NEW ELEMENTARY

MATHEMATICS

SYLLABUS D

1

SOLUTIONS

MANUAL

Authored by: Jennifer Hoerst
Printed by: Avyx, Inc.

Go to:
www.avyx.com

Or e-mail:
info@avyx.com

Or write:
Avyx, Inc.
8032 South Grant Way
Littleton, CO 80122-2705
USA
303-483-0140

ISBN 13: 978-1-8878-4077-4

Printed in the United States of America

Avyx, in an effort to help purchasers of the Singapore New Elementary Math 1 Textbook, is providing this Solutions Manual. Every effort has been made to eliminate errors. However, if you do find errors, we would also welcome your pointing these out to us. To give us feedback or to note error corrections, please send an email to the author at jenny@singmath.com. As errors are detected and corrected, you may find the error corrections posted online at the author's web site, http://www.singmath.com. **NOTE:** This site is the sole property of Jennifer Hoerst and is not a site maintained by Avyx. This site is offered solely as a courtesy to help purchasers see corrections as Jennifer Hoerst posts them. All corrections captured will be included in updates to the manuals prior to their reprinting.

Preface

This solutions manual is for instructors to help guide students to a solution; students should not to resort to it too soon. Much learning that occurs in wrestling with a challenging problem will be bypassed by looking up a solution too quickly, and the joy of discovery and accomplishment will be lost. If used too much, this manual will become a disservice.

Many problems have alternate solutions, not all of which are shown in this manual. You or your student may come up with a different approach in arriving at a solution, and in such cases this manual can be looked upon as a learning tool to show that alternate solutions are possible. Your solution may even be more elegant than that shown in this manual.

The solutions manual contains solutions only to the daily exercises, reviews, and miscellaneous exercises. Answers and solutions to class activities, challengers, problem solving, and investigations are in the Teacher Guides.

I am indebted to Hilary Miller for her invaluable help in proofing this manual, and for her encouragement. Its completion is as much due to her efforts as to mine. Special thanks goes to her father, Laurence R. Walker, a retired theoretical physicist, who helped me with solutions to some of the trickier problems and with whom I corroborated on errors I found in the text. Immeasurable thanks goes to my family members, who provided some of the solutions, as well as space and time.

Contents

Chapter 1

Exercise 1.1 (pp. 3-4)

Problems involving addition and subtraction can be solved by first determining the missing numbers for each place value independently. For addition, the tens in the answer can be removed by reducing a value in one of the addends in the next higher place value by one. (e.g. 1.(c)) For subtraction, tens in minuend can removed and by either reducing a value in the subtrahend in the next higher place value by one, (e.g. 1.(b)) or increasing a value in the minuend in the next higher place value by one.

1.(a)
```
    5 * 7
  + * 3 8
  -------
    8 0 5

    5 7 7
  + 3 3 8
  -------
  8 10 15

    1 1
    5 6 7
  + 2 3 8
  -------
    8 0 5
```

(b)
```
    1 * 6 *
  -   3 * 9
  ---------
    7 3 4

    1 10  6 13
  - 1  3  3  9
  ------------
       7  3  4

    1 0 6 3
  -   3 2 9
  ---------
    7 3 4
```

(c)
```
    7 * * 8 9
  +   9 9 * *
  -----------
    * 0 0 3 6

    7  1  1  8  9
  +     9  9  5  7
  ----------------
    * 10 10 13 16

    1 1 1 1
    7 0 0 8 9
  +   9 9 4 7
  -----------
    8 0 0 3 6
```

(d)
```
    2 3 * *
  - * * 6 9
  ---------
      1 3 3

    2 3  9 12
  - 2 2  6  9
  -----------
      1  3  3

        1
    2 3 0 2
  - 2 1 6 9
  ---------
      1 3 3
```

(e)
```
    * * * * 6
  - 2 8 9 7 *
  -----------
      2 1 4 2

    2 10 10 11 6
  - 2  8  9  7 4
  --------------
       2  1  4 2

    1 1 1
    3 1 1 1 6
  - 2 8 9 7 4
  -----------
      2 1 4 2
```

(c)
```
    7 * 4
  + * 8 *
  -------
    * 0 3

    7 2 4
  + * 8 9
  -------
  * 10 13

    1 1
    7 1 4
  + 1 8 9
  -------
    9 0 3
```

2.(a)
```
          4
        2 5
    x   * 9
    -------
    * * 5
    * 5 .
    -------
    4 * 5

        2 5
    x   * 9
    -------
    2 2 5
    * 5 .
    -------
    4 * 5

        2 5
    x   1 9
    -------
    2 2 5
    2 5 .
    -------
    4 7 5
```

(b)
```
        7 2 8
  x         * 4
  -------------
      2 9 1 2
  * * * * .
  -------------
  3 9 3 1 2

        7 2 8
  x         * 4
  -------------
        1
      2 9 1 2
    3 6 4 0 .
  -------------
  3 9 3 1 2

        7 2 8
  x         5 4
  -------------
      2 9 1 2
    3 6 4 0 .
  -------------
  3 9 3 1 2
```

(c)
```
          * 2
  12 ) 7  * 4
       * *
       ---
       2 4
       2 4
```
```
          * 2
  12 ) 7  * 4
       7 *
       ---
       2 4
       2 4
```
```
          6 2
  12 ) 7  4 4
       7 2
       ---
       2 4
       2 4
```

2.(d)

```
              5  5
   15 )  *  *  5
            *  5
            *  5
            *  5


              5  5
   15 )  8  2  5
         *  5
            *  5
            *  5


              5  5
   15 )  8  2  5
         7  5
            7  5
            7  5
```

(e)

```
                    6  5  4
   32 )  2  0  9  2  8
         *  *  *
               *  *  *
               *  *  *
                  *  *  *
                  *  *  *


                    6  5  4
   32 )  2  0  9  2  8
         1  9  2
            1  7  2
            1  6  0
               1  2  8
               1  2  8
```

(f)

```
                 1  *  *
        x          *  *
              1  1
           *  1  7  9
           7  8  6
         * 0  3  9


                 1  *  *
        x          *  *
           1  1  7  9
           7  8  6  .
         9 0 39


                   2
                 1  *  *
        x          6  9
           1  1  7  9
           7  8  6  .
         9  0  3  9


                 1  3  1
        x          6  9
           1  1  7  9
           7  8  6  .
         9  0  3  9
```

3 and 4 have multiple answers.

Exercise 1.2 (pp. 6-7)

1.(a) $\underline{4 \times 6} \div 8 + 32 - 12$
    $= \underline{24 \div 8} + 32 - 12$
    $= \underline{3 + 32} - 12$
    $= \underline{35 - 12}$
    $= \mathbf{23}$

(b) $\underline{42 \div 7} \times 3 - 11 + 9$
    $= \underline{6 \times 3} - 11 + 9$
    $= \underline{18 - 11} + 9$
    $= \underline{7 + 9}$
    $= \mathbf{16}$

(c) $16 - 7 + \underline{9 \times 5} \div 45$
    $= 16 - 7 + \underline{45 \div 45}$
    $= \underline{16 - 7} + 1$
    $= \underline{11 - 1}$
    $= \mathbf{10}$

(d) $23 + 80 - \underline{105 \div 7} \times 3$
    $= 23 + 80 - \underline{15 \times 3}$
    $= \underline{23 + 80} - 45$
    $= \underline{103 - 45}$
    $= \mathbf{58}$

(e) $54 - \underline{32 \times 8} \div 16 + 73$
    $= 54 - \underline{256 \div 16} + 73$
    $= \underline{54 - 16} + 73$
    $= \underline{38 + 73}$
    $= \mathbf{111}$

(f) $76 + \underline{24 \div 12} \times 7 - 26$
    $= 76 + \underline{2 \times 7} - 26$
    $= \underline{76 + 14} - 26$
    $= \underline{90 - 26}$
    $= \mathbf{64}$

2.(a) $72 \div \underline{(5 + 4)} \times 6$
    $= \underline{72 \div 9} \times 6$
    $= \underline{8 \times 6}$
    $= \mathbf{48}$

(b) $15 \times \underline{(34 - 29)} \div 25$
    $= \underline{15 \times 5} \div 25$
    $= \underline{75 \div 25}$
    $= \mathbf{3}$

(c) $56 \div 8 \times (24 + 11)$
$= 7 \times 35$
$= \mathbf{245}$

(d) $25 \times 9 \div (31 - 16)$
$= 225 \div 15$
$= \mathbf{15}$

3. (a) $36 \div (28 - 2 \times 8) \div 3$
$= 36 \div (28 - 16) \div 3$
$= 36 \div 12 \div 3$
$= 3 \div 3$
$= \mathbf{1}$

(b) $13 \times (5 - 45 \div 9) + 18$
$= 13 \times (5 - 5) + 18$
$= 13 \times 0 + 18$
$= 0 + 18$
$= \mathbf{18}$

(c) $6 + (7 \times 7 - 7) \div 6$
$= 6 + (49 - 7) \div 6$
$= 6 + 42 \div 6$
$= 6 + 7$
$= \mathbf{13}$

(d) $27 - (405 \div 45 \div 9) \times 4$
$= 27 - (9 \div 9) \times 4$
$= 27 - 1 \times 4$
$= 27 - 4$
$= \mathbf{23}$

4.(a) $(323 - 213) \times (161 - 153)$
$= 110 \times 8$
$= \mathbf{880}$

(b) $(126 + 30) \div (96 - 83)$
$= 156 \div 13$
$= \mathbf{12}$

(c) $(264 \div 12 - 3) \times (330 \div 15)$
$= (22 - 3) \times 22$
$= 19 \times 22$
$= \mathbf{418}$

(d) $(13 + 26 \times 5) \div (15 \times 6 - 79)$
$= (13 + 130) \div (90 - 79)$
$= 143 \div 11$
$= \mathbf{13}$

5.(a) $4 \times [(12 + 8) \times 2 + 3] + 4$
$= 4 \times [20 \times 2 + 3] + 4$
$= 4 \times (40 + 3) + 4$
$= 4 \times 43 + 4$
$= 172 + 4$
$= \mathbf{176}$

(b) $15 + [568 - (283 - 265) \times 12] \times 3$
$= 15 + [568 - 18 \times 12] \times 3$
$= 15 + (568 - 216) \times 3$
$= 15 + 352 \times 3$
$= 15 + 1056$
$= \mathbf{1071}$

(c) $300 - [(345 - 264) \times 3] \div 9$
$= 300 - (81 \times 3) \div 9$
$= 300 - 243 \div 9$
$= 300 - 27$
$= \mathbf{273}$

(d) $264 \div [(127 - 124) \times 4] - 22$
$= 264 \div (3 \times 4) - 22$
$= 264 \div 12 - 22$
$= 22 - 22$
$= \mathbf{0}$

6.(a) $\{[(174 - 120) \times 9 + 14] \times 5 - 24\} \times 7$
$= \{[54 \times 9 + 14] \times 5 - 24\} \times 7$
$= \{[486 + 14] \times 5 - 24\} \times 7$
$= (500 \times 5 - 24) \times 7$
$= (2,500 - 24) \times 7$
$= 2,476 \times 7$
$= \mathbf{17,332}$

(b) $\{[(211 - 102) \times 7 + 26] \times 3 - 312\} \div 15$
$= \{[109 \times 7 + 26] \times 3 - 312\} \div 15$
$= \{[763 + 26]\} \times 3 - 312\} \div 15$
$= (789 \times 3 - 312) \div 15$
$= (2367 - 312) \div 15$
$= 2055 \div 15$
$= \mathbf{137}$

(c) $\{[(185 + 19) \div 12 + 13] \div 2 + 66\} \div 9$
$= \{[204 \div 12 + 13] \div 2 + 66\} \div 9$
$= \{[17 + 13] \div 2 + 66\} \div 9$
$= (30 \div 2 + 66) \div 9$
$= (15 + 66) \div 9$
$= 81 \div 9$
$= \mathbf{9}$

(d) $3 \times \{81 + [13 - (7 + 5) \div 3]\}$
$= 3 \times \{81 + [13 - 12 \div 3]\}$
$= 3 \times \{81 + [13 - 4]\}$
$= 3 \times (81 + 9)$
$= 3 \times 90$
$= \mathbf{270}$

7.(a) <u>24 x 3</u> + 6 □ 2 = 75
        72 + 6 □ 2 = 75
     since 72 + 3 = 75 then [6 □ 2] = 3
                                6 ÷ 2 = 3
     24 x 3 + 6 ÷ 2 = 75

(b) 54 + 7 □ 3 - <u>20 ÷ 4</u> = 70
    54 + 7 □ 3 - 5 = 70
    Since 75 - 5 = 70 then 54 + 7 □ 3 = 75
    Since 54 + 21 = 75 then 7 □ 3 = 75
                              7 x 3 = 21
    54 + 7 **x** 3 - 20 ÷ 4 = 70

(c) <u>21 ÷ 3</u> □ 7 - 6 □ 4 = 47
       7 □ 7 - 6 □ 4 = 47
       7 x 7 - 6 □ 4 = 47
       7 x 7 - 6 + 4 = 47
    21 ÷ 3 **x** 7 - 6 **+** 4 = 47

(d) 16 □ 8 - 9 □ 9 x 2 = 0
    16 □ 8 = 9 □ 9 x 2
    16 ÷ 8 = 9 ÷ 9 x 2
    16 ÷ 8 - 9 ÷ 9 x 2 = 0

8. These are solved mostly by trial and error.

(a) 10 + 15 x (5 + 15) ÷ 5 = 70

(b) 38 + (21 - 7) x 15 = 248

(c) (32 - 13) x (16 - 5) = 209

(d) 18 ÷ [(12 - 9) x 2] = 3

Exercise 1.3 (p. 10)

1. Determine divisibility first by 2, then 3, then 4 etc. until the next number is one of the factors previously found. List in order.

(a) 1, 3, 5, 15

(b) 1, 2, 4, 7, 14, 28

(c) 1, 2, 3, 6, 7, 14, 21, 42

(d) 1, 2, 3, 6, 13, 26, 39, 78

(e) 1, 3, 7, 9, 21, 63

(f) 1, 2, 3, 4, 5, 6, 8, 10, 12, 15, 20, 24, 30, 40, 60, 120

2. (a) 3, 6, 9, 12, 15, 18, 21, 24, 27, 30

(b) 5, 10, 15, 20, 25, 30, 35, 40, 45, 50

(c) 6, 12, 18, 24, 30, 36, 42, 48, 54, 60

(d) 9, 18, 27, 36, 45, 54, 63, 72, 81, 90

(e) 15, 30, 45, 60, 75, 90, 105, 120, 135, 150

(f) 19, 38, 57, 76, 95, 114, 133, 152, 171, 190

3. (a) **1**, **2**, **3**, **4**, 5, **6**, 10, **12**, 15, 20, 30, 60
   (b) **1**, **2**, **3**, **4**, **6**, 8, **12**, 16, 24, 32, 48, 96
   Common factors: 1, 2, 3, 4, 6, 12

4. (a) 12, 24, **36**, 48, 60, **72**, 84, 96, **108**, 120, 132, **144**
   (b) 18, **36**, 54, **72**, 90, **108**, 126, **144**, 162, 180, 198, 216
   Common multiples: 36, 72, 108, 144

5. Perform division, answer is the whole number portion of the quotient multiplied by the divisor.

(a) 100 ÷ 7 = 14 r2
        14 x 7 = **98**

(b) 200 ÷ 7 = 28 r4
        28 x 7 = **196**

(c) 500 ÷ 7 = 71 r3
        71 x 7 = **497**

(d) 1000 ÷ 7 = 142 r6
         142 x 7 = **994**

Exercise 1.4 (p. 13)

1. (a) 5^2 (b) 3^3 (c) 17^3

   (d) $2^2 \times 7^3$ (e) $3^3 \times 5^2 \times 11^2$ (f) $7^2 \times 13 \times 17^2 \times 71$

2. (a) $2\mid \underline{10}$ (b) $3\mid \underline{15}$ (c) $2\mid \underline{16}$ (d) $2\mid \underline{18}$
        $5\mid \underline{\ \ 5}$ $5\mid \underline{\ \ 5}$ $2\mid \underline{\ \ 8}$ $3\mid \underline{\ \ 9}$
       $10 = \mathbf{2 \times 5}$ $15 = \mathbf{3 \times 5}$ $2\mid \underline{\ \ 4}$ $3\mid \underline{\ \ 3}$
                                           $2\mid \underline{\ \ 2}$ $18 = \mathbf{2 \times 3^2}$
                                        $16 = \mathbf{2^4}$

   (e) $2\mid \underline{20}$ (f) $2\mid \underline{36}$ (g) $2\mid \underline{48}$ (h) $2\mid \underline{72}$
        $2\mid \underline{10}$ $2\mid \underline{18}$ $2\mid \underline{24}$ $2\mid \underline{36}$
        $5\mid \underline{\ \ 5}$ $3\mid \underline{\ \ 9}$ $2\mid \underline{12}$ $2\mid \underline{18}$
       $20 = 2^2 \times 5$ $3\mid \underline{\ \ 3}$ $2\mid \underline{\ \ 6}$ $3\mid \underline{\ \ 9}$
                            $36 = \mathbf{2^2 \times 3^2}$ $3\mid \underline{\ \ 3}$ $3\mid \underline{\ \ 3}$
                                          $48 = \mathbf{2^4 \times 3}$ $72 = \mathbf{2^3 \times 3^2}$

   (i) $2\mid \underline{144}$ (j) $2\mid \underline{256}$
       $2\mid \underline{\ 72}$ $2\mid \underline{128}$
       $2\mid \underline{\ 36}$ $2\mid \underline{\ 64}$
       $2\mid \underline{\ 18}$ $2\mid \underline{\ 32}$
       $3\mid \underline{\ \ 9}$ $2\mid \underline{\ 16}$
       $3\mid \underline{\ \ 3}$ $2\mid \underline{\ \ 8}$
     $144 = \mathbf{2^4 \times 3^2}$ $2\mid \underline{\ \ 4}$
                      $2\mid \underline{\ \ 2}$
                 $256 = \mathbf{2^8}$

3. (a) $3\mid \underline{\ \ 9}$ (b) $2\mid \underline{12}$ (c) $3\mid \underline{21}$ (d) $2\mid \underline{24}$
        $3\mid \underline{\ \ 3}$ $2\mid \underline{\ \ 6}$ $7\mid \underline{\ \ 7}$ $\mid \underline{\ 12}$
       $9 = \mathbf{3 \times 3}$ $3\mid \underline{\ \ 3}$ $21 = \mathbf{3 \times 7}$ see 3(b)
                   $12 = \mathbf{2 \times 2 \times 3}$ $24 = \mathbf{2 \times 2 \times 2}$
                                                    $\mathbf{\times\ 3}$

   (e) $2\mid \underline{30}$ (f) $2\mid \underline{42}$ (g) $2\mid \underline{108}$ (h) $5\mid \underline{125}$
        $3\mid \underline{15}$ $3\mid \underline{21}$ $2\mid \underline{\ 54}$ $5\mid \underline{\ 25}$
        $5\mid \underline{\ \ 5}$ $7\mid \underline{\ \ 7}$ $3\mid \underline{\ 27}$ $5\mid \underline{\ \ 5}$
     $30 = \mathbf{2 \times 3 \times 5}$ $42 = \mathbf{2 \times 3 \times 7}$ $3\mid \underline{\ \ 9}$ $125 = \mathbf{5 \times 5 \times 5}$
                                          $3\mid \underline{\ \ 3}$
                                    $108 = \mathbf{2 \times 2 \times 3}$
                                            $\mathbf{\times\ 3 \times 3}$

   (i) $2\mid \underline{216}$ (j) $2\mid \underline{648}$
       $\mid \underline{108}$ $2\mid \underline{324}$
       see 3(g) $2\mid \underline{162}$
     $216 = \mathbf{2 \times 2 \times 2}$ $3\mid \underline{\ 81}$
            $\mathbf{\times\ 3 \times 3 \times 3}$ $3\mid \underline{\ 27}$
                              $\mid \underline{\ \ 9}$
                           see 3(a)
                   $648 = \mathbf{2 \times 2 \times 2}$
                   $\mathbf{\times\ 3 \times 3 \times 3 \times 3}$

4. Extend the sieve of Eratosthenes to 200.

  (a) 97   (b) 113   (c) 149   (d) 199

Exercise 1.5 (p.15)

1.(a) HCF = **1**

(b) HCF = **1**

(c)   2 | 12, 42
      3 | 6, 21
         2, 7
      HCF = 2 x 3 = **6**

(d) HCF = **1**

(e)   3 | 15, 27
         5, 9

      HCF = **3**

(f)   3 | 15, 42
         5, 14

      HCF = **3**

(g)   3 | 15, 60
      5 | 5, 20
         1, 4

      HCF = 3 x 5 = **15**

(h)   3 | 15, 63
         5, 21

      HCF = **3**

(i)   2 | 16, 56
      2 | 8, 28
      2 | 4, 14
         2, 7

      HCF = 2^3 = **8**

(j)   3 | 18, 45
      3 | 6, 15
         2, 5

      HCF = 3^2 = **9**

(k) HCF = **1**

(l) HCF = **1**

(m)   2 | 24, 48
      2 | 12, 24
      2 | 6, 12
      3 | 3, 6
         1, 2

      HCF = 2^3 x 3 = **24**

(n)   2 | 24, 108
      2 | 12, 54
      3 | 6, 27
         2, 9

      HCF = 2^2 x 3 = **12**

(o)   2 | 28, 54
         14, 27

      HCF = **2**

(p)   2 | 36, 162
      3 | 18, 81
      3 | 6, 27
         2, 9

      HCF = 2 x 3^2 = **18**

(q)   3 | 36, 243
      3 | 12, 81
         4, 9

      HCF = 3^2 = **9**

(r)   2 | 42, 36
      3 | 21, 12
         7, 4

      HCF = 2 x 3 = **6**

(s)   3 | 42, 63
      7 | 14, 21
         2, 3

      HCF 3 x 7 = **21**

(t)   3 | 45, 42
         15, 14

      HCF = **3**

(u)   2 | 60, 84
      2 | 30, 42
      3 | 15, 21
         5, 7

      HCF = 2^2 x 3 = **12**

(v)   2 | 96, 36
      2 | 48, 18
      3 | 24, 9
         8, 3

      HCF = 2^2 x 3 = **12**

(w)   2 | 108, 48
      2 | 54, 24
      3 | 27, 12
          9, 4

      HCF = 2^2 x 3 = **12**

(x)   3 | 165, 99
     11 | 55, 33
          5, 3

      HCF = 3 x 11 = **33**

(y)   5 |425, 200
      5 | 85, 40
          17,   8
   HCF = 5 x 5 = **25**

(z)   3 |546, 1521
     13 |182, 507
          14,   39
   HCF = 3 x 13 = **39**

2.(a) HCF = **1**

(b)   2 | 12, 42, 72
      3 | 6, 21, 36
          2,   7, 12
   HCF 2 x 3 = **6**

(c)   2 | 16, 72, 104
      2 | 8, 36, 52
      2 | 4, 18, 26
          2,   9, 13
   HCF = 2^3 = **8**

(d)   5 | 35,420, 245
      7 | 7, 84, 49
          1, 12,   7
   HCF = 5 x 7 = **35**

(e) HCF = **1**

(f) HCF = **1**

(g)   2 | 24,156,180, 204
      2 | 12, 78, 90, 102
      3 | 6, 39, 45, 51
          2, 13, 15, 17
   HCF = 2^2 x 3 = **12**

(h)   3 | 30,126,105, 255
          10, 42, 35, 85
   HCF = **3**

(i)   2 | 96,144,136,344
      2 | 48, 72, 68,172
      2 | 24, 36, 34, 86
          12, 18, 17, 43
   HCF = 2^3 = **8**

3. If the HCF is 12, both numbers must be divisible by 12. Numbers divisible by 12 are 12, 24, 36, 48, 60, 72. The two of these whose sum is 72 are **12** and **60**.

4. The numbers must be divisible by 8. They can be 8, 16, 24, 32, 40, 48, 56, 64, 72. Pairs whose sum are 72 and where the HCF is 8 are **64 and 8**, **56 and 16**, **32 and 40**.

Exercise 1.6 (p. 17)

1.(a) LCM = 2 x 17 = **34**

(b) LCM = 3 x 5 = **15**

(c) LCM = 4 x 9 = **36**

(d) LCM = 5 x 12 = **60**

(e)   3 | 6, 9
          2, 3
   LCM = 2 x 3^2 = **18**

(f)   2 | 6, 12
      3 | 3, 6
          1, 2
   LCM = 2^2 x 3 = **12**

(g)   3 | 6, 15
          2, 5
   LCM = 3 x 2 x 5 = **30**

(h)   2 | 12, 8
      2 | 6, 4
          3, 2
   LCM = 2^3 x 3 = **24**

(i)   3 | 12, 9
          4, 3
   LCM = 3^2 x 4 = **36**

(j)   2 | 12, 20
      2 | 6, 10
          3, 5
   LCM 2^2 x 3 x 5 = **60**

(k)   2 | 14, 6
          7, 3
   LCM = 2 x 7 x 3 = **42**

(l)   3 | 15, 9
          5, 3
   LCM 3^2 x 5 = **45**

(m) 5 | 15, 20
         3, 4
   LCM = 5 x 3 x 4 = **60**

(n)   2 | 16, 10
          8, 5
   LCM = 2 x 8 x 5 = **80**

(o)   2 | 16, 36
      2 | 8, 18
          4, 9
   LCM = 2^2 x 4 x 9 = **144**

(p) 3 | 18,   9
    3 | 6,   3
       2,   1
    LCM = 3^2 x 2 = **18**

(q) 2 | 18, 24
    3 | 9, 12
       3,   4
    LCM = 2 x 3^2 x 4 = **72**

(r) 5 | 20, 25
        4,   5
    LCM = 5^2 x 4 = **100**

(s) 2 | 78, 56
       39, 28
    LCM = 2 x 39 x 28 =
       2,184

(t) 3 | 81, 225
    3 | 27, 75
       9, 25
    LCM = 3^2 x 9 x 25 = **2,025**

(u) 2 |108, 132
    2 | 54, 66
    3 | 27, 33
       9, 11
    LCM = 2^2 x 3 x 9 x 11 =
       1,188

(v) 11 |110, 231
       10, 21
    LCM = 11 x 10 x 21 =
       2,310

(w) 3 |126, 195
       42, 65
    LCM = 3 x 42 x 65 = **8,190**

(x) 5 |135, 120
    3 | 27, 24
       9,   8
    LCM = 5 x 3 x 9 x 8 =
       1,080

(y) 2 |168, 248
    2 | 84, 124
    2 | 42, 62
       21, 31
    LCM = 2^3 x 21 x 31 =
       5,208

(z) 2 |700, 82
       350, 41
    LCM = 2 x 350 x 41 =
       28,700

2.(a) 2 | 8, 12, 18
      2 | 4, 6, 9
      3 | 2, 3 9
         2 1, 3
    LCM = 2^3 x 3^2 = **72**

(b) 2 | 20, 32, 18
    2 | 10, 16,   9
       5, 8,   9
    LCM = 2^2 x 5 x 8 x 9 =
       1,440

(c) 2 | 24, 18, 36
    3 | 12, 9, 18
    3 | 4, 3,   6
    2 | 4, 1   2
       2, 1,   1
    LCM = 2^3 x 3^2 = **72**

(d) 2 | 4, 8, 16, 20
    2 | 2, 4, 8, 10
    2 | 1, 2, 4, 5
       1, 1, 2, 5
    LCM = 2^4 x 5 = **80**

(e) 2 | 5, 12, 18, 20
    3 | 5, 6, 9, 10
    5 | 5, 2, 3, 10
    2 | 1, 2, 3, 2
       1, 1, 3, 1
    LCM = 2^2 x 3^2 x 5 = **180**

(f) 2 | 6, 12, 8, 18
    2 | 3, 6, 4,   9
    3 | 3, 3, 2,   9
       1, 1, 2,   3
    LCM = 2^3 x 3^2 = **72**

(g) 5 |135,175, 65
       27, 35, 13
    LCM = 5 x 27 x 35 x 13 =
       61,425

(h) 5 |140,385, 220
    7 | 28, 77, 44
    4 | 4, 11, 44
   11 | 1, 11, 11
       1, 1,   1
    LCM = 5 x 7 x 4 x 11 =
       1,540

(i) 3 |225,105, 252
    5 | 75, 35, 84
    7 | 15, 7, 84
    3 | 15, 1, 12
       5, 1,   4
    LCM = 3^2 x 5^2 x 7 x 4 =
       6,300

3.(a)   7 | 7, 28
         | 1,   4

    (i) HCF = 7
    (ii) LCM = 7 x 4 = 28
    (iii) product = 196
    product of numbers = **196**

  (c)   12, 35

    (i) HCF = 1
    (ii) LCM = 12 x 15 = 420
    (iii) product = 420
    product of numbers = **420**

  (b)   2 | 12, 18
       3 | 6,   9
          2,   3

    (i) HCF = 2 x 3 = 6
    (ii) LCM = 2^2 x 3^2 = 36
    (iii) product = 216
    product of numbers = **216**

  (d)   2 | 96, 120
       2 | 48, 60
       2 | 24, 30
       3 | 12, 15
          4,   5

    (i) HCF = 2^3 x 3 = 24
    (ii) LCM = 2^3 x 3 x 4 x 5 = 480
    (iii) product = 11,520
    product of numbers = **11,520**

4. The second number has to be a factor of 24. The factors of 24 other than 6 are 3, 4, and 8. 3 and 4 would have 12 as a LCM with 6. The other number is therefore **8**.

5. The product of these numbers is the product of the HCF and the LCM, or 91. The factors of 91 are 1, 7, 13, and 91. So the numbers could be **1 and 91 or 7 and 13**.

Exercise 1.7 (pp. 20-21)

1.(a) Square numbers.
   25, 36

  (c) Add 3 to previous term.
   13, 16

  (e) Add 6 to previous term.
   29, 35

 (b) Triangular numbers.
   15, 21

 (d) Double previous term.
   32, 64

 (f) Cubic numbers.
   125, 216

2.(a) Start with 2, add 5 to previous term.
   27, 32

  (c) Start at 81, subtract 5 from previous term.
   56, 51

  (e) Start at 384, halve previous term.
   12, 6

 (b) Start with 1, multiply previous term by 3.
   243, 729

 (d) Two series, alternating terms in list. First one starts with 3, add 4 to previous term. Second one starts with 9, add 4 to previous term. **15, 21**

 (f) Start with 6, add 3 to previous term.
   18, 21

3.(a) **30, 45**
   Triangular numbers x 3.
    10 x 3 = 30, 15 x 3 = 45

4.(a) 40, 60
   Triangular numbers x 4.
    10 x 4 = 40, 15 x 4 = 60

 (b) **16, 25**
   Square numbers.

 (b) **16, 25**
   Square numbers.

5.(a) Double previous term.   (b) 7, 21, 35

   (c) Each number is 7 x first term of sequence.   (d) 49 ÷ 7 = 7, so first term is 7.
                                                          7, 14, 28

Exercise 1.8 (pp. 24-25)

1. 4, 8, 10, 12, 14, 16, 18   2. 7, 9, 13, 15, 17, 19, 21

3. $a + 7 = b$ 4. $3p - 1 = q$

5.(a)

n	1	2	3	4	n	
m	1	4	9	16		
m	**1** x 1	**2** x 2	**3** x 3	**4** x 4	n x n	$m = n^2$

(b)

n	0	1	2	3	4	n	
m	-2	1	4	7	10		
m	0 - 2	3 - 2	6 - 2	9 - 2	12 - 2	n x f - 2	
m		**1** x 3 - 2	**2** x 3 - 2	**3** x 3 - 2	**4** x 3 - 2	**n** x 3 - 2	$m = 3n - 2$

As n increases by 1, m increases by 3, so m when n = 0 is 1 - 3 = -2. Express each m as a number - 2 (row 3 in table). That number for n = 1 will be the factor of n in the formula.

(c)

n	0	1	2	3	4	n	
m	0	2	4	6	8		
m		**1** x 2	**2** x 2	**3** x 2	**4** x 2	**n** x 2	$m = 2n$

As n increases by 1, m increases by 3, so the value for m when n = 0 is 0. So there is no addend as part of the formula.

(d)

n	0	1	2	3	4	n	
m	-1	5	11	17	23		
m	0 - 1	6 - 1	12 - 1	18 - 1	24 - 1	n x f - 1	
m		**1** x 6 - 1	**2** x 6 - 1	**3** x 6 - 1	**4** x 6 - 1	**n** x 6 - 1	$m = 6n - 1$

Here, the value for m when n = 0 is -1, so express each m as a (multiple of n) - 1. The multiple is the term when n = 1.

(e)

n	0	1	2	3	4	n	
m	-3	2	7	12	17		
m	0 - 3	5 - 3	10 - 3	15 - 3	20 - 3	n x f - 3	
m		**1** x 5 - 3	**2** x 5 - 3	**3** x 5 - 3	**4** x 5 - 3	**n** x 5 - 3	$m = 5n - 3$

(f)

n	0	1	2	3	4	n	
m	0	7	14	21	28		
m		**1** x 7	**2** x 7	**3** x 7	**4** x 7	**n** x 7	$m = 7n$

(g)

n	0	1	2	3	4	n	
m	86	81	76	71	66		
m	86 - 0	86 - 5	86 - 10	86 - 15	86 - 20	86 - n x f	
m		86 - **1** x 5	86 - **2** x 5	86 - **3** x 5	86 - **4** x 5	86 - **n** x 5	$m = 86 - 5n$

As n increases by 1, m decreases by 5, so the value for m when n = 0 is 81 + 5 = 86.
Express each m as 86 - a number. This number when n = 1 is the factor of n in the formula.

(h)

n	0	1	2	3	4	n
m		384	192	96	48	
m		2 x 192	2 x 96	2 x 48		
m		2^3 x 48	2^2 x 48	2^1 x 48	2^0 x 48	
m		2^{4-1} x 48	2^{4-2} x 48	2^{4-3} x 48	2^{4-4} x 48	2^{4-n} x 48

2^{4-n} x 48

A pattern can be determined by working from n = 4 to n = 1 and expressing each m as a value related to that of the next higher n. The answer m = 2^{4-n} x 48 is different from the answer in the text, but is equivalent, and more appropriate at this stage, since students have not yet worked with indices.

It can be simplified as follows: $48 \times 2^{4-n} = 3 \times 2^4 \times 2^{4-n} = 3 \times 2^{8-n}$

6.

T	0	1	2	3	4	n
M	1	3	5	7	9	
M	0 + 1	2 + 1	4 + 1	6 + 1	8 + 1	M x f + 1
M		**1** x 2 + 1	**2** x 2 + 1	**3** x 2 + 1	**4** x 2 + 1	**M** x 2 + 1

M = 2T +1

7.

S	0	1	2	3	4	n
D	2	4	6	8	10	
D	0 + 2	2 + 2	4 + 2	6 + 2	10 + 2	S x f + 2
D		**1** x 2 + 2	**2** x 2 + 2	**3** x 2 + 2	**4** x 2 + 2	**S** x 2 + 2

D = 2S +2

Exercise 1.9 (p. 27)

1. (a) commutative law of addition
   (c) associative law of addition
   (e) associative law of multiplication

   (b) associative law of addition
   (d) commutative law of multiplication
   (f) associative law of multiplication

2. (a) (3 x 4) + (3 x 5)
   (d) (5 x 4) + (2 x 4)

   (b) (3 x 7) + (3 x 2)
   (e) (3 x 7) + (1 x 7)

   (c) (3 x 8) + (3 x 4)
   (f) (7 x 11) + (4 x 11)

3. (a) 3 x **7** = 7 x 3 commutative law

   (c) 5 + **6** = 6 + 5 commutative law

   (e) (58 + **20**) x 4 = (58 x 4) + (20 x 4)
       distributive law

   (b) (7 x 8) x 3 = **7** x (8 x 3) associative law

   (d) **2** x (10 + 3) = (2 x 10) + (2 x 3)
       distributive law

   (f) (3 + 4) + **5** = 3 + (4 + 5)
       associative law

4. (a) True. a x 1 = 1 x a = a

   (b) True. a + 0 = 0 + a = a

5. (b) 5 + (3 + 2) = 5 + (2 + 3)
   (c) 4 x (3 + 7) = (4 x 3) + (4 x 7)
   (d) (6 + 3) x 4 = 4 x (6 + 3)
   (e) (7 + 4) x 2 = (4 + 7) x 2
   (f) (9 x 3) x 2 = 9 x (3 x 2)
   (g) (1 + 2) x (3 + 4) = (1 + 2) x 3 + (1 + 2) x 4

   (h) [(5 + 4) x 3] x 2 = (5 + 4) x (3 x 2)
   (i) (5 + 3) + 6 = 6 + (5 + 3)
   (j) 12 + (3 + 5) = (12 + 3) + 5

   (iv) commutative property of addition (for 5 + 3)
   (vii) distributive property
   (iii) commutative property of multiplication
   (ii) commutative property of addition
   (viii) associative property of multiplication

   (v) distributive property
   (vi) associative property of multiplication
   (ix) commutative property of addition
   (x) associative property of addition

Chapter 2

Exercise 2.1 (pp. 37-38)

1. (a) $\frac{5}{6}$ (b) $\frac{1}{4}$ (c) $\frac{3}{5}$ (d) $\frac{3}{8}$

$\frac{1}{3}$ $\left(\frac{1}{2}\text{ of }\frac{2}{3}=\frac{2}{6}=\frac{1}{3}\right)$ (f) $\frac{1}{4}$ (marked lines are equal, all 8 triangles have an

equal area, so shaded area is $\frac{1}{4}$)

2. (a)(i) AC = $\frac{1}{4}$ of AB   (ii) AD = $\frac{3}{4}$ of AB   (b)(i) PR = $\frac{3}{5}$ of PQ   (ii) PS = $\frac{4}{5}$ of PQ

3. (a) $\frac{3\times8}{7\times8}=\frac{24}{56}$ (b) $\frac{4\times6}{13\times6}=\frac{24}{78}$ (c) $\frac{9\times11}{17\times11}=\frac{99}{187}$

   $\frac{7\times7}{8\times7}=\frac{49}{56}$ $\frac{5\times13}{6\times13}=\frac{65}{78}$ $\frac{3\times17}{11\times17}=\frac{51}{187}$

   (d) $\frac{13\times7}{15\times7}=\frac{91}{105}$ (e) $\frac{11\times13}{12\times13}=\frac{143}{156}$ (f) $\frac{7\times15}{12\times15}=\frac{105}{180}$

   $\frac{9\times15}{7\times15}=\frac{135}{105}$ $\frac{12\times12}{13\times12}=\frac{144}{156}$ $\frac{6\times12}{15\times12}=\frac{72}{180}$

4. (a) $\frac{4+1}{2}=2\frac{1}{2}$ (b) $\frac{8+1}{4}=2\frac{1}{4}$ (c) $\frac{14+1}{2}=7\frac{1}{2}$

   (d) $\frac{15+3}{5}=3\frac{3}{5}$ (e) $\frac{144+38}{48}=3\frac{38}{48}=3\frac{19}{24}$ (f) $\frac{360+11}{36}=10\frac{11}{36}$

   (g) $\frac{121+2}{11}=11\frac{2}{11}$ (h) $\frac{234+12}{13}=18\frac{12}{13}$ (i) $\frac{240+87}{120}=2\frac{87}{120}=2\frac{29}{40}$

5. (a) $\frac{2\times2+1}{2}=\frac{5}{2}$ (b) $\frac{4\times3+1}{3}=\frac{13}{3}$ (c) $\frac{9\times11+3}{11}=\frac{102}{11}$

   (d) $\frac{11\times5+4}{5}=\frac{59}{5}$ (e) $\frac{12\times13+7}{13}=\frac{163}{13}$ (f) $\frac{17\times16+5}{16}=\frac{277}{16}$

   $\frac{64\times42+31}{42}=\frac{2,719}{42}$ (h) $\frac{78\times23+11}{23}=\frac{1,805}{23}$ (i) $\frac{37\times121+47}{121}=\frac{4,524}{121}$

6. (a) $\dfrac{7}{3}$ (b) $\dfrac{3}{5}$ (c) $\dfrac{3}{7}$

   (d) $\dfrac{11}{10}$ (e) $\dfrac{22}{8}$ (f) $\dfrac{21}{49}$

7. (a) $\dfrac{4 \times 3}{5 \times 3} = \dfrac{4}{5}$ (b) $\dfrac{1 \times 5}{6 \times 5} = \dfrac{1}{6}$ (c) $\dfrac{2 \ \times \ 7}{5 \ \times \ 7} = \dfrac{2}{5}$

   (d) $\dfrac{5 \times 3 \times 2}{6 \times 3 \times 2} = \dfrac{5}{6}$ (e) $\dfrac{3 \times 7}{7 \times 7} = \dfrac{3}{7}$ (f) $\dfrac{7 \times 6}{10 \times 6} = \dfrac{7}{10}$

   (g) $\dfrac{2 \times 13}{3 \times 13} = \dfrac{2}{3}$ (h) $\dfrac{27 \times 5}{33 \times 5} = \dfrac{9 \times 3}{11 \times 3} = \dfrac{9}{11}$ (i) $\dfrac{7 \times 10}{21 \times 10} = \dfrac{1 \times 7}{3 \times 7} = \dfrac{1}{3}$

   (j) $\dfrac{10 \times 9}{36 \times 9} = \dfrac{5 \times 2}{18 \times 2} = \dfrac{5}{18}$ (k) $\dfrac{90 \times 7}{96 \times 7} = \dfrac{15 \times 6}{16 \times 6} = \dfrac{15}{16}$ (l) $\dfrac{221 \times 3}{391 \times 3} = \dfrac{13 \times 17}{23 \times 17} = \dfrac{13}{23}$

8. (a) $(2 \times 10 = 20) < (3 \times 7 = 21)$ (b) $(2 \times 36 = 72) < (5 \times 15 = 75)$

$$\dfrac{2}{3} < \dfrac{7}{10} \qquad\qquad\qquad \dfrac{2}{5} < \dfrac{15}{36}$$

   (c) $\dfrac{1}{4}, \dfrac{9}{34}$ Fractions can be simplified before cross-multiplication   (d) $\dfrac{5}{6}, \dfrac{5}{6}$

$(1 \times 34 = 34) < (9 \times 4 = 46)$

$$\dfrac{2}{8} < \dfrac{18}{68} \qquad\qquad\qquad\qquad \dfrac{10}{12} = \dfrac{30}{36}$$

   (e) $\dfrac{1}{3}, \dfrac{7}{20}$ (f) $\dfrac{63}{78}, \dfrac{9}{11}$

$(1 \times 20 = 20) < (7 \times 3 = 21)$ $(63 \times 11 = 693) < (9 \times 78 = 702)$

$$\dfrac{7}{21} < \dfrac{14}{40} \qquad\qquad\qquad\qquad \dfrac{63}{78} < \dfrac{135}{165}$$

9. (a) $\dfrac{3}{8}, \dfrac{3}{5}$ If the numerator is the same, the fraction with the highest denominator is the smallest.   (b) $\dfrac{3}{8} < \dfrac{1}{2}$ Recognize that one more eighth is needed to make a half.

$$\dfrac{3}{8} < \dfrac{6}{15}$$

   (c) $\dfrac{3}{2}, \dfrac{13}{9}; \quad 1\dfrac{1}{2}, 1\dfrac{4}{9}$ (d) $(36 \times 29 = 1{,}044) < (34 \times 31 = 1{,}054)$

$\dfrac{1}{2} > \dfrac{4}{9}$ (4 is less than half of 9) $\dfrac{36}{31} < \dfrac{34}{29}$

$$\dfrac{18}{12} > \dfrac{26}{18}$$

(e) $(11 \times 135 = 1{,}485) > (16 \times 90 = 1{,}440)$ (f) $(21 \times 50 = 1{,}050) < (22 \times 49 = 1{,}078)$

$$\frac{11}{90} > \frac{\mathbf{16}}{\mathbf{135}}$$ $$\frac{\mathbf{21}}{\mathbf{49}} < \frac{22}{50}$$

10. Cross multiplication can be used here by multiplying the numerator of one fraction with the denominator of both of the other fractions. This is shown below without first simplifying the fraction, which could be done if the simplification is easy to see. If not, it is quicker to just do the multiplication.

(a) $17 \times 24 \times 27 = 11{,}016$; $18 \times 23 \times 27 = 11{,}178$; $20 \times 23 \times 24 = 11{,}040$

$$\frac{\mathbf{17}}{\mathbf{23}} < \frac{\mathbf{20}}{\mathbf{27}} < \frac{\mathbf{18}}{\mathbf{24}}$$

(b) $23 \times 28 \times 32 = 20{,}608$; $24 \times 27 \times 32 = 20{,}736$; $27 \times 27 \times 28 = 20{,}412$

$$\frac{\mathbf{27}}{\mathbf{32}} < \frac{\mathbf{23}}{\mathbf{27}} < \frac{\mathbf{24}}{\mathbf{28}}$$

(c) $30 \times 44 \times 43 = 56{,}760$; $50 \times 27 \times 43 = 58{,}050$; $49 \times 27 \times 44 = 58{,}212$

$$\frac{\mathbf{30}}{\mathbf{27}} < \frac{\mathbf{50}}{\mathbf{44}} < \frac{\mathbf{49}}{\mathbf{43}}$$

(d) $32 \times 106 \times 53 = 179{,}776$; $96 \times 35 \times 53 = 178{,}080$; $47 \times 35 \times 106 = 174{,}370$

$$\frac{\mathbf{47}}{\mathbf{53}} < \frac{\mathbf{96}}{\mathbf{106}} < \frac{\mathbf{32}}{\mathbf{35}}$$

(e) $123 \times 110 \times 342 = 4{,}627{,}260$; $82 \times 171 \times 342 = 4{,}795{,}524$; $500 \times 110 \times 171 = 9{,}405{,}000$

$$\frac{\mathbf{123}}{\mathbf{171}} < \frac{\mathbf{82}}{\mathbf{110}} < \frac{\mathbf{500}}{\mathbf{342}}$$

(f) $64 \times 158 \times 234 = 2{,}366{,}208$; $128 \times 78 \times 234 = 2{,}336{,}256$; $184 \times 78 \times 158 = 2{,}267{,}616$

$$\frac{\mathbf{184}}{\mathbf{234}} < \frac{\mathbf{128}}{\mathbf{158}} < \frac{\mathbf{64}}{\mathbf{78}}$$

Exercise 2.2 (p. 41)

1. (a) $\dfrac{3}{8} + \dfrac{1}{4} = \dfrac{3}{8} + \dfrac{2}{8}$ (b) $\dfrac{2}{11} + \dfrac{5}{22} = \dfrac{4}{22} + \dfrac{5}{22}$ (c) $\dfrac{1}{8} + \dfrac{5}{12} + \dfrac{7}{16} = \dfrac{6}{48} + \dfrac{20}{48} + \dfrac{21}{48}$

$$= \frac{\mathbf{5}}{\mathbf{8}}$$ $$= \frac{\mathbf{9}}{\mathbf{22}}$$ $$= \frac{\mathbf{47}}{\mathbf{48}}$$

(d) $\dfrac{4}{5} - \dfrac{8}{15} = \dfrac{12}{15} - \dfrac{8}{15}$ (e) $\dfrac{17}{20} - \dfrac{8}{15} = \dfrac{51}{60} - \dfrac{32}{60}$ (f) $\dfrac{9}{10} - \dfrac{5}{16} - \dfrac{7}{20} = \dfrac{72}{80} - \dfrac{25}{80} - \dfrac{28}{80}$

$$= \frac{4}{15}$$ $$= \frac{\mathbf{19}}{\mathbf{60}}$$ $$= \frac{\mathbf{19}}{\mathbf{80}}$$

2. (a) $\dfrac{5}{8}+\dfrac{1}{8}-\dfrac{3}{8}=\mathbf{\dfrac{3}{8}}$

(b) $\dfrac{7}{9}+\dfrac{1}{9}-\dfrac{5}{9}=\dfrac{3}{9}=\mathbf{\dfrac{1}{3}}$

(c) $\dfrac{4}{5}+\dfrac{3}{10}-\dfrac{8}{15}=\dfrac{24}{30}+\dfrac{9}{30}-\dfrac{16}{30}$

$=\mathbf{\dfrac{17}{30}}$

(d) $\dfrac{7}{9}+\dfrac{2}{15}-\dfrac{29}{45}=\dfrac{35}{45}+\dfrac{6}{45}-\dfrac{29}{45}$

$=\dfrac{12}{45}$

$=\mathbf{\dfrac{4}{15}}$

(e) $\dfrac{3}{8}-\dfrac{3}{4}+\dfrac{11}{12}=\dfrac{9}{24}-\dfrac{18}{24}+\dfrac{22}{24}$

$=\dfrac{22}{24}+\dfrac{9}{24}-\dfrac{18}{24}$ Move terms to avoid negative numbers.

$=\mathbf{\dfrac{13}{24}}$

(f) $\dfrac{4}{9}-\dfrac{7}{12}+\dfrac{23}{36}=\dfrac{16}{36}-\dfrac{21}{36}+\dfrac{23}{36}$

$=\dfrac{23}{36}+\dfrac{16}{36}-\dfrac{21}{36}$

$=\dfrac{18}{36}$

$=\mathbf{\dfrac{1}{2}}$

3. These can be converted to mixed fractions after adding (a, b, c) or before (d, e, f)

(a) $\dfrac{12}{5}+\dfrac{17}{15}=\dfrac{36}{5}+\dfrac{17}{15}$

$=\dfrac{53}{15}$

$=\mathbf{3\dfrac{8}{15}}$

(b) $\dfrac{7}{4}+\dfrac{9}{5}=\dfrac{35}{20}+\dfrac{36}{20}$

$=\dfrac{71}{20}$

$=\mathbf{3\dfrac{11}{20}}$

(c) $\dfrac{11}{3}-\dfrac{12}{5}=\dfrac{55}{15}-\dfrac{36}{15}$

$=\dfrac{19}{15}$

$=\mathbf{1\dfrac{4}{15}}$

(d) $\dfrac{17}{4}-\dfrac{13}{6}=4\dfrac{1}{4}-2\dfrac{1}{6}$

$=(4-2)+\left(\dfrac{3}{12}-\dfrac{2}{12}\right)$

$=\mathbf{2\dfrac{1}{12}}$

(e) $\dfrac{33}{8}+\dfrac{25}{14}=4\dfrac{1}{8}+1\dfrac{11}{14}$

$=5+\left(\dfrac{7}{56}+\dfrac{44}{56}\right)$

$=\mathbf{5\dfrac{51}{56}}$

(f) $\dfrac{31}{9}-\dfrac{19}{15}=3\dfrac{4}{9}-1\dfrac{4}{15}$

$=2+\left(\dfrac{20}{45}-\dfrac{12}{45}\right)$

$=\mathbf{2\dfrac{8}{45}}$

4. (a) $2\dfrac{2}{3}+4\dfrac{3}{5}=6+\dfrac{10}{15}+\dfrac{9}{15}$

$=6\dfrac{19}{15}$

$=\mathbf{7\dfrac{4}{15}}$

(b) $3\dfrac{1}{3}-1\dfrac{1}{5}=2+\dfrac{5}{15}-\dfrac{3}{15}$

$=\mathbf{2\dfrac{2}{15}}$

(c) $6\dfrac{1}{9}+3\dfrac{8}{21}=9+\dfrac{7}{63}+\dfrac{24}{63}$

$=\mathbf{9\dfrac{31}{63}}$

(d) $\quad 2\dfrac{12}{17}+4\dfrac{10}{34}=6+\dfrac{24}{34}+\dfrac{10}{34}$

$\qquad\qquad\quad =6\dfrac{34}{34}$

$\qquad\qquad\quad =\mathbf{7}$

(e) $\quad 5\dfrac{8}{15}-2\dfrac{8}{25}=3+\dfrac{40}{75}-\dfrac{24}{75}$

$\qquad\qquad\quad =\mathbf{3\dfrac{16}{75}}$

(f) $\quad 9\dfrac{5}{14}-4\dfrac{10}{21}=5\dfrac{15}{42}-\dfrac{20}{42}$

$\qquad\qquad\quad =4\dfrac{57}{42}-\dfrac{20}{42}$

$\qquad\qquad\quad =\mathbf{4\dfrac{37}{42}}$

5. (a) $\quad 3\dfrac{5}{6}+1\dfrac{1}{2}-2\dfrac{1}{4}=2+\dfrac{10}{12}+\dfrac{6}{12}-\dfrac{3}{12}$

$\qquad\qquad\qquad\qquad =2\dfrac{13}{12}$

$\qquad\qquad\qquad\qquad =\mathbf{3\dfrac{1}{12}}$

(b) $\quad 4\dfrac{3}{8}+2\dfrac{5}{12}-3\dfrac{1}{6}=3+\dfrac{9}{24}+\dfrac{10}{24}-\dfrac{4}{24}$

$\qquad\qquad\qquad\qquad =3\dfrac{15}{24}$

$\qquad\qquad\qquad\qquad =\mathbf{3\dfrac{5}{8}}$

(c) $\quad 5\dfrac{1}{2}-2\dfrac{1}{3}+1\dfrac{5}{6}=4+\dfrac{3}{6}-\dfrac{2}{6}+\dfrac{5}{6}$

$\qquad\qquad\qquad\qquad =4\dfrac{6}{6}$

$\qquad\qquad\qquad\qquad =\mathbf{5}$

(d) $\quad 2\dfrac{7}{9}+1\dfrac{2}{3}+3\dfrac{5}{12}=6+\dfrac{28}{36}+\dfrac{24}{36}+\dfrac{15}{36}$

$\qquad\qquad\qquad\qquad =6\dfrac{67}{36}$

$\qquad\qquad\qquad\qquad =\mathbf{7\dfrac{31}{36}}$

(e) $\quad 6\dfrac{3}{8}-2\dfrac{5}{6}-2\dfrac{1}{4}=2+\dfrac{9}{24}-\dfrac{20}{24}-\dfrac{6}{24}$

$\qquad\qquad\qquad\qquad =1\dfrac{24}{24}+\dfrac{9}{24}-\dfrac{20}{24}-\dfrac{6}{24}$

$\qquad\qquad\qquad\qquad =\mathbf{1\dfrac{7}{24}}$

(f) $\quad 4\dfrac{3}{4}-2\dfrac{1}{3}-1\dfrac{3}{10}=1+\dfrac{45}{60}-\dfrac{20}{60}-\dfrac{18}{60}$

$\qquad\qquad\qquad\qquad =\mathbf{1\dfrac{7}{60}}$

6. (a) $\quad 3\dfrac{17}{18}+\left(4\dfrac{5}{6}-1\dfrac{7}{9}\right)=6+\dfrac{17}{18}+\dfrac{15}{18}-\dfrac{14}{18}$

$\qquad\qquad\qquad\qquad\qquad =6\dfrac{18}{18}$

$\qquad\qquad\qquad\qquad\qquad =\mathbf{7}$

(b) $\quad 11\dfrac{7}{18}+\left(12\dfrac{5}{6}+3\dfrac{7}{9}\right)=26+\dfrac{7}{18}+\dfrac{15}{18}+\dfrac{14}{18}$

$\qquad\qquad\qquad\qquad\qquad =26\dfrac{36}{18}$

$\qquad\qquad\qquad\qquad\qquad =\mathbf{28}$

(c) $\quad 3\dfrac{11}{12}-\left(4\dfrac{7}{9}-5\dfrac{3}{8}\right)=(3-4+5)+\left(\dfrac{66}{72}-\dfrac{56}{72}+\dfrac{27}{72}\right)$

$\qquad\qquad\qquad\qquad\qquad =(5+3-4)+\dfrac{37}{72}$

$\qquad\qquad\qquad\qquad\qquad =\mathbf{4\dfrac{37}{72}}$

The subtraction follows the distributive law of multiplication: -1(a - b) = -a + b. Alternatively, operations within the parenthesis can be performed first.
Rearrange terms to avoid negative numbers.

(d) $\quad 5\dfrac{8}{9}-\left(15\dfrac{13}{18}-12\dfrac{5}{6}\right)=(5-15+12)+\left(\dfrac{16}{18}-\dfrac{13}{18}+\dfrac{15}{18}\right)$

$\qquad\qquad\qquad\qquad\qquad =(12+5-15)+\dfrac{18}{18}$

$\qquad\qquad\qquad\qquad\qquad =\mathbf{3}$

(e)
$$12\frac{5}{6} + \left(5\frac{8}{9} - 9\frac{13}{18}\right) = 8 + \frac{15}{18} + \frac{16}{18} - \frac{13}{18}$$
$$= 8\frac{18}{18}$$
$$= \mathbf{9}$$

(f)
$$92\frac{8}{35} - \left(41\frac{3}{7} - 32\frac{17}{20}\right) = (92 - 41 + 32) + \left(\frac{32}{140} - \frac{60}{140} + \frac{119}{140}\right)$$
$$= 83\frac{91}{140}$$
$$= \mathbf{83\frac{13}{20}}$$

Exercise 2.3 (pp. 44-45)

1. (a)
$$\frac{5 \times 14}{6} = \frac{5 \times 7}{3}$$
$$= \frac{35}{3}$$
$$= \mathbf{11\frac{2}{3}}$$

(b)
$$\frac{843 \times 10}{100} = \frac{843}{10}$$
$$= \mathbf{84\frac{3}{10}}$$

(c)
$$\frac{19 \times 3}{12 \times 38} = \frac{1 \times 1}{4 \times 2}$$
$$= \mathbf{\frac{1}{8}}$$

(d)
$$\frac{105 \times 40}{82 \times 7} = \frac{15 \times 20}{41}$$
$$= \frac{300}{41}$$
$$= \mathbf{7\frac{13}{41}}$$

(e)
$$\frac{2 \times 4 \times 7}{3 \times 5 \times 4} = \frac{2 \times 7}{3 \times 5}$$
$$= \mathbf{\frac{14}{15}}$$

(f)
$$\frac{5 \times 12 \times 3}{4 \times 20 \times 7} = \frac{1 \times 3 \times 3}{1 \times 4 \times 7}$$
$$= \mathbf{\frac{9}{28}}$$

2. (a) $\mathbf{\frac{5}{3}}$ (b) $\mathbf{\frac{8}{3}}$ (c) $\mathbf{\frac{8}{7}}$ (d) $\mathbf{\frac{10}{9}}$

(e) $\mathbf{\frac{1}{5}}$ (f) $\mathbf{\frac{1}{10}}$ (g) $\mathbf{\frac{3}{5}}$ (h) $\mathbf{1}$

3. (a)
$$\frac{3 \times 1}{5 \times 5} = \mathbf{\frac{3}{25}}$$

(b)
$$\frac{39 \times 7}{26} = \frac{3 \times 7}{2}$$
$$= \frac{21}{2}$$
$$= \mathbf{10\frac{1}{2}}$$

(c)
$$\frac{21 \times 24}{12 \times 19} = \frac{21 \times 2}{1 \times 19}$$
$$= \frac{42}{19}$$
$$= \mathbf{2\frac{4}{19}}$$

(d) $\dfrac{32 \times 51}{17 \times 11} = \dfrac{32 \times 3}{1 \times 11}$

$= \dfrac{96}{11}$

$= \mathbf{8\dfrac{8}{11}}$

(e) $\dfrac{3 \times 6 \times 15}{4 \times 5 \times 2} = \dfrac{3 \times 3 \times 3}{4 \times 1 \times 1}$

$= \dfrac{27}{4}$

$= \mathbf{6\dfrac{3}{4}}$

(f) $\dfrac{3 \times 15 \times 115}{23 \times 2 \times 30} = \dfrac{3 \times 1 \times 5}{1 \times 2 \times 2}$

$= \dfrac{15}{4}$

$= \mathbf{3\dfrac{3}{4}}$

4. (a) $\dfrac{16 \times 21}{3 \times 4} = \dfrac{4 \times 7}{1 \times 1}$

$= \mathbf{28}$

(b) $\dfrac{24 \times 35}{5 \times 8} = \dfrac{3 \times 7}{1 \times 1}$

$= \mathbf{21}$

(c) $\dfrac{15 \times 26}{4 \times 15} = \dfrac{1 \times 13}{2 \times 1}$

$= \dfrac{13}{2}$

$= \mathbf{6\dfrac{1}{2}}$

(d) $\dfrac{5}{2} \div \dfrac{5}{3} = \dfrac{5 \times 3}{2 \times 5}$

$= \dfrac{3}{2}$

$= \mathbf{1\dfrac{1}{2}}$

(e) $\dfrac{14}{3} \div \dfrac{35}{3} = \dfrac{14 \times 3}{3 \times 35}$

$= \dfrac{2}{5}$

(f) $\dfrac{63}{8} \div \dfrac{11}{4} = \dfrac{63 \times 4}{8 \times 11}$

$= \dfrac{63 \times 1}{2 \times 11}$

$= \dfrac{63}{22}$

$= \mathbf{2\dfrac{19}{22}}$

5. (a) $\dfrac{5}{2} \times \dfrac{17}{5} \div \dfrac{4}{5} = \dfrac{5 \times 17 \times 5}{2 \times 5 \times 4}$

$= \dfrac{5 \times 17 \times 1}{2 \times 1 \times 4}$

$= \dfrac{85}{8}$

$= \mathbf{10\dfrac{5}{8}}$

(b) $\dfrac{22}{7} \div \dfrac{11}{4} \times \dfrac{3}{8} = \dfrac{22 \times 4 \times 3}{7 \times 11 \times 8}$

$= \dfrac{2 \times 1 \times 3}{7 \times 1 \times 2}$

$= \dfrac{1 \times 1 \times 3}{7 \times 1 \times 1}$

$= \mathbf{\dfrac{3}{7}}$

(c) $\dfrac{3}{4} \times \dfrac{5}{6} + 3 \times \dfrac{4}{3} = \dfrac{3 \times 5}{4 \times 6} + \dfrac{3 \times 4}{3}$

$= \dfrac{1 \times 5}{4 \times 2} + \dfrac{1 \times 4}{1}$

$= \dfrac{5}{8} + 4$

$= \mathbf{4\dfrac{5}{8}}$

(d) $\dfrac{1}{6} \div \dfrac{3}{4} \div \left(\dfrac{3}{8} \div \dfrac{1}{4}\right) = \dfrac{1}{6} \times \dfrac{4}{3} \div \left(\dfrac{3 \times 4}{8 \times 1}\right)$

$= \dfrac{1 \times 4 \times 8 \times 1}{6 \times 3 \times 3 \times 4}$

$= \dfrac{1 \times 2 \times 2 \times 1}{3 \times 3 \times 3 \times 1}$

$= \mathbf{\dfrac{4}{27}}$

(e) $\dfrac{7}{15} \div \dfrac{22}{12} \times \left(\dfrac{1}{6} + \dfrac{2}{3}\right) = \dfrac{7 \times 12}{15 \times 22} \times \left(\dfrac{1}{6} + \dfrac{4}{6}\right)$

$\qquad\qquad = \dfrac{7 \times 4}{5 \times 22} \times \dfrac{5}{6}$

$\qquad\qquad = \dfrac{7 \times 1 \times 1}{1 \times 11 \times 3}$

$\qquad\qquad = \dfrac{\mathbf{7}}{\mathbf{33}}$

(f) $\dfrac{4}{7} \div \dfrac{1}{14} \times \dfrac{5}{2} + \dfrac{5}{2} = \dfrac{4 \times 14 \times 5}{7 \times 1 \times 2} + \dfrac{5}{2}$

$\qquad\qquad = \dfrac{2 \times 2 \times 5}{1 \times 1 \times 1} + \dfrac{5}{2}$

$\qquad\qquad = 20 + 2\dfrac{1}{2}$

$\qquad\qquad = \mathbf{22\dfrac{1}{2}}$

6. (a) $\dfrac{3 \times 4 - 8}{18 \times 14} = \dfrac{12 - 8}{18 \times 14}$

$\qquad\quad = \dfrac{4}{18 \times 14}$

$\qquad\quad = \dfrac{1}{9 \times 7}$

$\qquad\quad = \dfrac{\mathbf{1}}{\mathbf{63}}$

(b) $\dfrac{21 + 3^2}{18 \div 5} = 21 + 9 \div \dfrac{18}{5}$

$\qquad\quad = \dfrac{30 \times 5}{18}$

$\qquad\quad = \dfrac{5 \times 5}{3}$

$\qquad\quad = \dfrac{25}{3}$

$\qquad\quad = \mathbf{8\dfrac{1}{3}}$

(c) $\dfrac{2 \times 3 - 3 \div 5}{6 \times 7 \div 2} = \dfrac{6 - \dfrac{3}{5}}{\dfrac{6 \times 7}{2}}$

$\qquad\qquad = 5\dfrac{2}{5} \div \dfrac{6 \times 7}{2}$

$\qquad\qquad = \dfrac{27}{5} \times \dfrac{2}{6 \times 7}$

$\qquad\qquad = \dfrac{9 \times 1}{5 \times 1 \times 7}$

$\qquad\qquad = \dfrac{\mathbf{9}}{\mathbf{35}}$

(d) $\dfrac{4 \times 8 \div 2}{2 \times 5 - 3} = \dfrac{4 \times \dfrac{8}{2}}{10 - 3}$

$\qquad\qquad = \dfrac{4 \times 4}{7}$

$\qquad\qquad = \dfrac{16}{7}$

$\qquad\qquad = \mathbf{2\dfrac{2}{7}}$

(e) $\dfrac{5^3 - 14 \times 3}{24 \div 6 - 3} = \dfrac{125 - 42}{4 - 3}$

$\qquad\qquad = \dfrac{83}{1}$

$\qquad\qquad = \mathbf{83}$

(f) Since negative numbers have not yet been discussed in NEM 1, this problem is inappropriate here and may be skipped.

$\dfrac{2 \times 3 - 1}{31 + 4 \times 3} - 2 \div \dfrac{3}{4} = \dfrac{6 - 1}{31 + 12} - 2 \times \dfrac{4}{3}$

$\qquad\qquad = \dfrac{5}{43} - \dfrac{8}{3}$

$\qquad\qquad = \dfrac{15}{129} - \dfrac{344}{129}$

$\qquad\qquad = -\dfrac{329}{129}$

$\qquad\qquad = \mathbf{-2\dfrac{71}{129}}$

Exercise 2.4 (p. 49)

1. (a) 0.11 x 10 = **1.1**
         0.11 x 100 = **11**
         0.11 x 1,000 = **110**

   (b) 0.012 x 10 = **0.12**
        0.012 x 100 = **1.2**
        0.012 x 1,000 = **12**

   (c) 8.001 x 10 = **80.01**
        8.001 x 100 = **800.1**
        8.001 x 1,000 = **8,001**

   (d) 95 x 10 = **950**
        95 x 100 = **9,500**
        95 x 1000 = **95,000**

   (e) 101.35 x 10 = **1,013.5**
        101.35 x 100 = **10,135**
        101.35 x 1000 = **101,350**

   (f) 5,683.053 x 10 = **56,830.53**
        5,683.053 x 100 = **568,305.3**
        5,683.053 x 1,000 = **5,683,053**

2. (a) 71÷10 = **7.1**
         71 ÷ 100 = **0.71**
         71 ÷ 1,000 = **0.071**

   (b) 100.51 ÷ 10 = **10.051**
        100.51 ÷ 100 = **1.0051**
        100.51 ÷ 1,000 = **0.10051**

   (c) 0.017 ÷ 10 = **0.0017**
        0.017 ÷ 100 = **0.00017**
        0.017 ÷ 1,000 = **0.000017**

   (d) 0.0084 ÷10 = **0.00084**
        0.0084÷ 100 = **0.000084**
        0.0084÷ 1,000 = **0.0000084**

   (e) 7,088.4 ÷ 10 = **708.84**
        7,088.4 ÷ 100 = **70.884**
        7,088.4 ÷ 1,000 = **7.0884**

   (f) 452,063.25 ÷ 10 = **45,206.325**
        452,063.25 ÷ 100 = **4,520.6325**
        452,063.25 ÷ 1,000 = **452.06325**

3. (a)   0.76
         + 29.93
         30.69

   (b)   33.80
         + 9.35
         43.15

   (c)   28.320
          32.099
        + 1.320
         61.739

   (d)   21.138
            9.019
         +123.020
         153.177

4. (a)   82.72
         - 61.83
          20.89

   (b)   31.03
         - 3.94
          27.09

   (c)   13.00
         - 0.13
          12.87

   (d)   22.00
         - 1.63
          20.37

   (e)   46.340
         - 19.003
          27.337

   (f)   62.123
         - 4.240
          57.883

5. (a)   52.70
         - 21.07
          31.63
         - 9.80
          21.83

   (b)   32.10
         + 4.26
          36.36
         - 20.07
          16.29

   (c)   63.123
         - 36.740
          26.383
         + 1.200
          27.583

   (d)   78.007
         - 3.260
          74.747
         + 1.713
          76.460

6. (a) **36.18**
   (b) **284.9**
   (c) **20.37**
   (d) **34.19**
   (e) **622.326**
   (f) **638.82**

7. (a) $\dfrac{46.5}{5} = \mathbf{9.3}$

(b) $\dfrac{13.14}{6} = \mathbf{2.19}$

(c) $\dfrac{32.2 \times 10}{1.4 \times 10} = \dfrac{322}{14}$
$= \mathbf{23}$

(d) $\dfrac{57.5 \times 100}{0.23 \times 100} = \dfrac{5{,}750}{23}$
$= \mathbf{250}$

(e) $\dfrac{10.56 \times 10}{4.4 \times 10 \times 48} = \dfrac{105.6}{44 \times 48}$
$= \mathbf{0.05}$

(f) $\dfrac{12.96 \times 10{,}000}{3.6 \times 10 \times 0.012 \times 1{,}000}$
$= \dfrac{129{,}600}{36 \times 12}$
$= \mathbf{300}$

8. (a) $14.7 \div 1.2 \times (8.4 - 3.5) = \dfrac{14.7 \times 10}{1.2 \times 10} \times 4.9$
$= \dfrac{147 \times 4.9}{12}$
$= \mathbf{60.025}$

(b) $1.2 + 8.8 \div (0.05 \times 40) = 1.2 + \dfrac{8.8}{2}$
$= 1.2 + 4.4$
$= \mathbf{5.6}$

(c) $1.8^2 - 0.8^2 \times 3 = 3.24 - 0.64 \times 3$
$= 3.24 - 1.92$
$= \mathbf{1.32}$

(d) $1.2^3 - 1.2^2 \div 1.2 = 1.728 - \dfrac{1.2 \times 1.2}{1.2}$
$= 1.728 - 1.2$
$= \mathbf{0.528}$

(e) $9.8 \div 1.4^2 \times 2.1 = \dfrac{9.8 \times 2.1}{1.4 \times 1.4}$
$= \dfrac{9.8 \times 10 \times 2.1 \times 10}{1.4 \times 10 \times 1.4 \times 10}$
$= \dfrac{98 \times 21}{14 \times 14}$
$= \dfrac{7 \times 3}{1 \times 2}$
$= \mathbf{10.5}$

(f) $9.8 \div 1.4 \times 1.4 \times 2.1 = \dfrac{9.8 \times 1.4 \times 2.1}{1.4}$
$= 9.8 \times 2.1$
$= \mathbf{20.58}$

Exercise 2.5a (pp. 52-53)

1. A: 4 cm   B: 4 cm

2. (a) 6 kg

(b) 5 kg

3. (a) 30 ml

(b) 50 ml

4. (a)(i) 451,470
   (ii) 451,500
   (iii) 451,000
   (iv) 450,000

(b)(i) 675,900
   (ii) 675,900
   (iii) 676,000
   (iv) 680,000

(c)(i) 872,600
   (ii) 872,600
   (iii) 873,000
   (iv) 870,000

(d)(i) 965,350
   (ii) 965,400
   (iii) 965,000
   (iv) 970,000

(e)(i) 810,300
   (ii) 810,300
   (iii) 810,000
   (iv) 810,000

(f)(i) 405,000
   (ii) 405,000
   (iii) 405,000
   (iv) 400,000

5. (a)(i) 61
   (ii) 61.2
   (iii) 61.24
   (iv) 61.235

(b)(i) 30
   (ii) 29.6
   (iii) 29.60
   (iv) 29.595

(c)(i) 26
   (ii) 26.0
   (iii) 26.00
   (iv) 25.995

(d)(i) 88
   (ii) 88.3
   (iii) 88.32
   (iv) 88.320

(e)(i) 64
   (ii) 63.6
   (iii) 63.64
   (iv) 63.638

(f)(i) 58
   (ii) 57.6
   (iii) 57.63
   (iv) 57.628

6 (a)(i) $12.31
   (ii) $12

(b)(i) $45.56
   (ii) $46

(c)(i) $52.19
   (ii) $52

(d)(i) $28.81
   (ii) $29

(e)(i) $288.94
   (ii) $289

(f)(i) $167.56
   (ii) $168

7. (a)(i) 110 kg
   (ii) 108 kg
   (iii) 108.3 kg
   (iv) 108.33 kg

(b)(i) 120 ℓ
   (ii) 124 ℓ
   (iii) 124.3 ℓ
   (iv) 124.29 ℓ

(c)(i) 150 cm
   (ii) 147 cm
   (iii) 146.7 cm
   (iv) 146.67 cm

(d)(i) 130 m
   (ii) 131 m
   (iii) 131.4 m
   (iv) 131.43 m

(e)(i) 590 g
   (ii) 591 g
   (iii) 590.6 g
   (iv) 590.59 g

(f)(i) 210 km
   (ii) 212 km
   (iii) 211.8 km
   (iv) 211.82 km

Exercise 2.5b (pp. 56-57)

1. (a)(i) 1,300 km
   (ii) 1,320 km

(b)(i) 5,400 km
   (ii) 5,410 km

(c)(i) 4,000 km (4 and 0 are significant)
   (ii) 4,010 km

(d)(i) 6,000 km (6 and 0 are significant)
   (ii) 6,020 km

(e)(i) 8,000 ℓ (8 and 0 are significant)
   (ii) 8,000 ℓ (8 and 2 0's are significant)

(f)(i) 4.5 m
   (ii) 4.46 m

(g)(i) 15 m
   (ii) 15.4 m

(h)(i) 21 m
   (ii) 20.9 m

(i)(i) 50. cm (including the decimal can indicate the preceding 0's are significant)
   (ii) 50.0 cm (all 0's after a decimal are significant)

(j)(i) 0.023 km (leading 0's are not significant)
   (ii) 0.0235 km
(m)(i) 1.0 km
   (ii) 0.995 km

(k)(i) 0.00056 km
   (ii) 0.000564 km

(n)(i) 64,000 kg
   (ii) 64,100 kg

(l)(i) 0.98 km
   (ii) 0.983 km

(o)(i) 74,000 kg
   (ii) 74,000 kg (one of the 0's is significant)

2. (a) 1. The 6.

(b) 3. All 0's after the decimal are significant, so all 3 digits are significant.

(c) 2. Leading 0's are not significant.

(d) 4

(e) 4. See above explanation.

(f) 5

3. (a) 3   (b) 4   (c) 3

   (d) 4. The measurement is   (e) 2   (f) 2
       correct to the nearest g,
       so the 0 in the units place
       and the preceding 0's are
       significant.

4. (a) 2   (b) 3. The 0 in the 100s place   (c) 2
                                      is significant since the
                                      measurement was to the
                                      nearest 100 km.

   (d) 2. The 0 in the 10,000   (e) 4. The 0 in the 100 place is   (f) 5. The last 0 is not
       place is significant.   significant.   significant since it was
                                                                          measured to the nearest
                                                                          10.

5. (a) ans. = 12.194   (b) ans. = 18.758   (c) ans. = 44.79
       (i) 12   (i) 19   (i) 45
       (ii) 12.2   (ii) 18.8   (ii) 44.8

   (d) ans. = 2,556   (e) ans. = 74.325   (f) ans. = 0.09142
       (i) 2,600   (i) 74   (i) 0.091
       (ii) 2,560   (ii) 74.3   (ii) 0.0914

Exercise 2.6 (pp. 61-62)

1. (a) $0.375 = \dfrac{375}{1,000}$ (b) $0.016 = \dfrac{16}{1,000}$ (c) $3.2 = 3\dfrac{2}{10}$

   $\quad\quad = \dfrac{3 \times 125}{8 \times 125}$ $\quad\quad = \dfrac{2 \times 8}{125 \times 8}$ $\quad\quad = \mathbf{3\dfrac{1}{5}}$

   $\quad\quad = \dfrac{\mathbf{3}}{\mathbf{8}}$ $\quad\quad = \dfrac{\mathbf{2}}{\mathbf{125}}$

   (d) $0.0001 = \dfrac{\mathbf{1}}{\mathbf{10,000}}$ (e) $0.005 = \dfrac{5}{1,000}$ (f) $1.004 = 1\dfrac{4}{1,000}$

   $\quad\quad\quad\quad\quad = \dfrac{\mathbf{1}}{\mathbf{200}}$ $\quad\quad\quad\quad = \mathbf{1\dfrac{1}{250}}$

2. (a) $\dfrac{1}{2} = \dfrac{1 \times 5}{2 \times 5}$ (b) $\dfrac{3}{8} = \dfrac{3 \times 125}{8 \times 125}$ (c) $\dfrac{11}{25} = \dfrac{11 \times 4}{25 \times 4}$

   $\quad = \dfrac{5}{10}$ $\quad = \dfrac{375}{1,000}$ $\quad = \dfrac{44}{100}$

   $\quad = \mathbf{0.5}$ $\quad = \mathbf{0.375}$ $\quad = \mathbf{0.44}$

   (d) $\dfrac{1}{5} = 1 \div 5 = \mathbf{0.2}$ (e) $\dfrac{13}{52} = 13 \div 52 = \mathbf{0.25}$ (f) $\dfrac{18}{25} = 18 \div 25 = \mathbf{0.72}$

Repeating decimals can also be represented by placing a line over the digits that repeat. This representation is used here since it is common in the US.

3. (a) $\dfrac{2}{11} = \mathbf{0.\overline{18}}$

(b) $\dfrac{1}{6} = \mathbf{0.1\overline{6}}$

(c) $\dfrac{1}{9} = \mathbf{0.\overline{1}}$

(d) $\dfrac{1}{3} = \mathbf{0.\overline{3}}$

(e) $\dfrac{2}{9} = \mathbf{0.\overline{2}}$

(f) $\dfrac{13}{66} = \mathbf{0.1\overline{96}}$

(g) $\dfrac{27}{37} = \mathbf{0.\overline{729}}$

(h) $\dfrac{99}{101} = \mathbf{0.\overline{9801}}$

4. (a) ans. = 0.1538...
(i) 0.15
(ii) 0.154

(b) ans. = 0.4783...
(i) 0.48
(ii) 0.478

(c) ans. = 0.6316...
(i) 0.63
(ii) 0.632

(d) ans. = 0.7647...
(i) 0.76
(ii) 0.765

(e) ans. = 0.9130...
(i) 0.91
(ii) 0.913

(f) ans. = 0.46396...
(I) 0.46
(ii) 0.464

5. (a) $\dfrac{2}{5} = 0.4$ $\dfrac{3}{7} = 0.429...$

(b) $\dfrac{5}{11} = 0.\overline{45}$ $\dfrac{3}{8} = 0.375$

$\dfrac{2}{5} < 0.419 < \dfrac{3}{7} < 0.43$

$\dfrac{3}{8} < 0.39 < 0.411 < \dfrac{5}{11}$

(c) $\dfrac{3}{7} = 0.429...$ $\dfrac{3}{8} = 0.375$ $\dfrac{4}{9} = 0.4\overline{4}$ $\dfrac{6}{13} = 0.\overline{461538}$

$\dfrac{3}{8} < \dfrac{3}{7} < \dfrac{4}{9} < \dfrac{6}{13}$

(d) $\dfrac{5}{9} = 0.5\overline{5}$ $\dfrac{7}{15} = 0.4\overline{6}$ $\dfrac{9}{20} = 0.45$ $\dfrac{11}{21} = 0.524...$

$\dfrac{9}{20} < \dfrac{7}{15} < \dfrac{11}{21} < \dfrac{5}{9}$

6. (a) $2\dfrac{1}{5} + 2.6 = 2\dfrac{1}{5} + 2\dfrac{6}{10}$

$\phantom{2\dfrac{1}{5} + 2.6} = 2\dfrac{1}{5} + 2\dfrac{3}{5}$

$\phantom{2\dfrac{1}{5} + 2.6} = \mathbf{4\dfrac{4}{5}}$

$2\dfrac{1}{5} + 2.6 = 2.2 + 2.6$

$\phantom{2\dfrac{1}{5} + 2.6} = \mathbf{4.8}$

(b) $3.2 - 1\dfrac{1}{4} = 3\dfrac{2}{10} - 1\dfrac{1}{4}$

$\phantom{3.2 - 1\dfrac{1}{4}} = 3\dfrac{4}{20} - 1\dfrac{5}{20}$

$\phantom{3.2 - 1\dfrac{1}{4}} = 2\dfrac{24}{20} - 1\dfrac{5}{20}$

$\phantom{3.2 - 1\dfrac{1}{4}} = \mathbf{1\dfrac{19}{20}}$

$3.2 - 1\dfrac{1}{4} = 3.2 - 1.25$

$\phantom{3.2 - 1\dfrac{1}{4}} = \mathbf{1.95}$

(c)
$$1.75 + 1\frac{1}{5} \times 0.25 = 1\frac{3}{4} + \frac{6}{5} \times \frac{1}{4}$$
$$= 1\frac{15}{20} + \frac{6}{20}$$
$$= 1\frac{21}{20}$$
$$= \mathbf{2\frac{1}{20}}$$

$$1.75 + 1\frac{1}{5} \times 0.25 = 1.75 + 1.2 \times 0.25$$
$$= 1.75 + 0.3$$
$$= \mathbf{2.05}$$

(d)
$$2\frac{1}{4} + 0.6 \div \frac{2}{5} = 2\frac{1}{4} + \frac{6}{10} \div \frac{2}{5}$$
$$= 2\frac{1}{4} + \frac{3}{5} \times \frac{5}{2}$$
$$= 2\frac{1}{4} + \frac{3}{2}$$
$$= 2\frac{1}{4} + 1\frac{2}{4}$$
$$= \mathbf{3\frac{3}{4}}$$

$$2\frac{1}{4} + 0.6 \div \frac{2}{5} = 2.25 + 0.6 \div 0.4$$
$$= 2.25 + 1.5$$
$$= \mathbf{3.75}$$

(e)
$$4\frac{1}{2} \times 3.25 \div \left(1.2 - \frac{3}{4}\right) = \frac{9}{2} \times 3\frac{1}{4} \div \left(\frac{12}{10} - \frac{3}{4}\right)$$
$$= \frac{9}{2} \times \frac{13}{4} \div \left(\frac{24}{20} - \frac{15}{20}\right)$$
$$= \frac{9 \times 13}{2 \times 4} \div \frac{9}{20}$$
$$= \frac{9 \times 13 \times 20}{2 \times 4 \times 9}$$
$$= \frac{1 \times 13 \times 5}{1 \times 2 \times 1}$$
$$= \frac{65}{2}$$
$$= \mathbf{32\frac{1}{2}}$$

$$4\frac{1}{2} \times 3.25 \div \left(1.2 - \frac{3}{4}\right) = \frac{4.5 \times 3.25}{1.2 - 0.75}$$
$$= \frac{4.5 \times 3.25}{0.45}$$
$$= \frac{4.5 \times 10 \times 3.25 \times 10}{0.45 \times 100}$$
$$= \frac{45 \times 32.5}{45}$$
$$= \mathbf{32.5}$$

(f)

$$2.5 \div 1\frac{1}{4} \times \left(\frac{4}{5} + 1.125\right) = 2\frac{1}{2} \div \frac{5}{4} \times \left(\frac{4}{5} + 1\frac{1}{8}\right)$$

$$= \frac{5}{2} \times \frac{4}{5} \times \left(\frac{4}{5} + \frac{9}{8}\right)$$

$$= \frac{5 \times 4}{2 \times 5} \times \left(\frac{32}{40} + \frac{45}{40}\right)$$

$$= 2 \times \frac{77}{40}$$

$$= \frac{77}{20}$$

$$= 3\frac{17}{20}$$

$$2.5 \div 1\frac{1}{4} \times \left(\frac{4}{5} + 1.125\right) = \frac{2.5}{1.25} \times (0.8 + 1.125)$$

$$= \frac{2.5 \times 100}{1.25 \times 100} \times 1.925$$

$$= \frac{250}{125} \times 1.925$$

$$= 2 \times 1.925$$

$$= \textbf{3.85}$$

7. (a)

$$\frac{0.312 \times 0.02}{0.8 \times 0.05} = \frac{0.312 \times 0.02 \times 1000}{0.8 \times 10 \times 0.05 \times 100}$$

$$= \frac{312 \times 0.020}{8 \times 5}$$

$$= \frac{39 \times 0.004}{1 \times 1}$$

$$= 0.156$$

$$= \textbf{0.2}$$

correct to one decimal place

(b)

$$\frac{0.16 \times 1.24}{0.14 \times 0.02} = \frac{0.16 \times 100 \times 1.24 \times 100}{0.14 \times 100 \times 0.02 \times 100}$$

$$= \frac{16 \times 124}{14 \times 2}$$

$$= \frac{8 \times 62}{7 \times 1}$$

$$= 70.857...$$

$$= \textbf{70.9}$$

correct to one decimal place

(c)

$$\frac{56.4 \times 0.27}{0.03 \times 40} = \frac{56.4 \times 0.27 \times 100}{0.03 \times 100 \times 40}$$

$$= \frac{56.4 \times 27}{3 \times 40}$$

$$= \frac{14.1 \times 9}{1 \times 10}$$

$$= 12.69$$

$$= \textbf{12.7}$$

correct to one decimal place

(d)

$$\frac{31.88 \times 2.12}{24.8 \times 11.2} = \frac{31.88 \times 2.12 \times 100}{24.8 \times 10 \times 11.2 \times 10}$$

$$= \frac{31.88 \div 4 \times 212 \div 4}{248 \div 4 \times 112 \div 4}$$

$$= \frac{7.97 \times 53}{62 \times 28}$$

$$= 0.243...$$

$$= \textbf{0.2}$$

correct to one decimal place

8. (a)

$$\frac{1.2^2 \times 3.1 - 1.3}{3.1 \times 1.5 + 2.3} = \frac{1.44 \times 3.1 - 1.3}{4.65 + 2.3}$$

$$= \frac{4.464 - 1.3}{6.95}$$

$$= \frac{3.164}{6.95}$$

$$= 0.455...$$

$$= \textbf{0.46}$$

correct to two decimal places

(b)

$$\frac{3.2 \times 1.2 \div 1.25}{3.5 - 1.3^2} = \frac{3.072}{3.5 - 1.69}$$

$$= \frac{3.072}{1.81}$$

$$= 1.697...$$

$$= \textbf{1.70}$$

correct to two decimal places

(c) $\dfrac{1.2 \times 1.3}{3.6} + \dfrac{2.7}{1.2} = \dfrac{12 \times 1.3}{36} + \dfrac{27}{12}$

$\qquad\qquad = \dfrac{4 \times 1.3}{12} + \dfrac{27}{12}$

$\qquad\qquad = \dfrac{5.2 + 27}{12}$

$\qquad\qquad = \dfrac{32.2}{12}$

$\qquad\qquad = 2.68\overline{3}$

$\qquad\qquad = \mathbf{2.68}$

correct to two decimal places

(d) Since negative numbers have not yet been discussed in NEM 1, this problem is inappropriate and may be skipped.

$\dfrac{3.7 \div 2.5}{3.3} - \dfrac{1}{0.11} = \dfrac{1.4.8}{3.3} - \dfrac{100}{11}$

$\qquad\qquad = \dfrac{14.8}{33} - \dfrac{300}{33}$

$\qquad\qquad = \dfrac{-285.2}{33}$

$\qquad\qquad = -8.642...$

$\qquad\qquad = \mathbf{-8.64}$

correct to two decimal places

Exercise 2.7 (pp. 63-64)

1. (a) $8.65 - 28.28 + 118.36 \approx 9 - 30 + 100 = 100 - 30 + 9 \approx 79$ **(iii)** 98.73

   (b) $99.25 - 9.25 \times 8.24 \approx 100 - 9 \times 8 = 100 - 72 \approx 30$ **(iii)** 23.03

   (c) $82.45 \times 9.78 \approx 82 \times 10 = 820$ **(ii)** 806.361

   (d) $205.4 \times 66.4 \approx 200 \times 70 = 14,000$ **(ii)** 13,638.56

   (e) $30.03 \times 0.065 \approx 30 \times 0.1 = 3$ **(i)** 1.95195

   (f) $0.31002 \div 0.025 \approx 0.3 \div 0.03 = 30 \div 3 = 10$ **(iii)** 12.4008

   (g) $151.5 \div 0.96 \approx 151 \div 1 = 151$ **(ii)** 157.8125

   (h) $8,486.2 \div 1.25 \approx 8,000 \div 1 = 8,000$ **(i)** 6,788.96

   (i) $0.2342 \div 0.025 \approx 0.25 \div 0.025 = 10$ **(iii)** 9.368

   (j) $33.34 \times 16.01 \div 25.5 \approx 30 \times 20 \div 30 = 20$ **(i)** 20.93229

2. (a) $\dfrac{4.426 \times 7.201^2}{20.34} \approx \dfrac{4 \times 7 \times 7}{21}$

   $\qquad\qquad\qquad \approx 7$

   incorrect; ans. = 11.28

   (b) $\dfrac{12.316 \times 4.123^2}{3.621} \approx \dfrac{12 \times 4 \times 4}{4}$

   $\qquad\qquad\qquad \approx 48$

   (c) $\dfrac{13 \times 6.993}{2.3 \times 2} \approx \dfrac{13 \times 7}{4}$

   $\qquad\qquad\qquad \approx 3 \times 7$

   $\qquad\qquad\qquad \approx 21$

   incorrect; ans. = 19.76

   (d) $\dfrac{47 \times 9.072}{6.3 - 0.8} \approx \dfrac{47 \times 9}{5}$

   $\qquad\qquad\qquad \approx 9 \times 9$

   $\qquad\qquad\qquad \approx 81$

   incorrect; ans. = 77.52

   (e) $\dfrac{45 \times 11.8^2}{15.1 \times 4.8} \approx \dfrac{45 \times 12 \times 12}{15 \times 5}$

   $\qquad\qquad\qquad \approx 3 \times 2 \times 12$

   $\qquad\qquad\qquad \approx 72$

   (f) $\dfrac{5.3 \times 12.4^2}{11.3 \times 5.6} \approx \dfrac{5 \times 12 \times 12}{11 \times 6}$

   $\qquad\qquad\qquad \approx 5 \times 2$

   $\qquad\qquad\qquad \approx 10$

   incorrect; ans. = 12.88

   (g) $9.62 \times 1.58 + 1.143 \times 3.81 \approx 10 \times 2 + 1 \times 3 = 20 + 3 = 23$
   incorrect; ans. = 19.55

   (h) $10.32 \times 14.3 - 9.51 \times 2.1 \approx 10 \times 14 - 9 \times 2 = 140 - 18 = 122$

(i) $$\frac{7.2^2 + 5.6^2}{4.4^2 - 3.2^2} \approx \frac{7^2 + 6^2}{4^2 - 3^2}$$

$$\approx \frac{49 + 36}{16 - 9}$$

$$\approx \frac{85}{7}$$

$$\approx 12$$

incorrect; ans. = 9.12

(j) $$\frac{9.8^2 + 6.7^2}{5.6^2 - 4.6^2} \approx \frac{10^2 + 7^2}{6^2 - 5^2}$$

$$\approx \frac{100 + 49}{36 - 25}$$

$$\approx \frac{149}{11}$$

$$\approx 13$$

(k) $$\frac{7.24 + 8.43^2}{4.321} \approx \frac{7 + 8^2}{4}$$

$$\approx \frac{7 + 64}{4}$$

$$\approx \frac{71}{4}$$

$$\approx 18$$

incorrect; ans. = 18.12

(l) $$\frac{9.45 \times 9.23^2}{2.81 \times 2} \approx \frac{9 \times 9 \times 9}{3 \times 2}$$

$$\approx \frac{3 \times 81}{2}$$

$$\approx 3 \times 40$$

$$\approx 120$$

incorrect; ans. = 143.25

3. (a) 31.60   (b) 436.16   (c) 243.36   (d) 0.50

   (e) 6.71   (f) 1.11   (g) 4.36   (h) 0.84

   (i) 238.86   (j) 27.60   (k) 0.24   (l) 1.30

   (m) 6.07   (n) 1.23

Chapter 3

Exercise 3.1 (p. 76)

1. (a)   1 m = 100 cm
       2.5 m = 2.5 x 100 cm
       2.5 m = **250 cm**

   (b) 100 cm = 1 m
       1 cm = 1 ÷ 100 m
       1 cm = **0.01 m**

   (c)   1 cm = 0.01 m
       7.6 cm = 7.6 x 0.01 m
       7.6 cm = **0.076 m**

   (d)   1 km = 1,000 m
       3.8 km = 3.8 x 1,000 m
       3.8 km = **3,800 m**

   (e) 1,000 m = 1 km
       1 m = 1 ÷ 1,000 km
       1 m = **0.001 km**

   (f)   1 m = 0.001 km
       11.8 m = 11.8 x 0.001 km
       11.8 m = **0.0118 km**

   (g)   1 km = 1,000 m
       1 m = 100 cm
       1,000 m = 1,000 x 100 cm
       1 km = 100,000 cm
       2 km = 2 x 100,000 cm
       2 km = **200,000 cm**

   (h) 1,000 mg = 1 g
       1 mg = 1 ÷ 1,000 g
       1 mg = **0.001 g**

   (i)   1 mg = 0.001 g
       5.5 mg = 5.5 x 0.001 g
       5.5 mg = **0.0055 g**

   (j) 1,000 g = 1 kg
       1 g = 1 ÷ 1,000 kg
       1 g = **0.001 kg**

   (k)   1 g = 0.001 kg
       3.3 g = 3.3 x 0.001 kg
       3.3 g = **0.0033 kg**

   (l)   1 kg = 1,000 g
       1 g = 1,000 mg
       1,000 g = 1,000 x 1,000 mg
       1 kg = 1,000,000 mg
       8.5 kg = 8.5 x 1,000,000 mg
       8.5 kg = **8,500,000 mg**

   (m) 1 tonne = 1,000 kg
       3.5 tonnes = 3.5 x 1,000 kg
       3.5 tonnes = **3,500 kg**

   (n) 1,000 kg = 1 tonne
       1 kg = 1 ÷ 1,000 tonnes
       1 kg = 0.001 tonnes
       2,570 kg = 2,750 x 0.001 tonnes
       2,570 kg = **2.75 tonnes**

   (o) 1 kg = 1,000 g
       4.5 kg = 4.5 x 1,000 g
       4.5 kg = **4,500 g**

   (p) 1,000 ml = 1 ℓ
       1 ml = 1 ÷ 1,000 ℓ
       1 ml = 0.001 ℓ
       20 ml = 20 x 0.001 ℓ
       20 ml = **0.02 ℓ**

   (q)   1 L = 1,000 ml
       2.6 L = 2.6 x 1,000 ml
       2.6 L = **2,600 ml**

   (r)   1 min = 60 s
       35 min = 35 x 60 s
       35 min = **2,100 s**

   (s)   1 h = 60 min
       3 h = 3 x 60 min
       3 h = **180 min**

   (t)   1 h = 60 min
       1 min = 60 s
       60 min = 60 x 60 s
       1 h = 3,600 s
       2 h = 2 x 3,600 s
       2 h = **7,200 s**

(u)   60 min = 1 h
        1 min = 1 ÷ 60 h
     690 min = 690 ÷ 60 h
     690 min = **11.5 h**

2. (a)   1,000 g = 1 kg
         5,252 g = (5 x 1,000) + 252 g
         5,252 g = **5 kg 252 g**

(b)   1,000 g = 1 kg
      4,211 g = (4 x 1,000) + 211 g
      4,211 g = **4 kg 211 g**

(c)   1,000 m = 1 km
      3,215 m = (3 x 1,000) + 215 m
      3,215 m = **3 km 215 m**

(d)   1,000 m = 1 km
      1,268 m = (1 x 1,000) + 268 m
      1,268 m = **1 km 268 m**

(e)   100 cm = 1 m
      462 cm = (4 x 100) + 62 cm
      462 cm = **4 m 62 cm**

(f)   100 cm = 1 m
      801 cm = (8 x 100) + 1 cm
      801 cm = **8 m 1 cm**

(g)   1,000 ml = 1 ℓ
      6,523 ml = (6 x 1,000) + 523 ml
      6,523 ml = **6 ℓ 523 ml**

(h)   1 h = 60 min
      6 h = 6 x 60 min
      6 h = **360 min**

(i)   60 s = 1 min
      215 s = (3 x 60) + 35 s
      215 s = **3 min 35 s**

(j)   60 min = 1 h
      121 min = (2 x 60) + 1 min
      121 min = **2 h 1 min**

(k)   1 h = 3600 s
      2 h = 2 x 3,600 s = 7,200 s
      1 min = 60 s
      5 min = 5 x 60 s = 300 s
      2 h 5 min = 7,200 s + 300 s
      2 h 5 min = **7,500 s**

(l)   1 h = 3,600 s
      1 min = 60 s
      20 min = 20 x 60 s = 1,200 s
      1 h 20 min 3 s = 3,600 s + 1,200 s + 3 s
      1 h 20 min 3 s = **4,803 s**

(m) 3,600 s = 1 h
     4,625 s = 1 h 1,025 s
        60 s = 1 min
     1,025 s = (17 x 60) + 5 s
     1,025 s = 17 min 5 s
     4,625 s = **1 h 17 min 5 s**

(n)   3,600 s = 1 h
      3,679 s = 1 h 79 s
        60 s = 1 min
      79 s = (1 x 60) + 19 s
      79 s = 1 min 19 s
      3,679 s = **1 h 1 min 19 s**

Exercise 3.2 (pp. 77-81)

1. (a)   12 pens = $24
         1 pen = $24 ÷ 12
              = **$2**

(b)   1 pen = $2
      30 pens = $2 x 30
            = **$60**

(c) $2 = 1 pen
      $1 = 1 ÷ 2 pens
      $30 = 30 ÷ 2 pens
          = **15 pens**

2. (a)   Hours before lunch = 12 h 30 min - 9 h = **3 h 30 min**
   (b)   Hours after lunch = 17 h - 13 h 30 min = 16 h 60 min - 13 h 30 min = **3 h 30 min**
   (c)   Total hours = 3 h 30 min + 3 h 30 min = **7 h**
   (d)   Hours for 1 day = 7 h
         Hours for 5 days = 7 x 5 = **35 h**
   (e)   Pay for 1 h = $8
         Pay for 35 h = $8 x 35 = **$280**
   (f) $280 for 1 week
         $1 for 1 ÷ 280 weeks
         $1,120 for 1,120 ÷ 280 weeks = **4 weeks**

3. (a) Age of John when he got married = 32 - 7 = **25 years**
    (b) Age of Ann 3 years before John got married = 21.
         ∴ Age when John got married = 21 + 3 = **24 years**
    (c) Current age of Ann = 24 + 7 = **31 years.**
         Or, Ann is 1 year younger than John, so her age now is 32 - 1 = 31 years.

4. (a) The jug holds 3 ℓ more than the mug = 3 + 1 = **4 ℓ**
    (b) The bottle holds 2 ℓ less than the jug = 4 - 2 = **2 ℓ**
    (c) Total capacity = 1 + 4 + 2 = **7 ℓ**
    (d) 7 ℓ = $10.50
         1 ℓ = $10.50 ÷ 7 = $1.5
         Cost per liter = **$1.50**

5. (a) Number that worked overtime = $\frac{2}{5}$ x 85 = 2 x 17 = **34**
    (b) Each earned $300 for overtime
         34 earned 34 x $300 = **$10,200**
    (c) Amount paid as salary = amount paid salary + overtime - amount paid overtime
                        = $112,200 - $10,200 = **$102,000**
    (d) Salary for 85 workers = $102,000
         Salary for 1 worker = $102,000 ÷ 85 = **$1,200**

6. (a) Cost of 15 m = $60
         Cost of 1 m = $60 ÷ 15 = **$4**
    (b) Cost of 90 m = $4 x 90 = **$360**
    (c) 5 curtains = 90 m
         1 curtain   = 90 m ÷ 5 = 18 m
    (d) 3 curtains = 18 m x 3 = **54 m**
    (e) Cost of 1 m = $4
         Cost of 18 m = $4 x 18 = **$72**

7. (a) **5** buses stop at D
    (b) **5** buses stop at both B and E
    (c) The 13:55 bus reaches E at 16:13
         16 h 13 min - 13 h 55 min = 15 h 73 min - 13 h 55 min = **2 h 18 min**
    (d) The bus that has the most stops will take the longest. It leaves at 14:11 and arrives at
         17:50
         17 h 50 min - 14 h 11 min = **3 h 39 min**
    (e) He would take the 14:22 bus, which arrives at E at **16:15**

8. (a) From Town J to D takes **8 min** (column 2, row 7 of travel time)
    (b) The largest value is **20 min** (column 5, bottom row), from Town G to Town A.
    (c) Peter's fare from K to D is 80¢ (column 8, top row of fare). The fare from D to I is 60¢
         (column 8, row 3 of fare), for both it is 2 x 60¢ = 120¢.
         Total fare = 80¢ + 120¢ = 200¢ = **$2.00**
    (d) Time from Town H to Town A is 12 min. He arrives at town A 12 minutes after 08:15, or
         08:27
    (e) The fare was 80¢ for 12 minutes. $\frac{80¢}{12min}$ = **6$\frac{2}{3}$** ¢/min.

9. (a) The team that has won the last match in each group will go into the second round; they
        are teams **E, F, K, and S**.
   (b) E played **2** games (vs. D, then A)
        F played **2** games (vs. G, then J)
        K played **3** games (vs. L, then M, then O)
        S played **2** games (vs. R, then P)
   (c) E: $(4 + 3) \div 2 = 7 \div 2 =$ **3.5 goals**
        F: $(3 + 2) \div 2 = 5 \div 2 =$ **2.5 goals**
        K: $(2 + 3 + 1) \div 3 = 6 \div 3 =$ **2 goals**
        S: $(4 + 3) \div 2 = 7 \div 2 =$ **3.5 goals**

10.(a) Score was **4-1**; **E** won (home team score is given first).
   (b) Score was **6-0**; **E** won
   (c) Each team played 3 home games and 3 away games; **6 games** total.
   (d) Home games (first number in first row): $3 + 4 + 6 = 15$ goals.
        Away games (second number in first column): $0 + 4 + 5 = 9$ goals.
        Total goals scored for E = $15 + 9 =$ **22 goals**
   (e) Home games (second number in first row): $2 + 1 + 0 = 3$
        Away games (first number in first column): $3 + 5 + 5 = 13$
        Total goals against E = $3 + 13 =$ **16 goals**.

11.(a) If the first number in the row for that time is bigger, the team won that match. If the
        second number in the column for that team is bigger, the team won that match. If they
        are the same, the match was a draw. For goals scored, add the first numbers in the row
        and last numbers in the column, for goals scored against add the second numbers in the
        row and first numbers in the column. No. of points awarded is (2 x no. of matches won)
        + no. of matches drawn.

	No. of matches won	No. of matches drawn	No. of matches lost	No. of goals scored for	No. of goals scored against	No. of points awarded
E	**3**	**1**	**2**	**22**	**16**	**7**
F	**3** 2 home 1 away	**1** 1 home	**2** 0 home 2 away	**13** $3 + 1 + 4$ $2 + 1 + 2$	**10** $0 + 1 + 2$ $3 + 3 + 1$	**7** 2(3) + 1
K	**4** 3 home 1 away	**1** 1 away	**1** 0 home 1 away	**14** $5 + 3 + 3$ $1 + 1 + 1$	**12** $4 + 1 + 2$ $4 + 1 + 0$	**9** 2(4) + 1
S	**0** 0 home 0 away	**1** 1 home	**5** 2 home 3 away	**10** $5 + 1 + 0$ $0 + 2 + 2$	**21** $5 + 2 + 1$ $6 + 4 + 3$	**1** 2(0) + 1

   (b) **K and E** (E had more goals than F)
   (c) **E** scored the most goals
   (d) **S** scored the least goals
   (e) **12** goals were scored against K

Exercise 3.3 (pp. 83-85)

1. Average temperature = (24.5 + 23.8 + 22.4 + 25.6 + 26.0 + 23.1 + 24.0) ÷ 7
                                    = **24.2°C**

2. Increase in temperature for 10 s = 35 - 25 = 10°C
    Increase in temperature for   1 s = 10 ÷ 10 = **1°C**

3. Number of weekdays worked = 4 weeks x 6 days/week = 24 days (includes Saturday)
    Pay for weekdays = 24 x $30 = $720
    Number of Sundays worked = 4
    Pay for Sundays = 4 x $45 = $180
    Total pay = $720 + $180 = **$900**

4. Total cost of 12 bags = $50 x 12 = $600
    Total cost including transport = $600 + $15 = $615
    Profit = $650 - $615 = $35
    Or: Net profit = $650 - [($50 x 12) + $15) = **$35**

5. 2 hours = 120 minutes
    Packets of biscuits packed by A in 2 hours = 120 s x 152 packets/s
                                        = 18,240 packets
    Packets of biscuits packed by B in 2 hours = 120 s x 205 packets/s
                                        = 24,600 packs
    Total packets 18,240 + 24,600 = 42,840 packets
    Or: Total packets = (152 packets/s x 2 h x 60 s/h) + (205 packets/s x 2 h x 60 s/h)
                        = **42,840 packets**

6. Price for 16 pieces = cost + profit = $3 + $5 = $8
    Price for   1 piece = $8 ÷ 16 = **$0.50**

7. Total oranges bought = 10 x 30 = 300
    Total oranges sold = 300 - 50 = 250
    Price for 250 oranges = $45
    Price for   1 orange = $45 ÷ 250 = **$0.18**
    Or: Price/orange = $45 ÷ (10 cartons x 30 oranges/carton - 50 oranges) = **$0.18**

8. Cost of 5 lemons = $0.25 x 5 = $1.25
    Cost of $\frac{1}{2}$ kg mutton = $8.36 x $\frac{1}{2}$ = $4.18
    Cost of $\frac{1}{2}$ ℓ milk = $0.85
    Cost of 1 ℓ of milk = $0.85 x 2 = $1.70
    Cost of 2.5 ℓ of milk = $1.70 x 2.5 = $4.25
    Total cost = $1.25 + $4.18 + $4.25 = **$9.68**

    Or: Total cost = ($0.25 x 5) + ($8.36 x $\frac{1}{2}$) + $\left(\dfrac{\$0.85}{\frac{1}{2}} \times 2.5 \right)$ = $9.68

9.   Cost of 2 durians = cost of 6 mangoes
      Cost of 1 durian = cost of 6 ÷ 2 = 3 mangoes
      Cost of 4 durians = cost of 3 x 4 = 12 mangoes
      Cost of 3 mangoes + cost of 4 durians = $30
      Cost of 3 mangoes + cost of 12 mangoes = $30
      Cost of 15 mangoes = $30
      Cost of 1 mango = **$2**

10.   Admission = (3 adults x $5/adult) + (4 children x $2/child) = $23
      Change = $50 - $23 = **$27**

11.   Payment if no vases were broken = 120 x $2 = $240
      Payment lost for broken vases = $240 - $165 = $75
      Number of broken vases = $75 ÷ $15/vase = **5 vases**

12.   Total money she had = (2 x $10) + (1 x $5) + (7 x $1) + (8 x $0.10) = $32.80
      Total money she spent = $5.60 + $1.25 + $7.30 + $6.60 = $20.75
      Money left = $32.80 - $20.75 = **$12.05**

13.   The eldest brother received $\frac{3}{5} = \frac{6}{10}$ of the money = $108

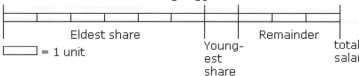

      Eldest share   Young-   Remainder   total
      $\square$ = 1 unit   est   salary
                              share

      6 units = $108
      1 unit = $108 ÷ 6 = $18
      The youngest got 1 unit = $18
      The middle brother got 3 units = $18 x 3 = **$54**
      Or: $\frac{3}{5}$ of the money = $108

          Total money = $108 ÷ $\frac{3}{5}$ = $108 x $\frac{5}{3}$ = $36 x 5 = $180

          Younger brother got $\frac{1}{10}$ x 180 = $18

          Middle brother got $180 - $108 - $18 = $54

14.   Fraction given to friend = $\frac{1}{4} \times \left(1 - \frac{2}{5}\right) = \frac{1}{4} \times \frac{3}{5} = \frac{3}{20}$

      Remaining tarts = $200 - \left(\frac{2}{5} \times 200\right) - \left(\frac{3}{20} \times 200\right) = 200 - 80 - 30 =$ **90 tarts**

15. Fraction of chairs that are yellow = $1 - \dfrac{2}{5} - \dfrac{3}{7} = \dfrac{35}{35} - \dfrac{14}{35} - \dfrac{15}{35} = \dfrac{6}{35}$

There are 24 yellow chairs.

$\dfrac{6}{35}$ of the chairs = 24

$\dfrac{1}{35}$ of the chairs = 24 ÷ 6 = 4

Blue chairs = $\dfrac{15}{35}$ of the chairs = 4 x 15 = **60**

16. 3 people pay $1 - \dfrac{1}{6} = \dfrac{5}{6}$ of the bill.

1 person pays $\dfrac{5}{6} \div 3 = \dfrac{5}{6} x \dfrac{1}{3} = \dfrac{\mathbf{5}}{\mathbf{18}}$ of the bill.

17. Cost of container with coffee = (30 packets x \$2/packet) + \$3 = \$63
Cost of 60 containers + delivery = (60 x \$63) + \$20 = **\$3,800**

18. Earnings per week = \$780 ÷ 6 = \$130
Earnings per day = \$130 ÷ 5 = \$26
Pay - transport = \$26 - \$2 = \$24
Number of hours worked = \$24 ÷ \$4/h = **6 h**

19. Fraction left to fill = $1 - \dfrac{3}{5} = \dfrac{2}{5}$

$\dfrac{2}{5}$ tin = 3.5 ℓ

$\dfrac{2}{5}$ tin = 3.5 ℓ ÷ 2 = 1.75 ℓ

$\dfrac{5}{5}$ tin = 1.75 ℓ x 5 = 8.75 ℓ

8.75 ℓ = \$28

1 ℓ = \$28 ÷ 8.75 = \$3.20

$\dfrac{1}{4}$ ℓ = \$3.20 ÷ 4 = \$0.80

$\dfrac{3}{4}$ ℓ = \$0.80 x 3 = **\$2.40**

20. Total cost = 20 x $16 = $320
     Total good apples = (64 apples/box x 20 boxes) - 30 apples = 1,250 apples
     Selling price = cost + profit = $320 + $55 = $375
     Price per apple = $375 ÷ 1,250 apples = **$0.30**

21. Selling price for all eggs = cost + profit = $15.20 + $7.60 = $22.80
     Number of eggs sold at 12¢ each = $22.80 ÷ $0.12 = 190
     Number of eggs discarded = 200 - 190 = **10**

22. Find total earnings first.
     To find earnings on weekend, hourly wages on weekdays is needed.
     Hours worked weekdays = 7 h/day x 5 days = 35 h
     Hourly wage weekdays = $140 ÷ 35 h = $4/h
     Hourly wage on weekend = 2 x $4 = $8
     Hours worked on weekend = 4 h x 2 = 8 h
     Earnings on weekend = 8 x $8 = $64
     Total earnings = $64 + $140 = $204
     Money spent on holiday = $204 - 54 = $150
     He spent $50 per day, so number of days = $150 ÷ $50/day = **3 days**

23. Fraction spent on food = $\dfrac{5}{8} \times \dfrac{3}{5} = \dfrac{15}{40}$

     Fraction spent on other items = $\dfrac{3}{8} \times \dfrac{3}{5} = \dfrac{9}{40}$

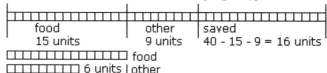

     □ = 1 unit

     He spent 6 units more on food than other items.
     6 units = $600
     1 unit = $600 ÷ 6 = $100
     He saved 16 units
     16 units = $100 x 16 = $1,600
     He saved **$1,600**

24. From 10:15 to 10:35, 20 min, the temperature increased 2.5°C/min
     Total increase in temperature = 20 min x 2.5°C/min = 50°C
     The temperature falls to 12.5°C above the starting temperature.
     Total decrease in temperature from to 10:35 to 11:05, 30 min, = 50 - 12.5 = 37.5°C
     Rate of temperature fall = 37.5°C ÷ 30 min = 1.25°C

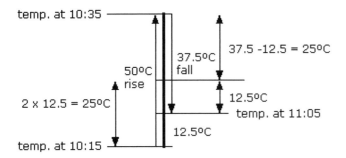

     The time when the temperature is 12.5°C above what it is at 11:05 will be when it is 25°C
     more than the temperature at 10:05 and when it is 25°C less than the temperature at 10:35.
     Rate of temperature increase is 2.5°C/min
     2.5°C → 1 min
     1°C   → 1 ÷ 2.5 = 0.4 min
     25°C → 0.4 x 25 = 10 min
     (Or: 25°C ÷ 2.5°C/min = 10 min)
     The temperature was 12.5°C higher than at 11:05 at 10:15 + 10 min = 10:25.
     Rate of temperature decrease is 1.25°C.
     This is half the rate of temperature increase, so it will take twice as long to fall 25°C as it took
     to rise 25°C, or 2 x 10 min = 20 min
     (Or: 25°C ÷ 1.25°C/min = 20 min)
     The temperature was 12.5°C higher than at 11:05 at 10:35 + 20 min = 10:55
     So the temperature is 12.5°C higher than at 11:05 at **10:25** and at **10:55**.

Chapter 4

Exercise 4.1 (pp. 95-96)

1.

2. (a) 5 > 3   (b) 7 > -4   (c) -8 < -1

   (d) 125 > -3   (e) 0 < 4   (f) 6 > -8

   (g) -3 > -12   (h) 0 > -9   (i) -12 < 10

3. (a) 5   (b) 7   (c) 0

   (d) 7   (e) 18   (f) 18

4. (a) **12** is larger than -14   (b) **-14** is numerically larger (14) than 12

5. (a) **-18** is smaller than -14   (b) **-14** is numerically (14) smaller than - 18 (18)

6. (a) **24** has the greater value than   (b) **-25** has the greater absolute value (25) than
       -25   24

7. (a) **-16** has the smaller value than   (b) **-15** has the smaller absolute value (15) than -
       -15   16 (16)

8. (a)   4, 3, 2, 1, 0, **-1, -2, -3** (decreasing by 1)
   (b)   2, 4, 6, 8, **10, 12, 14** (increasing by 2)
   (c)   -8, -6, -4, -2, **0, 2, 4** (increasing by 2)
   (d)   -4, **-3**, -2, -1, 0, **1, 2, 3** (increasing by 1)
   (e)   -6, -3, **0, 3**, 6, **9** (increasing by 3)
   (f)   -2, **-3, -4, -5**
   (g)   -5, **-7, -9, -11**
   (h)   -4, **-6, -8, -10**
   (I)   3, **2, 1, 0, -1**
   (j)   -3, **-4, -5, -6, -7**
   (k)   9, **6, 3, 0, -3**
   (l)   -9, **-6, -3, 0, 3**

Exercise 4.2 (pp. 100-102)

1. (a)

   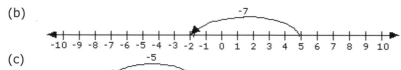

   (b)

   (c)

   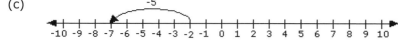

2. (a) -7 + 16 = 16 - 7   (b) -3 + (-9) = -(3 + 9)   (c) 15 + (-19) = -(19 - 15)
            = **9**   = **-12**   = **-4**

(d) $-21 + 16 = -(21 - 16)$
$= \mathbf{-5}$

(e) $-5 + -(20) = -(5 + 20)$
$= \mathbf{-25}$

(f) $-7 + 7 = 7 - 7$
$= \mathbf{0}$

(g) $-5 + (-2) = -(5 + 2)$
$= \mathbf{-7}$

(h) $5 + (-10) = -(10 - 5)$
$= \mathbf{-5}$

(i) $-7 + 5 = -(7 - 5)$
$= \mathbf{-2}$

(j) $3 + (-7) = -(7 - 3)$
$= \mathbf{-4}$

(k) $-23 + (-13)$
$= -(23 + 13)$
$= \mathbf{-36}$

(l) $-45 + 18 = -(45 - 18)$
$= \mathbf{-27}$

(m) $27 + (-32)$
$= -(32 - 27)$
$= \mathbf{-5}$

(n) $-38 + 81 = 81 - 38$
$= \mathbf{43}$

(o) $55 + (-42) = 55 - 42$
$= \mathbf{13}$

(p) $-37 + 37 = 37 - 37$
$= \mathbf{0}$

(q) $-64 + (-64)$
$= -(64 + 64)$
$= \mathbf{-128}$

(r) $-129 + 107$
$= -(129 - 107)$
$= \mathbf{-22}$

3. (a) $7 - 3 = \mathbf{4}$

(b) $5 - 8 = -(8 - 5)$
$= \mathbf{-3}$

(c) $-5 - 8 = -(5 + 8)$
$= \mathbf{-13}$

(d) $-5 - 3 = -(5 + 3)$
$= \mathbf{-8}$

(e) $8 - (-3) = 8 + 3$
$= \mathbf{11}$

(f) $5 - (-7) = 5 + 7$
$= \mathbf{12}$

(g) $-6 - (-8) = -6 + 8$
$= 8 - 6$
$= \mathbf{2}$

(h) $-8 - (-4) = -8 + 4$
$= -(8 - 4)$
$= \mathbf{-4}$

(i) $-34 - (-74) = -34 + 74$
$= 74 - 34$
$= \mathbf{40}$

(j) $-52 - (-31) = -52 + 31$
$= -(52 - 31)$
$= \mathbf{-21}$

(k) $38 - (-8) = 38 + 8$
$= \mathbf{46}$

(l) $-45 - (-12) = -45 + 12$
$= -(45 - 12)$
$= \mathbf{-33}$

(m) $-24 - (-32) = -24 + 32$
$= 32 - 24$
$= \mathbf{8}$

(n) $82 - (-18) = 82 + 18$
$= \mathbf{100}$

(o) $14 - (-56) = 14 + 56$
$= \mathbf{70}$

(p) $-92 - (-92) = -92 + 92$
$= 92 - 92$
$= \mathbf{0}$

(q) $107 - 128$
$= -(128 - 107)$
$= \mathbf{-21}$

((r) $-351 - (-101)$
$= -351 + 101$
$= -(351 - 101)$
$= \mathbf{-250}$

4. (a) $24 - (-12) = 24 + 12$
$= \mathbf{36}$

(b) $-156 - 342 = -(156 + 342)$
$= \mathbf{-498}$

(c) $342 - (-32) = 342 + 32$
$= \mathbf{374}$

(d) $765 - (-342) = 765 + 342$
$= \mathbf{1,107}$

(e) $-(-682) + 402 = 682 + 402$
$= \mathbf{1,084}$

(f) $-345 + (-284) = -(345 + 284)$
$= \mathbf{-629}$

(g) $354 - (-404) = 354 + 404$
$= \mathbf{758}$

(h) $432 - (-135) = 432 + 135$
$= \mathbf{567}$

(i) $426 - (-12) + 28 = 426 + 12 + 28$
$= \mathbf{466}$

(j) $255 - (-122) - 201 = 255 + 122 - 201$
$= 377 - 201$
$= \mathbf{176}$

(k) -(-234) - 111 - 182 = 234 - 111 - 182
                       = 123 - 182
                       = -(182 - 123)
                       = **-59**

(l) 365 + (-182) - (-222)
    = 365 - 182 + 222
    = 183 + 222
    = **405**

(m) 562 - (-100) - 201
    = 562 + 100 - 201
    = 662 - 201
    = **461**

(n) -(-800) + (-510) - (120)
    = 800 - 510 - 120
    = 290 - 120
    = **170**

(o) -285 - (-124) - (-321)
    = -285 + 124 + 321
    = -285 + 445
    = 445 - 285
    = **160**

(p) -379 - (-128) - (-251)
    = -379 + 128 + 251
    = -379 + 379
    = 379 - 379
    = **0**

5.

Original Temperature	Change	New Temperature	Mathematical Sentence
5°C	-3°C	2°C	5 + (-3) = 2
12°C	+10°C	22°C	**12 + 10 = 22**
15°C	-13°C	**2°C**	**15 + (-13) = 2**
15°C	-18°C	**-3°C**	**15 + (-18) = -3**
-8°C	+14°C	**6°C**	**-8 + 14 = 6**
-18°C	+9°C	**-9°C**	**-18 + 9 = -9**
-21°C	-13°C	**-33°C**	**-21 + (-13) = -33**

6.

Checks(C) and Bills (B) ($)		Total amount in box ($)	Mathematical Sentence
C: 10	B: 15	-5	10 + (-15) = -5
C: 25	B: 17	8	**25 + (-17) = 8**
C: 7	B: 10	**-3**	**7 + (-10) = -3**
B: 25	C: 18	**-7**	**-25 + 18 = -7**
B: 18	C: 25	**7**	**-18 + 25 = 7**
C: 16	C: 17	**33**	**16 + 17 = 33**
B: 19	B: 25	**-44**	**-19 + (-25) = -44**

7.

Checks (C) and Bills (B) ($)			Total amount ($)	Re-moved ($)	Amount Left ($)	Mathematical Sentence
C: 10	C: 30	B: 16	24 *10 + 30 + (-16)*	C: 30	-6	24 - 30 = -6
B: 37	C: 15	C: 10	-12 *-37 + 15 + 10*	C: 10	-22	**-12 - 10 = -22**
C: 52	B: 10	B: 12	**30** *52 + (-10) + (-12)*	B: 12	42	**30 - (-12) =** *30 + 12 = **42***
C: 25	B: 15	B: 20	**-10** *25 + (-15) + (-20)*	B: 15	**5**	**-10 - (-15) =** *-10 + 15 = **5***
C: 33	C: 15	B: 10	38 *33 + 15 + (-10)*	C: 15	**23**	**38 - 15 = 23**
C: 20	B: 42	B: 18	**-40** *20 + (-42) + (-18)*	B: 18	**-22**	**-40 - (-18) =** *-40 + 18 = **-22***

8. (a)   Jan. +$5,000   Feb. +$2,000   Mar. -$6,000
          Apr. +$1,000   May +$4,000   Jun. -$3,000
    (b)   In thousands: 5 + 2 - 6 + 1 + 4 - 3 = 3 Total income = **$3,000**
    (c)   In thousands: 5 + 2 - 6 = 1   Income first 3 months = **$1,000**
    (d)   In thousands: -6 + 1 + 4 - 3 = -4 Income Mar. - Jun. = **-$4,000**

9. The difference in temperature = 35ºC - (-5ºC) = 35ºC + 5ºC = 40ºC
    1:00 to 4:00 = 3 h.
    Temperature decrease from 1:00 - 4:00 = 3 h x 0.5ºC/h = 1.5ºC
    Temp. at 4:00 = -5ºC - 1.5ºC = **-6.5ºC**

10.(a)   **13,000 m + 5,000 m + (-3,000) m**
   (b)   **15,000 m**

Exercise 4.3 (pp. 107 - 108)

1. (a) 3 x (-5) = -(3 x 5)   (b) 4 x (-1) = -(4 x 1)
             = **-15**   = **-4**

    (c) -3 x -2 = 3 x 2   (d) 0 x (-3) = **0**
             = **6**

    (e) - 5 x 0 = **0**   (f) 18 x 11 = **198**

    (g) -14 x (-7) = 14 x 7   (h) -7 x (-2) x 3 = 7 x 2 x 3
             = **98**   = **42**

    (i) -3 x 4 x (-5) = 3 x 4 x 5   (j) 5 x (-2) x 7 = -(5 x 2 x 7)
             = **60**   = **-70**

    (k) 3 x (-8) x 0 = **0**   (l) -7 x (-3) x (-2) = -(7 x 3 x 2)
                                                  = **-42**

    (m) -5 x (-8) x (-3) = -(5 x 8 x 3)   (n) -2 x (-3) x (-4) x (-5)
             = **-120**   = 2 x 3 x 4 x 5
                                                  = **120**

    (o) -3 x 4 x (-8) x (-7) = -(3 x 4 x 8 x 7)   (p) -2 x 0 x 3 x (-5) = **0**
             = **-672**

    (q) -12 x (-11) x (-321) = -(12 x 11 x 321)   (r) -25 x (-26) x 123 = 25 x 26 x 123
             = **-42,372**   = **79,950**

    (s) -16 x (-123) x (-37) = -(16 x 123 x 37)   (t) -214 x (-15) x (-125)
             = **-72,816**   = -(214 x 15 x 125)
                                                      = **-401,250**

    (u) 13 x (-10) x (-301) = 13 x 10 x 301   (v) 45 x (-14) x 377 = -(45 x 14 x 377)
             = **39,310**   = **-237,510**

    (w) 6 x (-18) x (-7) = 6 x 18 x 7   (x) -27 x 8 x (-15) = 27 x 8 x 15
             = **756**   = **3,240**

    (y) 5 x (-19) x (-102) = 5 x 19 x 102   (z) -25 x 6 x (-200) = 25 x 6 x 200
             = **9,690**   = **30,000**

2. (a) $15^2 = 15 \times 15 = \mathbf{225}$

(c) $106^2 = 106 \times 106 = \mathbf{11,236}$

(b) $(-45)^2 = -45 \times (-45) = \mathbf{2,025}$

(d) $(-312)^2 = -312 \times (-312) = \mathbf{97,344}$

3. (a) $121 = 11 \times 11$ or $-11 \times (-11)$
   11, -11

(c) $625 = 5 \times 5 \times 5 \times 5$
   $= (5 \times 5)^2$
   $= 25 \times 25$ or $-25 \times (-25)$
   25, -25

(b) $256 = 2 \times 2 \times 2 \times 2 \times 2 \times 2 \times 2 \times 2$
   $= (2 \times 2 \times 2 \times 2)^2$
   $= 16 \times 16$ or $-16 \times (-16)$
   16, -16

(d) $1,225 = 5 \times 5 \times 7 \times 7$
   $= (5 \times 7)^2$
   $= 35 \times 35$ or $-35 \times (-35)$
   35, -35

4. (a) $441 = 3 \times 3 \times 7 \times 7 = 21 \times 21$
   $\sqrt{441} = \mathbf{21}$

(c) $4,624 = 2^4 \times 17^2 = (2 \times 2 \times 17)^2$
   $-\sqrt{4,624} = \mathbf{-68}$

(b) $576 = 2^6 \times 3^2 = (2 \times 2 \times 2 \times 3)^2$
   $-\sqrt{576} = \mathbf{-24}$

(d) $7,396 = 2 \times 2 \times 43 \times 43 = (2 \times 43)^2$
   $\sqrt{7,396} = \mathbf{86}$

5. (a) $11^3 = 11 \times 11 \times 11$
   $= \mathbf{1,331}$

(c) $(-30)^3 = -30 \times (-30) \times (-30)$
   $= -(30 \times 30 \times 30)$
   $= \mathbf{-27,000}$

(b) $(-25)^3 = -25 \times (-25) \times (-25)$
   $= -(25 \times 25 \times 25)$
   $= \mathbf{-15,625}$

(d) $42^3 = 42 \times 42 \times 42$
   $= \mathbf{74,088}$

6. (a) $125 = 5 \times 5 \times 5$
   $\sqrt[3]{125} = \mathbf{5}$

(c) $-8,000 = -(8 \times 100)$
   $= -(2^3 \times 10^3)$
   $= -(2 \times 10)^3$
   $= -(20)^3$
   $\sqrt[3]{-8,000} = \mathbf{-20}$

(b) $-1,728 = -(2^6 \times 3^3)$
   $= -(2 \times 2 \times 3)^3$
   $= -(12)^3$
   $\sqrt[3]{-1,728} = \mathbf{-12}$

(d) $12,167 = 23 \times 23 \times 23$
   $\sqrt[3]{-12,167} = \mathbf{23}$

7. (a) $512 = 2^9$
   $= (2 \times 2 \times 2)^3$
   $= 8^3$
   $\sqrt[3]{512} = \mathbf{8}$

(c) $9,261 = 3^3 \times 7^3$
   $= (3 \times 7)^3$
   $= 21^3$
   $\sqrt[3]{9,261} = \mathbf{21}$

(b) $1,331 = 11 \times 11 \times 11$
   $\sqrt[3]{-1,331} = \mathbf{-11}$

(d) $15,625 = 5^6$
   $= (5 \times 5)^3$
   $= 25^3$
   $\sqrt[3]{-15,625} = \mathbf{-25}$

8. Keying order differs among calculators.

9. (a) $-(-32) \times (-12)^2 = 32 \times 144$
                        $= \mathbf{4,608}$

(b) $31^2 \times [-(-31)] = 961 \times 31$
                        $= \mathbf{29,791}$

(c) $13^3 \times \{-[-(-30)]\} = 2,197 \times (-30)$
                        $= \mathbf{-65,910}$

(d) $-\{-[-(-23)]\} \times [-(-71)^3]$
                        $= 23 \times -(-357,911)$
                        $= \mathbf{8,231,953}$
(answer in text is incorrect)

Exercise 4.4 (pp. 109-110)

1. $-8 \div 4 = -(8 \div 4)$
              $= \mathbf{-2}$

2. $-24 \div 6 = -(24 \div 6)$
              $= \mathbf{-4}$

3. $-45 \div 9 = -(45 \div 9)$
              $= \mathbf{-5}$

4. $9 \div (-3) = -(9 \div 3)$
              $= \mathbf{-3}$

5. $42 \div (-7) = -(42 \div 7)$
              $= \mathbf{-6}$

6. $0 \div (-18) = \mathbf{0}$

7. $72 \div (-6) = -(72 \div 6)$
              $= \mathbf{-12}$

8. $-9 \div (-3) = 9 \div 3$
              $= \mathbf{3}$

9. $-32 \div (-8) = 32 \div 8$
              $= \mathbf{4}$

10. $-72 \div (-9) = 72 \div 9$
              $= \mathbf{8}$

11. $-123 \div 3 = -(123 \div 3)$
              $= \mathbf{-41}$

12. $-456 \div 6 = -(456 \div 6)$
              $= \mathbf{-76}$

13. $448 \div (-8) = -(448 \div 8)$
              $= \mathbf{-56}$

14. $207 \div (-9) = -(207 \div 9)$
              $= \mathbf{-23}$

15. $-244 \div (-4) = 244 \div 4$
              $= \mathbf{61}$

16. $-560 \div (-5) = 560 \div 5$
              $= \mathbf{112}$

17. $-504 \div (-9) = 504 \div 9$
              $= \mathbf{56}$

18. $576 \div (-24) = -(576 \div 24)$
              $= \mathbf{-24}$

19. $384 \div (-32) = -(384 \div 32)$
              $= \mathbf{-12}$

20. $-144 \div (-12) = 144 \div 12$
              $= \mathbf{12}$

21. $-345 \div (-15) = 345 \div 15$
              $= \mathbf{23}$

22. $-252 \div 18 = -(252 \div 18)$
              $= \mathbf{-14}$

23. $-220 \div 22 = -(220 \div 22)$
              $= \mathbf{-10}$

24. $237 \div (-79) = -(237 \div 79)$
              $= \mathbf{-3}$

25. $-168 \div (-42) = 168 \div 42$
              $= \mathbf{4}$

26. $-713 \div 31 \div (-23) = 713 \div 31 \div 23$
              $= \mathbf{1}$

27. $325 \div (-13) \div [-(-5)] = -(325 \div 13) \div 5$
              $= -(25 \div 5)$
              $= \mathbf{-5}$

28. $-112 \div (-4)^2 \div 7 = -112 \div 16 \div 7$
              $= -(112 \div 16 \div 7)$
              $= \mathbf{-1}$

29. $616 \div [-(-11)] \div (-28) = -(616 \div 11 \div 28)$
              $= \mathbf{-2}$

30. $-384 \div 96 \div [-(-4)] = -(384 \div 96 \div 4)$
              $= \mathbf{-1}$

Exercise 4.5 (pp. 113-114)

1. (a) **true**: $-a \times (-b) = a \times b$ where a and b are rational numbers.

(b) **true**: $-a \times 0 = -(a \times 0) = -0 = 0$ where a is a rational number.

(c) **false**: $0 \times -1 = 0$

(d) **true**: $-a \times b = -(a \times b)$ where a and b are rational numbers.

(e) **false**: they are either both negative or both positive.

(f) **false**: they could both be negative.

2. (a)
$$-\frac{1}{2} + \frac{1}{3} = \frac{1}{3} - \frac{1}{2}$$
$$= \frac{2-3}{6}$$
$$= -\frac{1}{6}$$

(b)
$$-\frac{3}{4} + \left(-\frac{1}{2}\right) = \frac{-3 + (-2)}{4}$$
$$= \frac{-5}{4}$$
$$= -1\frac{1}{4}$$

(c)
$$-\frac{9}{16} + \frac{9}{16} = \frac{9}{16} - \frac{9}{16}$$
$$= 0$$

(d)
$$\frac{1}{4} + \left(-\frac{2}{3}\right) = \frac{3-8}{12}$$
$$= -\frac{5}{12}$$

(e)
$$-\frac{9}{7} + \left(-\frac{4}{9}\right) = \frac{-81 + (-28)}{63}$$
$$= \frac{-109}{63}$$
$$= -1\frac{46}{63}$$

(f)
$$-3\frac{3}{5} + \frac{9}{10} = \frac{9}{10} - 3\frac{6}{10}$$
$$= \frac{9-36}{10}$$
$$= \frac{-27}{10}$$
$$= -2\frac{7}{10}$$

3. (a)
$$\frac{2}{7} - \left(-\frac{1}{3}\right) = \frac{6+7}{21}$$
$$= \frac{13}{21}$$

(b)
$$-\frac{4}{5} - \left(-\frac{4}{5}\right) = -\frac{4}{5} + \frac{4}{5}$$
$$= 0$$

(c)
$$\frac{3}{2} - \left(-\frac{2}{3}\right) = \frac{9+4}{6}$$
$$= \frac{13}{6}$$
$$= 2\frac{1}{6}$$

(d)
$$-\frac{2}{11} - \left(-\frac{1}{3}\right) = \frac{-6+11}{33}$$
$$= \frac{5}{33}$$

(e)
$$\frac{21}{25} - \left(-\frac{23}{50}\right) = \frac{42+23}{50}$$
$$= \frac{65}{50}$$
$$= 1\frac{3}{10}$$

(f)
$$-\frac{25}{72} - \frac{15}{36} = \frac{-25-30}{72}$$
$$= -\frac{55}{72}$$

4. (a)
$$-\frac{2}{3} \times \left(-\frac{3}{4}\right) = \frac{2 \times 3}{3 \times 4}$$
$$= \frac{1}{2}$$

(b)
$$-\frac{14}{15} \times \left(-\frac{6}{7}\right) = \frac{14 \times 6}{15 \times 7}$$
$$= \frac{4}{5}$$

(c)
$$\frac{9}{18} \times \left(-\frac{9}{4}\right) = -\frac{9 \times 9}{18 \times 4}$$
$$= -\frac{9}{8}$$
$$= -1\frac{1}{8}$$

(d)
$$\frac{15}{4} \times \left(-\frac{1}{2}\right) = -\frac{15 \times 1}{4 \times 2}$$
$$= -\frac{15}{8}$$
$$= -1\frac{7}{8}$$

(e)
$$-\frac{35}{6} \times \left(-\frac{10}{21}\right) = \frac{35 \times 10}{6 \times 21}$$
$$= \frac{5 \times 5}{3 \times 3}$$
$$= \frac{25}{9}$$
$$= 2\frac{7}{9}$$

(f)
$$-\frac{2,148,214}{5,732,195} \times 0 = 0$$

5. (a) $-\dfrac{2}{3} \div \left(-\dfrac{4}{7}\right) = \dfrac{2 \times 7}{3 \times 4}$

   $= \dfrac{7}{6}$

   $= \mathbf{1\dfrac{1}{6}}$

(b) $-\dfrac{3}{5} \div \dfrac{9}{5} = -\dfrac{3 \times 5}{5 \times 9}$

   $= -\dfrac{\mathbf{1}}{\mathbf{3}}$

(c) $-\dfrac{18}{5} \div \dfrac{3}{10} = -\dfrac{18 \times 10}{5 \times 3}$

   $= -(6 \times 2)$

   $= \mathbf{-12}$

(d) $-5 \div \left(-\dfrac{3}{4}\right) = \dfrac{5 \times 4}{3}$

   $= \dfrac{20}{3}$

   $= \mathbf{6\dfrac{2}{3}}$

(e) $-\dfrac{3}{7} \div (-3) = \dfrac{3 \times 1}{7 \times 3}$

   $= \dfrac{\mathbf{1}}{\mathbf{7}}$

(f) $27 \div \left(-\dfrac{15}{7}\right) = -\dfrac{27 \times 7}{15}$

   $= -\dfrac{9 \times 7}{5}$

   $= -\dfrac{63}{5}$

   $= \mathbf{-12\dfrac{3}{5}}$

6. (a) $\dfrac{-2}{3} = -\dfrac{\mathbf{2}}{\mathbf{3}}$

(b) $\dfrac{4}{-5} = -\dfrac{\mathbf{4}}{\mathbf{5}}$

(c) $\dfrac{3}{-7} = -\dfrac{\mathbf{3}}{\mathbf{7}}$

(d) $\dfrac{5}{-16} = -\dfrac{\mathbf{5}}{\mathbf{16}}$

(e) $-\dfrac{3}{-7} = \dfrac{\mathbf{3}}{\mathbf{7}}$

(f) $\dfrac{-4}{9} = -\dfrac{\mathbf{4}}{\mathbf{9}}$

(g) $\dfrac{-5}{-24} = \dfrac{\mathbf{5}}{\mathbf{24}}$

(h) $\dfrac{-7}{20} = -\dfrac{\mathbf{7}}{\mathbf{20}}$

(i) $\dfrac{-9}{-10} = \dfrac{\mathbf{9}}{\mathbf{10}}$

(j) $-\dfrac{8}{-15} = \dfrac{\mathbf{8}}{\mathbf{15}}$

(k) $\dfrac{-84}{-11} = \dfrac{\mathbf{84}}{\mathbf{11}}$

(l) $\dfrac{-678}{5} = -\dfrac{\mathbf{678}}{\mathbf{5}}$

7. (a) $-1 > -2$

(b) $-\dfrac{3}{4} < \dfrac{1}{2}$

(c) $-2\dfrac{8}{10} < -2\dfrac{5}{10}$

(d) $2\dfrac{3}{4} > -4\dfrac{1}{4}$

(e) $-2.3 < 1.4$

(f) $3.6 > -4.4$

(g) $-5.5 < -2.8$

(h) $-8.6 < -1.1$

8. Fractions, repeating decimals, and the roots of squares are all rational. The roots of non-square numbers are irrational. So only $\sqrt{3}$, $\sqrt{8}$, and $\sqrt{5}$ are irrational.

9. (a) 1.414   (b) 1.732   (c) 2.449   (d) 2.449

   (e) 4.243   (f) 2.449   (g) 1.260   (h) 1.442

   (I) 1.817   (j) 1.817   (k) 2.289   (l) 1.260

Exercise 4.6 (pp. 115-116)

1. $[34 + 21 + (-12)] \times 5 = \underline{43 \times 5} = \textbf{215}$

2. $[\underline{5 + (-18)}] + [\underline{24 + (-30)}] \times (-7) = -13 + \underline{(-6) \times (-7)} = -13 + 42 = \textbf{29}$

3. $\{[\underline{12 - (-8)}] \times 2 + 3\} \times 4 = \{\underline{20 \times 2} + 3\} \times 4 = \{\underline{40 + 3}\} \times 4 = 43 \times 4 = \textbf{172}$

4. $-15 \times [\underline{13 + (-8)}] \times 23 = -15 \times 5 \times 23 = \textbf{-1,725}$

5. $237 - \underline{48 \times (-35)} + (-59) = \underline{237 - (-1,680)} + (-59) = 1,917 - 59 = \textbf{1,858}$

6. $-85 + (\underline{-92 + 78}) \times (-15) = -85 + \underline{(-14) \times (-15)} = -85 + 210 = \textbf{125}$

7. $\underline{-18 \times (-15)} + 28 - (-39) = 270 + 28 + 39 = \textbf{337}$

8. $48 - 34 + 29 \times [\underline{43 - (-32)}] = \underline{48 - 34} + \underline{29 \times 75} = 14 + 2,175 = \textbf{2,189}$

9. $52 \underline{- (-23)} + (-24) \times [\underline{78 + (-68)}] = \underline{52 + 23} + \underline{(-24) \times 10} = 75 + (-240) = \textbf{-165}$

10. $\underline{75 \times (-23)} - [\underline{43 + (-12)}] = -1,725 - 31 = \textbf{-1,756}$

11. $(\underline{-19 + 52}) \times (-23) - (-42) = \underline{33 \times (-23)} + 42 = -759 + 42 = \textbf{-717}$

12. $24 + (-57) - 28 \times [\underline{53 + (-48)}] = -33 + \underline{(-28) \times 5} = -33 - 140 = \textbf{-173}$

13. $[\underline{32 + (-21)}] \times [\underline{-15 + 16}] = 11 \times 1 = \textbf{11}$

14. $(\underline{178 - 168}) \times (-12) - [\underline{-150 + 120}] \times 3 = \underline{10 \times (-12)} - (-30) \times 3$
    $$= -120 - \underline{(-30) \times 3} = -120 - (-90) = \textbf{-30}$$

15. $\{56 - [\underline{28 + (-26)}] \times 12\} + 86 = \{56 + \underline{(-2) \times 12}\} + 86 = (\underline{56 - 24}) + 86 = \textbf{118}$

16. $248 + 84 - [\underline{36 + (-78)}] \times 3 + (-29) = 332 - \underline{(-42) \times 3} + (-29)$
    $$= 332 - (-126) - 29 = \textbf{429}$$

17. $-\left[\dfrac{1}{2} + \left(-\dfrac{1}{8}\right)\right] \times \dfrac{3}{4} + \dfrac{3}{8} = -\left(\dfrac{4}{8} - \dfrac{1}{8}\right) \times \dfrac{3}{4} + \dfrac{3}{8} = -\dfrac{3}{8} \times \dfrac{3}{4} + \dfrac{3}{8} = -\dfrac{9}{32} + \dfrac{12}{32} = \dfrac{\textbf{3}}{\textbf{32}}$

18. $\left[\left(\dfrac{5}{6} - \dfrac{1}{3}\right) \div 1\dfrac{1}{3} + \dfrac{1}{2}\right] \div \left(-\dfrac{2}{3}\right) = \left[\left(\dfrac{5}{6} - \dfrac{2}{6}\right) \div \dfrac{4}{3} + \dfrac{1}{2}\right] \times \left(-\dfrac{3}{2}\right)$

    $$= \left(\dfrac{3}{6} \times \dfrac{3}{4} + \dfrac{1}{2}\right) \times \left(-\dfrac{3}{2}\right) = \left(\dfrac{9}{24} + \dfrac{12}{24}\right) \times \left(-\dfrac{3}{2}\right) = -\left(\dfrac{21}{24} \times \dfrac{3}{2}\right) = -\dfrac{21}{16} = -1\dfrac{\textbf{5}}{\textbf{16}}$$

19. $\left[-\dfrac{1}{5} + \left(-\dfrac{1}{10}\right)\right] \div \left[\dfrac{1}{2} - \left(-\dfrac{1}{4}\right)\right] \div \dfrac{1}{6} = \left[-\left(\dfrac{2}{10} + \dfrac{1}{10}\right)\right] \div \left(\dfrac{2}{4} + \dfrac{1}{4}\right) \div \dfrac{1}{6}$

    $$= -\dfrac{3}{10} \div \dfrac{3}{4} \div \dfrac{1}{6} = -\dfrac{3 \times 4 \times 6}{10 \times 3 \times 1} = -\dfrac{1 \times 2 \times 6}{5} = -\dfrac{12}{5} = -2\dfrac{\textbf{2}}{\textbf{5}}$$

20. $-\dfrac{1}{2} + \left[\left(-\dfrac{1}{8}\right) \times \dfrac{1}{4} - \left(-\dfrac{1}{2}\right) - \dfrac{1}{4}\right] \div \dfrac{1}{8} = -\dfrac{1}{2} + \left[-\dfrac{1}{32} + \dfrac{16}{32} - \dfrac{8}{32}\right] \times \dfrac{8}{1}$

    $$= -\dfrac{1}{2} + \dfrac{7}{32} \times 8 = -\dfrac{1}{2} + \dfrac{7}{4} = -\dfrac{2}{4} + \dfrac{7}{4} = \dfrac{5}{4} = 1\dfrac{\textbf{1}}{\textbf{4}}$$

Exercise 4.7 (pp. 119-120)

Thinking processes can vary. One possibility for each problem is offered here.

1. (a) $\frac{1}{4}$ of $72 = **$18**

Decompose 72 into multiples of 4.

$\frac{1}{4}$ of $60 + $\frac{1}{4}$ of $12 = $15 + $3

$\qquad\qquad\qquad = $18

(b) $\frac{3}{4}$ of $104 = **$78**

find $\frac{1}{4}$ and multiply that by 3:

$\frac{1}{4}$ of $104 = $\frac{1}{4}$ of $100 + $\frac{1}{4}$ of 4

$\qquad\qquad = $25 + $1

3 x ($25 + $1) = $75 + $3

(c) $1\frac{1}{4}$ of $832 = **$1,040**

Find a fourth of 832 and add 832

$\frac{1}{4}$ of $832 = $\frac{1}{4}$ of $800 + $\frac{1}{4}$ of 32

$\qquad\qquad = $200 + $8

$832 + 200 + $8 = $1,032 + 8

$\qquad\qquad = $1,040

(d)   0.55 x 44 = **24.2**

Decompose 0.55
0.55 = 0.5 + 0.05

0.5 x 44 = $\frac{1}{2}$ x 44 = 22

0.05 x 44 would be a tenth or 2.2
22 + 2.2 = 24.2

(e)   0.145 x 64 = **9.28**

64 is a multiple of 8, and 0.125 is one eighth
0.145 = 0.125 + 0.02

$\qquad = \frac{1}{8} + \frac{2}{100}$

$\frac{1}{8}$ x 64 = 8

$\frac{2}{100}$ x 64 = 0.64 x 2 = 1.28

8 + 1.28 = 9.28

(f)   0.09 x 256 = **23.04**

Rewrite 0.09
0.09 = 0.1 - 0.01
0.1 x 256 = 25.6
0.01 x 256 = 2.56
25.6 - 2.56 = (25 - 2) + (0.6 - 0.56)

$\qquad\qquad = 23 + 0.04$

$\qquad\qquad = 23.04$

2. (a)   4,920 x 125 = **615,000**

125 is an eighth of a thousand.
Decompose 4,920 into easy multiples of 8.

$125 = \frac{1,000}{8}$

4,920 = 4,000 + 800 + 120

$\frac{1}{8}$ x 4,000 = 500

$\frac{1}{8}$ x 800 = 100

$\frac{1}{8}$ x 120 = 15

500 + 100 + 15 = 615
615 x 1,000 = 615,000

(b)   525 ÷ 25 = **21**

Recognize 25 as $\frac{100}{4}$

525 ÷ 25 = 525 x $\frac{4}{100}$

525 x 4 = 500 x 4 + 25 x 4

$\qquad\qquad = 2,000 + 100$

$\qquad\qquad = 2,100$

2,100 ÷ 100 = 21

(c)   3,128 x 5 = **15,640**

5 is equivalent to $\frac{10}{2}$

3,128 x 5 = 3,128 ÷ 2 x 10
$\qquad$ = (1,500 + 64) x 10
$\qquad$ = 15,640

(d)   112 ÷ 125 = **0.896**

Recognize 125 = $\frac{1,000}{8}$

112 ÷ 125 = 112 x $\frac{8}{1,000}$

112 x 8 = 896
896 ÷ 1,000 = 0.896

(e)   824 x 25 = **20,600**

Recognize 25 as $\frac{100}{4}$

824 ÷ 4 = (800 ÷ 4) + (24 ÷ 4)
= 200 + 6 = 206
206 x 100 = 20,600

(f)   7,325 ÷ 5 = **1,465**

Dividing by 5 is equivalent to doubling
and dividing by 10
7,325 x 2 = 14,650
14,650 ÷ 10 = 1,465

3. (a)   7 + 4 + 5 + 3 + 8 + 6 = **33**

7 + 3 = 10
4 + 6 = 10
8 + 5 = 13
$\qquad\qquad$ 33

(b)   7 + 8 + 7 + 9 + 4 - 15 = **20**

8 = 7 + 1
9 = 7 + 2
4 + 1 + 2 = 7
5 x 7 = 35
35 - 15 = 20

(c)   6 + 7 - 9 + 3 + 6 - 10 = **3**

7 + 3 - 10 = 0
6 - 9 + 6 = (6 - 6) + (6 - 30) = 3

(d)   24 - 34 + 42 - 21 + 39 = **50**

24 - 21 = 3
39 - 34 = 5
42 + 3 + 5 = 50

(e)   15 x 25 x 2 x 114 x 4 = **342,000**

25 x 4 = 100
15 x 2 = 30
30 x 100 = 3,000
3,000 x 114 = 342,000

(f)   42 x 72 ÷ 7 ÷ 12 x 125 = **4,500**

42 ÷ 7 = 6
72 ÷ 12 = 6
6 x 6 = 36
125 = 100 + $\frac{100}{4}$
36 x 100 = 3,600
36 ÷ 4 x 100 = 900
3,600 + 900 = 4,500

4. (a)   7 x 99 = **693**

99 = 100 - 1
7 x 100 = 700
7 x 1 = 7
700 - 7 = 693

(b)   124 x 12 = **1,488**

12 = 10 + 2
124 x 10 = 1,240
124 x 2 = 248
1,240 + 248 = 1,488

(c)   992 + 528 + 107 = **1,627**

992 = 1,000 - 8
107 = $\underline{100 + 7}$
$\qquad$ 1,100 - 1
1,100 + 528 = 1,628
1,628 - 1 = 1,627

(d)   721 + 315 + 243 = **1,279**

700 + 300 + 200 = 1,200
21 + 15 = 36
36 + 43 = 79
1,200 + 79 = 1,279

(e)   321 - 175 + 412 = **558**

175 = 200 - 25
321 - 200 = 121
121 + 25 = 146
146 + 400 = 546
546 + 12 = 558

(f) $2\dfrac{5}{6} \times 4 = \mathbf{11\dfrac{1}{3}}$

$2\dfrac{5}{6} = 3 - \dfrac{1}{6}$

$3 \times 4 = 12$

$\dfrac{1}{6} \times 4 = \dfrac{2}{3}$

$12 - \dfrac{2}{3} = 11\dfrac{1}{3}$

(g)   15 x 112 = **1,680**

15 = 3 x 5
5 x 112 = 500 + 60 = 560
560 x 3 = 1,500 + 180 = 1,680

(h) $1\dfrac{1}{5} \div \dfrac{3}{10} = \mathbf{4}$

$1\dfrac{1}{5} \times 10 = 10 + 2 = 12$

$12 \div 3 = 4$

5. (a)   24 x 121 ≈ **3,000**

24 ≈ 25
121 ≈ 120
25 x 120 = 25 x 4 x 30
         = 100 x 30
         = 3,000

(b)   28 + 35 + 68 + 71 ≈ **200**

28 + 71 ≈ 100
35 + 68 ≈ 100

(c)   0.26 ÷ 0.124 ≈ **2**

$0.26 \approx 0.25 = \dfrac{1}{4}$

$0.124 \approx 0.125 = \dfrac{1}{8}$

$\dfrac{1}{4} \div \dfrac{1}{8} = \dfrac{1}{4} \times 8$

(d)   315 + 298 + 289 ≈ **900**

All 3 terms ≈ 300

(e)   0.52 x 0.24 ≈ **0.125**

$0.52 \approx \dfrac{1}{2}$

$0.24 \approx \dfrac{1}{4}$

$\dfrac{1}{2} \times \dfrac{1}{4} = \dfrac{1}{8} = 0.125$

(f)   126 x 7.9 ≈ **1,000**

$126 \approx \dfrac{1,000}{8}$

$7.9 \approx 8$

$\dfrac{1,000}{8} \times 8 = 1,000$

Revision Exercise 1

Revision 1A (pp. 124-125)

1. (a) 2 | 384   (b) 5 | 555   (c) 5 |1,045   (d) 2 |2,048
       2 | 192   3 | 111   11 | 209   2 |1,024
       2 | 96   37 | 37   19 | 19   2 | 512
       2 | 48   2 | 256
       2 | 24   555 = **3 x 5 x 37**   1,045 = **5 x 11 x 19**   2 | 128
       2 | 12   2 | 64
       2 | 6   2 | 32
       3 |___   2 | 16
                                                               2 | 8
       384 = **2^7 x 3**   2 | 4
                                                               2 | 2

                                                               2,048 = **2^{11}**

2. Find LCM. 15 = 5 x 3, 20 = 4 x 5, LCM = 3 x 4 x 5 = 60
   That number is the lowest that can be divided by 15 and 20 leaving no remainder. For
   remainders, add remainder to the LCM.

   (a) **60**   (b) **61**   (c) **62**

3. Four smaller tins = 500 g
   $1.80 x 4 = $7.20 which is more than one large tin at $7.10
   Large tin is the better buy.

4. (a)
   $$1 \text{ g} = \frac{1}{1,000} \text{ kg}$$

   $$14.7 \text{ g} = \frac{14.7}{1,000} \text{ kg}$$
   14.7 g = **0.0147 kg**

   (b)   60 min = 1 h
          116 min = (1 x 60) + 56 min
          116 min = **1 h 56 min**

5. (a)
   $$\frac{7}{38} \times \left(\frac{-}{-21}\right) + \frac{3}{2} + \frac{5}{2} = 3$$

   $$-\left(\frac{7 \times -}{38 \times 3 \times 7}\right) + \frac{8}{2} = 3$$

   $$-\left(\frac{-}{114}\right) + 4 = 3$$

   $$4 - \frac{-}{114} = 3$$

   $$1 = \frac{-}{114}$$
   $$= \overline{-}\textbf{114}$$

   Unknown value must be negative for
   fraction to be equivalent to positive 1.

   (b)
   $$\left(\frac{3}{-28}\right) + \left(\frac{-6}{-}\right) = 0$$

   $$\frac{-6}{-} - \frac{3}{28} = 0$$

   $$\frac{-6}{-} - \frac{3x2}{28x2} = 0$$

   $$\frac{-6}{-} - \frac{6}{56} = 0$$

   $$= -\textbf{56}$$
   Unknown value must be negative.

(c)
$$\frac{7}{38} \times \left(\frac{-}{-21}\right) + \frac{3}{2} + \frac{5}{2} = 3$$

$$-\left(\frac{7 \times \_}{38 \times 3 \times 7}\right) + \frac{8}{2} = 3$$

$$-\left(\frac{\_\_}{114}\right) + 4 = 3$$

$$4 - \frac{\_\_}{114} = 3$$

$$1 = \frac{\_\_}{114}$$

$$\_ = \mathbf{114}$$

(d)
$$\left(\frac{-5}{19}\right) + \left(\frac{-10}{-38}\right) - \left[\frac{4}{15} \times \frac{\_}{-12} \times 2\right] = 2$$

$$\frac{-10 + 10}{38} - \left(\frac{4 \times \_ \times 2}{-15 \times 3 \times 4}\right) = 2$$

$$0 + \left(\frac{\_ \times 2}{45}\right) = 2$$

$$2 \times \frac{\_}{45} = 2$$

$$\_ = \mathbf{45}$$

6. (a) $5 > 3$

(b) $-2 < -1$

(c) $-4 < 0$

(d) $6 > -8$

(e) $-16 > -17$

(f) $(-1) \times (-2) > 1 \times (-3)$
positive side will be greater

(g) $13 + 4 \times 5 > (-4) \times 20$
positive side will be greater

(h) $3 \times 6 + 4 - 2 \_\_\_ 6 \times (-3) + 4 \times 2$
$18 + 2 \_\_\_ -18 + 8$
$20 > -10$

7. (a) $192 + 48 - \{[\underline{36 + (-78)}] \times 8 + (-92)\} = 240 - \{\underline{(-42) \times 8} + (-92)\}$
$= 240 - \{\underline{-336 + (-92)}\}$
$= 240 \underline{- (-428)}$
$= \underline{240 + 428}$
$= \mathbf{668}$

(b) $(187 - 168) \times (-21) - [\underline{(-150) + 141}] \times 3 = \underline{19 \times (-21)} - \underline{(-9) \times 3}$
$= -399 \underline{- (-27)}$
$= \underline{-399 + 27}$
$= \mathbf{-372}$

8. $\frac{5.96}{2.02} \approx \frac{6}{2} = \mathbf{3}$ $\frac{596}{0.202} = \frac{5.96 \times 100}{2.02 \times 0.1} = \frac{5.69}{1.02} \times 1{,}000 \approx 3 \times 1{,}000 = \mathbf{3{,}000}$

9.   Cost for 3 adults = $4 \times 3 = $12
Cost for 4 children = $2 \times 4 = $8
Total cost = $12 + $8 = $20
Change = $100 - 20 = **$80**

10.   ▯▯▯▯▯▯▯▯ = $14   3 tins beans + 5 cans beans = $14

▯▯▯▯▯▯▯▯▯▯▯▯▯▯
| biscuits |beans| 3 tins biscuits = 3 x 3 = 9 cans beans
▯ = 1 unit   9 cans beans + 5 cans beans = 14 units
                          14 units = $14
                          1 unit = $1
                          1 can beans = **$1**

Revision 1B (pp. 125-126)

1.(a) 3 |1,155   (b) The largest factor is **385** (3 x 385 = 1,155)
       5 | 385
       7 | 77
      11 | 11

       1155 = **3 x 5 x 7 x 11**

2. (a) 2 | 32, 12   (b) 3 | 5, 9,12, 16   (c) 2 |52, 28, 20   (d) 5 |15, 25, 10, 35
       2 | 16, 6   2 | 5, 3, 4, 16   2 |26, 14, 10   3, 5, 2, 7
       2 | 8, 3   2 | 5, 3, 2, 8   13, 7, 5
       2 | 4, 3   5, 3, 1, 4   LCM = 2 x 3
       2, 3   LCM = 2^2 x 5   x 5^2 x 7
                           LCM = 2^4 x 3^2 x 5   x 7 x 13   = **1,050**
   LCM = 2^5 x 3= **96**   = **720**   = **1,820**

3. (a)   72.342 x 84.5 = **6,112.899**   (b)   11.001 x 5.428 = 59.713428
                                                      ≈ **59.713**

   (c) $\frac{23}{3} = 7.\bar{6} ≈ \textbf{7.667}$ (d) $\frac{103}{17} = 6.0588... ≈ \textbf{6.059}$

4.

   Bulan Ave. = $120\frac{5}{8}$

   Bintang Ave. = $\frac{4}{5}$ of Bulan Ave.

   Mata Hari Ave. = $\frac{11}{8}$ of Bintang Ave.

   Length of Mata Hari = $\frac{11}{8} \times \frac{4}{5} = \frac{11}{10}$ of Bulan Ave. So Mata Hari is $\frac{1}{10}$ longer than Bulan Ave.

   $\frac{1}{10} \times 120\frac{5}{8} = \left(\frac{1}{10} \times 120\right) + \left(\frac{1}{10} \times \frac{5}{8}\right) = 12\frac{1}{16}$

   The difference in length between Bulan Ave. and Mata Hari Ave. is **$12\frac{1}{16}$** m.

5. (a)   6 _ 2 3   (b)   _ 4 _
         - 1 5   5   +   8 7 6
          _ 8 7 _   1 2 _ 1

           5 13 11 13   3 5 5
         - 1 5 4 5   +   8 7 6
           4 8 7 8   1 2 12 11

           6 **4** 2 3   3 4 **5**
         - 1 5 **4** 5   +   8 7 6
           4 8 7 8   1 2 **2** 1

6. (a) 11:30 is $\frac{1}{2}$ an hour before noon. **$-\frac{1}{2}$**

    (b) 15:00 is 3 hours after noon. **+3**

    (c) 23:30 is $11\frac{1}{2}$ hours after noon. **$+11\frac{1}{2}$**

(d) 06:00 is 6 hours before noon. **-6**

(e) 03:30 is 8 $\frac{1}{2}$ hours before noon. **-8$\frac{1}{2}$**

7. (a) -{[456 - (-122)] x 4} - 192 = -{578 x 4} - 192 = -2,312 - 192 = **-2,504**

    (b) [(-21) - (-221)] x [(-151) + 162] x 4 = 200 x 11 x 4 = **8,800**

8. Medicine taken each day = 3 x 6 ml = 18 ml
Medicine taken for 1 week = 18 ml x 7 = 126 ml
Medicine remaining = 150 ml - 126 ml = **24 ml**

9. $\dfrac{1.584 \times 0.14}{0.2 \times 4.5} = \dfrac{1.584 \times 0.14 \times 100}{0.2 \times 4.5 \times 100} = \dfrac{1.584 \times 14}{2 \times 45} = \dfrac{0.176 \times 7}{5} = \dfrac{1.232}{5} = 0.2464 \approx \mathbf{0.25}$

10. $\dfrac{10.9 \times 0.642}{2.190} \approx \dfrac{11 \times 0.64}{2.2} = \dfrac{11 \times 0.64 \times 10}{2.2 \times 10} = \dfrac{11 \times 6.4}{22} = \dfrac{6.4}{2} \approx \mathbf{3}$

Revision 1C

1. To find this number, multiply 6 x 8 = **48**.

2. Find the LCM first.

(a) 2 | 16, 24, 34
    4 | _8, 12_, 17
      2, 3, 17
    LCM = 2^2 x 3 x 4 x 17
        = 816
    ∴ smallest number giving remainder of 1 is 816 + 1 = **817**

(b) 2 | 20, 42, 63
    21 | 10, _21, 63_
       10, 1, 3
    LCM = 2 x 3 x 10 x 21
        = 1,260
    ∴ smallest number giving a remainder of 11 is 1,260 + 11 = **1,271**

(c) 5 | 5, 10, 22, 35
    2 | 1, 2, 22, 7
       1, 1, 11, 7
    LCM = 2 x 5 x 7 x 11
        = 770
    ∴ smallest number giving a remainder of 3 is 770 + 3 = **773**

3. (a) $\dfrac{22}{7}$ $\dfrac{25}{8}$ 3.13
    3.14.. 3.125 3.13
    $\dfrac{22}{7}$ is largest

(b) $\dfrac{1}{4}$ $\dfrac{1}{3}$ 0.22
    0.25 $0.3\overline{3}$ 0.22
    $\dfrac{1}{3}$ is largest

(c) $\dfrac{5}{8}$ $\dfrac{6}{11}$ 0.71
    0.624 $0.5\overline{4}$ 0.71
    0.71 is largest

(d) $\dfrac{9}{13}$ $\dfrac{11}{19}$ 0.62
    0.69... 0.58... 0.62
    $\dfrac{9}{13}$ is largest

(e) $\dfrac{15}{7}$ $\dfrac{23}{11}$ 2.23
    2.14 $2.\overline{09}$ 2.23
    2.23 is largest

4. Mass of durians is $\dfrac{24}{25}$ mass of basket.

$$\dfrac{24}{25} \times 55\dfrac{5}{9} = \dfrac{24}{25} \times 55 + \dfrac{24}{25} \times \dfrac{5}{9}$$

$$= \dfrac{24 \times 11}{5} + \dfrac{24}{45} = \dfrac{264}{5} + \dfrac{24}{45} = 52\dfrac{4}{5} + \dfrac{24}{45} = 52\dfrac{36}{45} + \dfrac{24}{45} = 52\dfrac{60}{45} = 53\dfrac{15}{45} = 53\dfrac{1}{3}$$

Mass of durians is $\mathbf{53\dfrac{1}{3}}$ **kg**.

5. (a) 18, 13, **8**, 3, **-2, -7**   (b) -52, **-38, -24**, -10, **4**, 18
        decreases by **3**   increases by **14**

6. X = +500 m, Y = -20 m, difference = 500 - (-20) = 500 + 20 = **520 m**

7. (a)
$$\dfrac{2}{3} + \left(-\dfrac{3}{4}\right) = \dfrac{8}{12} + \left(-\dfrac{9}{12}\right)$$
$$= -\left(\dfrac{9}{12} - \dfrac{8}{12}\right)$$
$$= -\dfrac{\mathbf{1}}{\mathbf{12}}$$

(b)
$$\dfrac{4}{5} + \dfrac{7}{12} = \dfrac{48 + 35}{60}$$
$$= \dfrac{83}{60}$$
$$= 1\dfrac{\mathbf{23}}{\mathbf{60}}$$

(c)
$$\dfrac{13}{28} + \dfrac{7}{14} - \left(-\dfrac{8}{21}\right) = \dfrac{39}{84} + \dfrac{42}{84} + \dfrac{32}{84}$$
$$= \dfrac{113}{84}$$
$$= 1\dfrac{\mathbf{29}}{\mathbf{84}}$$

(d)
$$-\dfrac{3}{25} + \left(-\dfrac{4}{15}\right) = -\left(\dfrac{9}{75} + \dfrac{20}{75}\right)$$
$$= \dfrac{\mathbf{29}}{\mathbf{75}}$$

(e)
$$-\dfrac{23}{32} - \dfrac{15}{24} = -\left(\dfrac{69}{96} + \dfrac{60}{96}\right)$$
$$= -\dfrac{129}{96}$$
$$= -1\dfrac{33}{96}$$
$$= -1\dfrac{\mathbf{11}}{\mathbf{32}}$$

8. (a) [(248 + 24) x 3 - 12] x 15 - 3 X (-12 - 124) = [272 x 3 - 12] x 15 - 3 x (-136)
                                                    = (816 - 12) x 15 - (-408)
                                                    = 804 x 15 + 408
                                                    = 12,060 + 408
                                                    = **12,468**

    (b) -15 + 2 x [(-38 - 10) x (-8) + 5] - (-17 - 19) = -15 + 2 x [(-48) x (-8) + 5] + 36
                                                       = -15 + 2 x [384 + 5] +36
                                                       = -15 + 2 x 389 + 36
                                                       = -15 + 778 + 36
                                                       = **799**

(c) $\{[(\underline{32-29}) \times (-4) + 5] \times 6 + (-2)\} - (\underline{12+8+7}) = \{[\underline{3 \times (-4)} + 5] \times 6 + (-2)\} - 27$
$$= [(\underline{-12+5}) \times 6 - 2] - 27$$
$$= [\underline{-7 \times 6} - 2] - 27$$
$$= [\underline{-42 - 2}] - 27$$
$$= \underline{-44 - 27}$$
$$= \mathbf{-71}$$

9.   The number can be found by division: $882 \div 7 = \mathbf{126}$

10.   6 apples

Cost of 6 apples = cost of 2 oranges
So 3 apples = 1 unit

Peter bought 3 apples and 5 oranges for $3
6 units = $3
1 unit = $3 ÷ 6 = $0.50
1 orange costs **$0.50.**

Revision 1D (pp. 127 - 128)

1.   Only b and c are prime. 87 is divisible by 3 since $8 + 7 = 15$. 201 is likewise divisible by 3. 437 is divisible by 19, and 1,331 is divisible by 11.

2. (a)   4 |384, 124, 64
          | 96, 31, 16

     HCF = **4**

   (b)   5 | 25, 60, 45
           | 5, 12, 9

     HCF = **5**

   (c)   7 | 42, 28, 63, 98
           | 6, 4, 9, 14

     HCF = **7**

   (d)   5 |180, 95,120, 350
           | 36, 19, 24, 70

     HCF = **5**

3. $2.4 \div \left(5\frac{1}{5} - \frac{5.2}{1.3}\right) = 2.4 \div \left(5\frac{1}{5} - 4\right) = 2.4 \div 1\frac{1}{5} = 2.4 \div \frac{6}{5} = \frac{2.4 \times 5}{6} = 0.4 \times 5 = \mathbf{2}$

4.   Remainder $= 23\frac{1}{4} - 12\frac{2}{3} = 11\frac{3}{12} - \frac{8}{12} = 10\frac{15}{12} - \frac{8}{12} = 10\frac{7}{12}$ m

$\frac{3}{5} \times 10\frac{7}{12} = \left(\frac{3}{5} \times 10\right) + \left(\frac{3}{5} \times \frac{7}{12}\right) = \mathbf{6\frac{7}{20}}$ **m**

5. (a) $1 - 7 = \mathbf{-6}$ (b) $-2 - (-8) = \mathbf{6}$ (c) $0 - 5 = \mathbf{-5}$
   (d) $-22 - (-18) = \mathbf{-4}$ (e) $50 - 21 = \mathbf{29}$

6. (a) $\left(-\frac{6}{11}\right) \times \frac{5}{18} = -\frac{6 \times 5}{11 \times 18}$
$$= -\frac{1 \times 5}{11 \times 3}$$
$$= -\frac{\mathbf{5}}{\mathbf{33}}$$

   (b) $\frac{27}{52} \times \frac{13}{135} = \frac{1 \times 1}{4 \times 5}$
$$= \frac{\mathbf{1}}{\mathbf{20}}$$

   (c) $\frac{49}{892} + \left(\frac{-84}{223}\right) = \frac{49}{892} - \frac{336}{892}$
$$= -\frac{\mathbf{287}}{\mathbf{892}}$$

(d)
$$\frac{98}{-125} \div \left(-\frac{63}{60}\right) = \frac{98}{125} \times \frac{60}{63}$$
$$= \frac{14 \times 12}{25 \times 9}$$
$$= \frac{14 \times 4}{25 \times 3}$$
$$= \frac{56}{75}$$

(e)
$$\frac{21}{462} \times \left(\frac{165}{-81} \div \frac{125}{135}\right) = \frac{1}{22} \times \left(-\frac{55}{27} \div \frac{25}{27}\right)$$
$$= \frac{1}{22} \times \left(-\frac{55}{27} \times \frac{27}{25}\right)$$
$$= \frac{1}{22} \times \left(-\frac{55}{25}\right)$$
$$= -\frac{1 \times 1}{2 \times 5}$$
$$= -\frac{1}{10}$$

(f)
$$7\frac{1}{7} \times \frac{14}{15} = \frac{50 \times 14}{7 \times 15}$$
$$= \frac{10 \times 2}{1 \times 3}$$
$$= \frac{20}{3}$$
$$= 6\frac{2}{3}$$

(g)
$$11\frac{7}{11} \times \left(\frac{15}{-86}\right) \times \left(5\frac{1}{24}\right) \times 2 \times \frac{11}{6}$$
$$= -\frac{128 \times 15 \times 121 \times 2 \times 11}{11 \times 86 \times 24 \times 6}$$
$$= -\frac{8 \times 5 \times 121 \times 1 \times 1}{1 \times 43 \times 1 \times 3}$$
$$= -\frac{4,840}{129}$$
$$= -37\frac{67}{129}$$

(h)
$$7\frac{5}{16} \div 62\frac{1}{48} = \frac{117}{16} \div \frac{2,977}{48}$$
$$= \frac{117}{16} \times \frac{48}{2,977}$$
$$= \frac{9 \times 3}{1 \times 229}$$
$$= \frac{27}{229}$$

(i)
$$\frac{51}{64} \div 7\frac{7}{16} = \frac{51}{64} \div \frac{119}{16}$$
$$= \frac{51 \times 16}{64 \times 119}$$
$$= \frac{3 \times 1}{4 \times 7}$$
$$= \frac{3}{28}$$

7. (a) $-\{[\underline{346 + (-265)}] \times 4\} + 22 = -(\underline{81 \times 4}) + 22$
$$= \underline{-324 + 22}$$
$$= \textbf{-302}$$

(b) $\{296 - [\underline{281 + (-125)}] \times 11\} + 68 = (296 - \underline{156 \times 11}) + 68$
$$= 296 - 1,716 + 68$$
$$= -(1,716 - 296 - 68)$$
$$= \textbf{-1,352}$$

(c) $[\underline{(-91) + 52}] \times (-12) - (-129) = \underline{-39 \times (-12)} + 129$
$$= 468 + 129$$
$$= \textbf{597}$$

8. Solve by trial and error.
   (a) $8 + 5 \times (9 - 6 \div 3) = 43$
   (b) $(10 + 2 \times 3) - (8 + 16 \div 4) = 4$

9. Pay for weekdays = 5 days/week x 3 weeks x $25 = $375
    Pay for Saturday = 3 x $50 = $150
    Total pay = $375 + $150 = **$525**

10. Total oranges to be sold = 20 boxes x 50 oranges/box - 50 oranges = 950 oranges
    Total cost = 20 x $30 = $600
    Sale = Cost + Profit = $600 + $65 = $665
    950 oranges = $665
       1 orange = $665 ÷ 950 = **$0.70**

Revision 1E (pp. 128-129)

1. 3,462 = (494 x 7) + 4. The remainder is **4**

2. $0.2 \times 0.3 \div 0.0012 = \dfrac{0.2 \times 0.3}{0.0012} = \dfrac{0.2 \times 0.3 \times 10{,}000}{0.0012 \times 10{,}000} = \dfrac{2 \times 3 \times 100}{12} = \mathbf{50}$

3. $35\dfrac{3}{5} + 32\dfrac{2}{5} + 39\dfrac{1}{2} = 106\dfrac{6}{10} + \dfrac{4}{10} + \dfrac{5}{10} = 106\dfrac{15}{10} = \mathbf{107\dfrac{1}{2}}$ **kg**

4. (a) **+120 m**   (b) **-50 m**   (c) **+200 m**   (d) **0 m**

5. (a) (42 + 21 - 8) x 15 = 55 x 15 = **825**

    (b) [6 + (-9)] - [24 + (-20)] x (-2) = (-3) - 4 x (-2) = -3 - (-8) = -3 + 8 = **5**

    (c) {[13 - (-8)] x 4 + 3} x (-4) = (21 x 4 + 3) x (-4)
                                     = (84 + 3) x (-4) = -(87 x 4) = **-348**

6.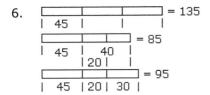

    (a) 3 fountain pens = $135
        1 fountain pen = **$45**

    (b) 1 fountain pen + 2 ball-point pens = $85
        2 ball-point pens = $85 - $45 = $40
        1 ball-point pen = $40 ÷ 2 = **$20**

    (c) 1 fountain pen + 1 ball-point pen + 1 pencil = $95
        1 pencil = $95 - $45 - $20 = **$30**

7. $\dfrac{0.24 \times 14.3}{5.2} = \dfrac{0.24 \times 14.3 \times 1000}{5.2 \times 1000} = \dfrac{24 \times 143}{52 \times 100} = \dfrac{6 \times 11}{2 \times 50} = \dfrac{666}{100} = \mathbf{0.66}$

8. (a) 0.027684 ≈ **0.028**   (b) 0.027684 ≈ **0.02768**

9. Total drink = 3 ℓ + 21 ℓ = 24 ℓ
    Sales = $3 x 8 = $24
    Cost = Sales - Profit = $24 - $12 = $12
    Cost per liter = $\dfrac{\$12}{24}$ = $0.50 per ℓ
    Cost price was **50¢** per liter.

10. Total days worked = 5 days/week x 4 weeks = 20 days
    Transport allowance = $2 x 20 = $40
    Pay = $640 - $40 = $600
    $5 = 1 h
    $1 = 0.20 h
    $600 = 0.20 x 600 = 120 h
    20 days = 120 h
    1 day = $\frac{120}{20}$ = 6 h

    He worked **6 hours per day**.

Miscellaneous Exercise 1 (pp. 130-132)

1. (a) The 7th to the 21st is (21 - 7) + 1 = 15 days.
       There were **15** performances.
    (b) Length of performance = 10 h 20 min - 7 h 45 min
                       = 9 h 80 min - 7 h 45 min = **2 h 35 min**
    (c) Total cost = ($11 x 263) + ($5.50 x 160) = $2,893 + $880 = **$3,773**

2. A number divisible by 5 and 9 would have to be divisible by the LCM, which is 45.
    45 x 2 = 90, which is not 3 digits. 45 x 3 = 135. So the smallest 3-digit number divisible by
    5 and 9 is **135**.

3. If the product of two numbers is divisible by 6, and each number is not, then one is divisible
    by 3 and the other by 2. The only number in the list that is divisible by 2 is 82, and the only
    one that is divisible by 3 is 45. So the two numbers are **45 and 82**.

4. This number would be a multiple of the LCM + 1 of 2, 3, and 5. The LCM is 2 x 3 x 5 = 30 so
    the lowest possible number would be **31**.

5. **13** is the prime number, and 4 and 9 are the composite numbers. 1, 3, 5, and 7, and 11
    would have a prime as one of the addends.

6. Find multiples of 13 where the multiple - 1 is a multiple of 5 and the value - 2 is also a
    multiple of 3.

multiple of 13	subtract 1	multiple of 5?	subtract 2	multiple of 3?
13	14	no		
26	25	yes	**24**	yes

So the man is **24 years** old.

7. Find the multiples of 8 - 1 that are multiples of 3.

multiple of 8	subtract 1	multiple of 3?
8	7	no
16	**15**	yes
24	23	no
32	31	no
40	**39**	yes
48	47	no
56	55	no
64	**63**	yes
72	71	no
80	79	no
88	**87**	yes

(a) **15 yrs. old**   (b) **39 yrs. old**   (c) **63 yrs. old**   (d) **87 yrs. old**

8. Start with multiples of 5.

multiple of 5	subtract 1	multiple of 3?	subtract 2	multiple of 2?
5	4	no		
10	9	yes	**8**	yes
15	14	no		
20	19	no		
25	24	yes	23	no
30	29	no		
35	34	no		
40	39	yes	**38**	yes
45	44	no		
50	49	no		
55	54	yes	53	no
60	59	no		
65	64	no		
70	69	yes	**68**	yes

(a) **8 yrs. old**   (b) **38 yrs. old**   (c) **68 yrs. old**

9.

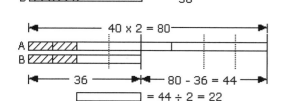

A has 4 more pupils than B. If A had 4 less it would have same number as B.
76 - 4 = 72. 72 ÷ 2 = 36
∴B has 36 pupils.
  A has 36 + 4 = 40 pupils

A has $1\frac{1}{2}$ times as many boys as B, and B has twice as many girls as A.

Double the number of pupils in A. This will give the same number of girls in both. The difference between the doubled A and B will be twice the number of boys in B.

B has **22** boys.

10. A length of 32.4 cm, correct to 1 decimal place, means that the length is greater than or equal to 32.35 and less than or equal to 32.44.
So 32.35 ≤ length ≤ 32.44
(a) **False**   (b) **False**   (c) **True**   (d) **True**   (e) **True**   (f) **True**

11. 365 ml correct to the nearest ml: 364.5 ≤ vol. ≤ 365.4
245 ml correct to the nearest ml: 244.5 ≤ vol. ≤ 245.4
The smallest volume the jug could now have would be when the smallest volumes are added, and the largest volume would be when the largest volumes are added.
∴ 609.0 ≤ final vol. ≤ 610.8
(a) **False**   (b) **False**   (c) **False**   (d) **False**   (e) **True**   (f) **True**

12. 610 ml correct to the nearest ml: 609.5 ≤ vol. ≤ 610.4
    245 ml correct to the nearest ml: 244.5 ≤ vol. ≤ 245.4
    If 245 ml is removed, the smallest volume in the jug would be the smallest original minus the
    largest removed, or 609.5 - 245.4 = 364.1. The largest volume would be the largest original
    volume minus the smallest removed, or 610.4 - 244.5 = 365.9.
    ∴ 364.1 ≤ final vol. ≤ 365.9
    (a) **False**   (b) **False**   (c) **False**   (d) **False**   (e) **True**   (f) **True**

13. These can be solved by educated guess. The number of choices can be reduced by rewriting
    the problem to what fractions have to be whole numbers. For example, in 3.(a) $\dfrac{x}{=\!=}$ would
    have to be a whole number, and so would have to be $\dfrac{9\ x}{3}\!=\!=$.

    (a) 1 x 9 ÷ 3 + 5 - 7 = 1   (b) (7 x 5 + 1) ÷ 3 - 9 = 3

    (c) 9 ÷ 3 x 1 + 7 - 5 = 5   (d) 9 - (3 + 7) ÷ 5 x 1 = 7

    (e) 5 x 9 ÷ 3 + 1 - 7 = 9

14. (a) (2 + 4) ÷ 6 x 10 - 8 = 2   (b) 8 - (4 + 2 x 10) ÷ 6 = 4

    (c) (10 + 6) x 4 ÷ 8 - 2 = 6   (d) 8 x 2 ÷ 4 + 10 - 6 = 8

    (e) (10 - 4) x 2 ÷ 6 + 8 = 10

15. The remainder in line d is a 1 digit number, and four more digits are added before another
    multiplication is performed. Therefore two of the digits in the dividend which are "brought
    down" must be 0. Since line e does not have a thousands digit, the first digit in line d must be
    1. Line d must be between 1,000 and 1,009. Since the difference between d and e is a
    single digit 5 (before more numbers are "brought down") line e must be between 995 and
    999 inclusive.

```
a              * * * * * * *
b     * * * ) 5 * * 0 0 * * * *
c            * * *
d            1 0 0 *
e             9 9 *
f              5 * *
g              * * *
h              * 5 * *
i              * * * *
j                    0
```

Since line e is a multiple of the divisor, the
divisor must be a factor of the numbers 995,
996, 997, 998, and 999. So the possible values
for the divisor are
199, 166, 332, 498, 499, 333, and 111.
995 through 999 are not possibilities for the
divisor, because the first digit in line c has to be
4 or 5.

Line h, and therefore line i, must be between 1,500 and 4,599, so the divisor x 9 has to be
greater than or equal to 1,500. This eliminates 111 and 166 as possible candidates. So the
possible candidates are now 199, 332, 333, 498, and 499

The first three digits for the dividend must be between 500 and 599. Since the difference
between it and line c is 1, line c must be between 499 and 597. The divisor must be a factor
of a number between 499 and 597 and one of the possible candidates already determined
above. The possible candidates are now 199 (199 x 3 = 597), 498, or 499.

The first three digits of line h must be between 150 and 459. Line f must be between 500 and
599. So line g must be between 41 (500 - 459) and 499 (599 - 150). It has to be greater

than 100, so g must be between 100 and 499. The divisor must be a factor of a number between 100 and 499 and one of the possible candidates already determined above. If it is 331, 332, 498, or 499, the other factor (in the quotient) cannot be greater than 1 or else line g would be greater than 499, which it cannot be. If g is 499 or 498, the first 3 digits of line h would have to be between 1 (500 - 499) and 101 (500 - 498), which is not possible with the given second digit of 5. So the divisor must be 199.

```
a              3 0 0 5 * * 8
b   1 9 9 ) 5 9 8 0 0 0 * * *
c         5 9 7
d         1 0 0 0
e           9 9 5
f               5 * *
g               * * *
h               * 5 * *
i               1 5 9 2
j                       0
```

The first digit in the quotient would have to be 3 for 5 to be the first digit in line c. So the second and third digit of the dividend is 9 and 8. The second and third digits in line a have to be 0. The next digit needs to be 5 to get the 99 in line e. This makes the last digit in line e 5, and the last digit in line d 0. Thus the 6th digit in the dividend must be 0.
The last digit of the quotient must be 8 to get a 5 in the second digit of line i.

```
a              3 0 0 5 0 2 8
b   1 9 9 ) 5 9 8 0 0 0 5 7 2
c         5 9 7
d         1 0 0 0
e           9 9 5
f               5 5 7
g               3 9 8
h               1 5 9 2
i               1 5 9 2
j                       0
```

So line h is 1592, and the last digit in the dividend must be 2. The first digit of line g must be 3 and the next to last digit of the quotient must be 2, making line g 398. So line f must be 159 + 398 = 557, making the 7th and 8th digit of the dividend 5 and 7 and the 5th digit of the quotient 0.

Chapter 5

Exercise 5.1 (pp. 138-140)

1.  ```
    |---x---|-----?-----|
    |-------100----------|
    ```
    ? = **100 − x**

2.  ```
    |---y---|-----7-----|
    |---------?----------|
    ```
    ? = **7 + y**

3.  ```
    |-----30-----| Jiaming and Abu
    |--p--|        Jiaming
          |------| Abu
    ```
    ? = **30 - p**

4. (a)   1 meter = 100 centimeters
          s meters = **100s** centimeters

    (b)   1 kilometers = 1,000 meters
          m kilometers = **1,000m** meters

    (c)   1 dollar = 100 cents
          q dollars = **100q** cents

    (d)   1 meter = 1,000 millimeters
          d meters = **1,000d** millimeters

    (e)   1 kilogram = 1,000 grams
          p kilograms = **1,000p** grams

    (f) s meters + t centimeters
          100s centimeters + t centimeters
          (**100s + t**) centimeters

    (g) p kilograms + q grams
          1,000p grams + q grams
          (**1,000p + q**) grams

5. x number
    $2x$ multiply it by 2
    2x - 5   subtract 5

6.  ```
    |--x--|         number
    |-----|-----|   other number
      2x
    ```

7. x number
    $x + 10$ add 10 to it
    $3(x + 10)$ multiply sum by 3
    $3x + 30$ distributive property
    $3x + 30 - x$ subtract given number
    2x + 30   combine terms

8. (a) **x - 5**
    (b) let x be 3
        3 - 5 = -2

9. (a) **k + 2**
    (b) Let k be (-14)
        (-14) + 2 = **-12**

10. (a) **2x + 11**
    (b) Let x be $-\dfrac{7}{16}$

        $2\left(-\dfrac{7}{16}\right) + 11 = -\dfrac{7}{8} + 11 = \mathbf{10\dfrac{1}{8}}$

11. x Tim's age
    x + 5   Nafa's age

12. x sister's age
    x - 8   boy's age

13.
   x son's age = $\dfrac{1}{7}$ of father's age

   7x father's age

14. x boys

    $\dfrac{2}{3}x$ girls

15. 1   house in x days

    $\dfrac{1}{x}$ house in $\dfrac{x}{x}$ = 1 day

16. $\dfrac{1}{6}$ in 1 hour

    $\dfrac{1}{6}y$ in y hours

Exercise 5.2 (p. 141)

1. (a) $a(b + c) = 2(4 + 3)$
           $= 2(7)$
           $= \mathbf{14}$

   (b) $e - (a + c) = 7 - (2 + 3)$
              $= 7 - 5$
              $= \mathbf{2}$

   (c) $e(f - c) = 7(6-3)$
           $= 7(3)$
           $= \mathbf{21}$

   (d) $d(e - b) = 5(7 - 4)$
            $= 5(3)$
            $= \mathbf{15}$

   (e) $c(f + b + a) = 3(6 + 4 + 2)$
                $= 3(12)$
                $= \mathbf{36}$

   (f) $f(b + c + d) = 6(4 + 3 + 5)$
                $= 6(12)$
                $= \mathbf{72}$

   (g) $a(e - a - b) = 2(7 - 2 - 4)$
                $= 2(1)$
                $= \mathbf{2}$

   (h) $b(f - c - a) = 4(6 - 3 - 2)$
                $= 4(1)$
                $= \mathbf{4}$

   (i) $a + b(c + d) = 2 + 4(3 + 5)$
               $= 2 + 4(8)$
               $= 2 + 32$
               $= \mathbf{34}$

   (j) $f + c(e - b) = 6 + 3(7 - 4)$
               $= 6 + 3(3)$
               $= 6 + 9$
               $= \mathbf{15}$

   (k) $b(c + d) + \dfrac{f}{e} = 4(3 + 5) + \dfrac{6}{7}$

                $= 4(8) + \dfrac{6}{7}$

                $= \mathbf{32\dfrac{6}{7}}$

   (l) $\dfrac{c}{d}(a + f) = \dfrac{3}{5}(2 + 6)$

              $= \dfrac{24}{5}$

              $= \mathbf{4\dfrac{4}{5}}$

   (m) $\dfrac{\frac{a}{b}}{c} = \dfrac{\frac{2}{4}}{3}$

        $= 2 \div \dfrac{4}{3}$

        $= 2 \times \dfrac{3}{4}$

        $= \mathbf{\dfrac{3}{2}}$

   (n) $\dfrac{\frac{a}{b}}{c} = \dfrac{\frac{2}{4}}{3}$

        $= \dfrac{2}{4} \div 3$

        $= \dfrac{2}{4} \times \dfrac{1}{3}$

        $= \mathbf{\dfrac{1}{6}}$

   (o) $\dfrac{\frac{d}{e}}{f} = \dfrac{\frac{5}{7}}{6}$

        $= 5 \div \dfrac{7}{6}$

        $= 5 \times \dfrac{6}{7}$

        $= \mathbf{\dfrac{30}{7}}$

2. (a)
$$\frac{a}{b}(b + e) = \frac{-2}{6}[6 + (-1)]$$
$$= \frac{-2 \times 5}{6}$$
$$= \frac{-5}{3}$$
$$= -1\frac{2}{3}$$

(b)
$$b\left(\frac{a}{b} + \frac{c}{d}\right) = 6\left(\frac{-2}{6} + \frac{-4}{7}\right)$$
$$= 6\left(\frac{-1}{3} + \frac{-4}{7}\right)$$
$$= 6\left(\frac{-7}{21} + \frac{-12}{21}\right)$$
$$= 6\left(-\frac{19}{21}\right)$$
$$= -\frac{114}{21}$$
$$= -5\frac{3}{7}$$

(c)
$$a\left(bc + de + \frac{f}{c}\right) = -2\left[6(-4) + 7(-1) + \frac{6}{-4}\right]$$
$$= -2\left(-24 - 7 - \frac{3}{2}\right)$$
$$= -2\left(-31 - \frac{3}{2}\right)$$
$$= -2\left(-\frac{62}{2} - \frac{3}{2}\right)$$
$$= -2 \times \left(-\frac{65}{2}\right)$$
$$= \mathbf{65}$$

(d)
$$d\left(df - bc + \frac{a}{d}\right) = 7\left[7(6) - 6(-4) + \frac{-2}{7}\right]$$
$$= 7\left(42 + 24 - \frac{2}{7}\right)$$
$$= 7\left(66 - \frac{2}{7}\right)$$
$$= (7 \times 66) - \left(7 \times \frac{2}{7}\right)$$
$$= 462 - 2$$
$$= \mathbf{460}$$

(e)
$$a + \{[b + c(d + f) + cd] + ef\} = -2 + \{[6 - 4(7 + 6) + (-4)7] + (-1)6\}$$
$$= -2 + [6 - (4 \times 13) - 28] -6$$
$$= -2 + (6 - 52 - 28) - 6$$
$$= \mathbf{-82}$$

(f)
$$b\{a + [e(a + b) + de] -cd\} = 6\{-2 + [(-1)(-2 + 6) + 7(-1)] - (-4)(7)\}$$
$$= 6\{-2 + [(-1)(4) + (-7)] + 28\}$$
$$= 6\{-2 + (-11) + 28\}$$
$$= 6\{15\}$$
$$= \mathbf{90}$$

(g)
$$ef + b\{[b + e(a + b) - f] + ag\} = (-1)(6) + 6\{[6 + (-1)(-2 + 6) - 6] + (-2)(6)\}$$
$$= -6 + 6\{[6 + (-4) - 6] + (-12)]\}$$
$$= -6 + 6(-16)$$
$$= -6 + (-96)$$
$$= \mathbf{-102}$$

(h)　$\dfrac{de}{a} - \left(\dfrac{a}{b} + \dfrac{c}{f}\right) + a^2 = \dfrac{(7)(-1)}{(-2)} - \left(\dfrac{-2}{6} + \dfrac{-4}{6}\right) + (-2)^2$

$$= \dfrac{7}{2} - \dfrac{-6}{6} + 4$$

$$= 3\dfrac{1}{2} + 1 + 4$$

$$= \mathbf{8\dfrac{1}{2}}$$

3. (a)　　　　　$ab + ac = a(b + c)$

$$\left(2 \times \dfrac{1}{4}\right) + (2 \times (-6)) = 2\left(\dfrac{1}{4} + (-6)\right)$$

$$\dfrac{1}{2} + (-12) = 2\left(\dfrac{1}{4} - \dfrac{24}{4}\right)$$

$$-11\dfrac{1}{2} = 2\left(-\dfrac{23}{4}\right)$$

$$-11\dfrac{1}{2} = -\dfrac{23}{2}$$

$$-11\dfrac{1}{2} = -11\dfrac{1}{2}$$

(b)　　　　　$ba + ca = (b + c)a$

$$\left(\dfrac{1}{4}x2\right) + ((-6) \times 2) = \left(\dfrac{1}{4} + (-6)\right) \times 2$$

$$\dfrac{1}{2} + (-12) = \left(\dfrac{1}{4} - \dfrac{24}{4}\right) \times 2$$

$$-11\dfrac{1}{2} = -\dfrac{23}{4} \times 2$$

$$-11\dfrac{1}{2} = -\dfrac{23}{2}$$

$$-11\dfrac{1}{2} = -11\dfrac{1}{2}$$

(c)　　　　　$ab - ac = a(b - c)$

$$\left(2x\dfrac{1}{4}\right) - (2 \times (-6)) = 2\left(\dfrac{1}{4} - (-6)\right)$$

$$\dfrac{1}{2} - (-12) = 2\left(\dfrac{1}{4} + \dfrac{24}{4}\right)$$

$$12\dfrac{1}{2} = 2 \times \dfrac{25}{4}$$

$$12\dfrac{1}{2} = \dfrac{25}{2}$$

$$12\dfrac{1}{2} = 12\dfrac{1}{2}$$

(d)　　　　　$ba - ca = (b - c)a$

$$\left(\dfrac{1}{4}x2\right) - ((-6) \times 2) = \left(\dfrac{1}{4} - (-6)\right) \times 2$$

$$\dfrac{1}{2} - (-12) = \left(\dfrac{1}{4} + \dfrac{24}{4}\right) \times 2$$

$$\dfrac{1}{2} + 12 = \dfrac{25}{4} \times 2$$

$$12\dfrac{1}{2} = \dfrac{25}{2}$$

$$12\dfrac{1}{2} = 12\dfrac{1}{2}$$

4. (a)　$2p + (x - y) = (2 \times 3) + \left[-4 - \left(-\dfrac{2}{3}\right)\right]$

$$= 6 + \left(-3\dfrac{1}{3}\right)$$

$$= 6 - 3\dfrac{1}{3}$$

$$= \mathbf{2\dfrac{2}{3}}$$

(b)　$\dfrac{1}{2}(p - 2q) + \dfrac{x}{y} = \dfrac{1}{2}\left[3 - \left(2 \times \dfrac{1}{2}\right)\right] + \dfrac{-4}{-\dfrac{2}{3}}$

$$= \dfrac{1}{2} \times (3 - 1) + \left(4 \div \dfrac{2}{3}\right)$$

$$= \dfrac{1}{2} \times 2 + \left(4 \times \dfrac{3}{2}\right)$$

$$= 1 + 6$$

$$= \mathbf{7}$$

(c)

$$5px^2 + 3qy^2 = \left[5 \times 3 \times (-4)^2\right] + \left[3 \times \frac{1}{2} \times \left(-\frac{2}{3}\right)^2\right]$$

$$= (15 \times 16) + \left(\frac{3}{2} \times \frac{4}{9}\right)$$

$$= 240 + \frac{1}{3}$$

$$= \mathbf{240\frac{2}{3}}$$

(d)

$$4\left(\frac{x}{p} - \frac{y}{q}\right) = 4\left(\frac{-4}{3} - \frac{-\frac{2}{3}}{\frac{1}{2}}\right)$$

$$= 4\left(-\frac{4}{3} + \frac{2}{3} \div \frac{1}{2}\right)$$

$$= 4\left(-\frac{4}{3} + \frac{2}{3} \times 2\right)$$

$$= 4\left(-\frac{4}{3} + \frac{4}{3}\right)$$

$$= 4 \times 0$$

$$= \mathbf{0}$$

(e)

$$pq\left(\frac{1}{x} - \frac{1}{y}\right) = \left(3 \times \frac{1}{2}\right) \times \left(\frac{1}{-4} - \frac{1}{-\frac{2}{3}}\right)$$

$$= \frac{3}{2} \times \left(-\frac{1}{4} - 1 \div \left(-\frac{2}{3}\right)\right)$$

$$= \frac{3}{2} \times \left(-\frac{1}{4} - \left(-\frac{3}{2}\right)\right)$$

$$= \frac{3}{2} \times \left(-\frac{1}{4} + \frac{6}{4}\right)$$

$$= \frac{3}{2} \times \frac{5}{4}$$

$$= \frac{15}{8}$$

$$= \mathbf{1\frac{7}{8}}$$

(f)

$$\left(\frac{3x + y}{p - q}\right)^2 = \left(\frac{(3 \times (-4)) + \left(-\frac{2}{3}\right)}{3 - \frac{1}{2}}\right)^2$$

$$= \left(\frac{-12 - \frac{2}{3}}{2\frac{1}{2}}\right)^2$$

$$= \left(-12\frac{2}{3} \div 2\frac{1}{2}\right)^2$$

$$= \left(-\frac{38}{3} \times \frac{2}{5}\right)^2$$

$$= \left(-\frac{76}{15}\right)^2$$

$$= \frac{5,776}{225}$$

$$= \mathbf{25\frac{151}{225}}$$

(g)

$$\frac{x+y}{p^2+q^2} = \frac{-4+\left(-\dfrac{2}{3}\right)}{3^2+\left(\dfrac{1}{2}\right)^2}$$

$$= -4\frac{2}{3} \div \left(9 + \frac{1}{4}\right)$$

$$= -\frac{14}{3} \times \frac{4}{37}$$

$$= -\frac{56}{111}$$

(h)

$$\left(\frac{1}{q^2} - 3p\right)(x+y) = \left(\frac{1}{\left(\dfrac{1}{2}\right)^2} - (3 \times 3)\right)\left(-4 + \left(-\dfrac{2}{3}\right)\right)$$

$$= \left(\left(1 \div \frac{1}{4}\right) - 9\right) \times \left(-4\frac{2}{3}\right)$$

$$= -5 \times \left(-\frac{14}{3}\right)$$

$$= \frac{70}{3}$$

$$= 23\frac{1}{3}$$

Exercise 5.3 (pp. 143-144)

To distinguish between multiplication and the variable x, $\cdot$ will be used for multiplication.

1. (a) $(3 + 5)a = $ **8a**   (b) $(6 + 6)b = $ **12b**   (c) $[(5 + (-8)]c = $ **-3c**

   (d) $(-5 + 8)c = $ **3c**   (e) $[-9 + (-3)]m = $ **-12m**   (f) $(4 + 1)x = $ **5x**

   (g) **4a + 3b**   (h) **5a + 5b**   (i) $(-9 + 14)ab = $ **5ab**

   (j) **12a²b + 17ab²**   (k) $(52 - 31)ab^2 = $ **21ab²**   (l) **32ab² - 32cb²**

2. (a) $2 \cdot 6 \cdot ab = $ **12ab**   (b) $-5 \cdot 3 \cdot ac = $ **-15ac**   (c) $6 \cdot 2 \cdot xy = $ **12xy**

   (d) $-3 \cdot 6 \cdot xz = $ **-18xz**   (e) $3 \cdot 5 \cdot nm = $ **15nm**   (f) $3 \cdot 6 \cdot np = $ **18np**

   (g) $-4 \cdot 3 \cdot pq = $ **-12pq**   (h) $-4 \cdot (-7) \cdot pr = $ **28pr**   (i) $-4 \cdot 3 \cdot (a^2)ab = $ **-12a³b**

   (j) $-12 \cdot 31 \cdot a \cdot a^2 \cdot b^2 \cdot b = $ **-372a³b³**

   (k) $-23 \cdot 23 \cdot x \cdot x^2 \cdot y = $ **-529x³y**

   (l) $-17 \cdot 14 \cdot x \cdot y \cdot y^2 = $ **-238xy³**

3. (a) $\dfrac{128a}{16a} = $ **8**   (b) $\dfrac{-28ab}{49b} = -\dfrac{\textbf{4a}}{\textbf{7}}$ (c) $\dfrac{33m}{44mn} = \dfrac{\textbf{3}}{\textbf{4n}}$

   (d) $\dfrac{17pq}{-34qp} = -\dfrac{\textbf{1}}{\textbf{2}}$ (e) $\dfrac{-32xy}{-12yz} = \dfrac{\textbf{8x}}{\textbf{3z}}$ (f) $\dfrac{-22xy}{-55yz} = \dfrac{\textbf{2x}}{\textbf{5z}}$

4. (a) $(3 + 7)a = $ **10a**   (b) $3 \cdot 7 \cdot a \cdot a = $ **21a²**

   (c) $(3 - 7)b = $ **-4b**   (d) $3 \cdot (-7) \cdot b \cdot b = $ **-21b²**

   (e) $(3 + 5)a + (-7b) = $ **8a - 7b**   (f) $3 \cdot 5 \cdot (-7) \cdot a \cdot a \cdot b = $ **-105a²b**

   (g) $(-5 - 6)c + 2c^2 = $ **2c² - 11c**   (h) $-5 \cdot (-6) \cdot 2 \cdot c^2 \cdot c^2 = $ **60c⁴**

   (i) $4d + (5 + 3)de = $ **4d + 8de**   (j) $4 \cdot 5 \cdot 3 \cdot d \cdot de \cdot de = $ **60d³e²**

   (k) $(4 + 9)f + 4fg = $ **13f + 4fg**   (l) $4 \cdot 4 \cdot 9 \cdot f \cdot f \cdot fg = $ **144f³g**

(m) $(4 - 3 - 7)b =$ **-6b**

(n) $\dfrac{(-3)(7)(ab)(a)}{42b} = -\dfrac{\mathbf{a^2}}{\mathbf{2}}$

(o) $\dfrac{-5x}{(15)(4)(y)(xy)} = -\dfrac{\mathbf{1}}{\mathbf{12y^2}}$

(p) $(-7 - 14)a^2 + 7ab =$ **7ab - 21a²**

(q) $\dfrac{(-32)(5)(x)(yz)}{4y} =$ **-40xz**

(r) $\dfrac{72xy}{(8)(4)(yz)(zx)} = \dfrac{\mathbf{9}}{\mathbf{4z^2}}$

Exercise 5.4 (p. 146)

1. (a) $a(b - c) =$ **ab - ac**

(b) $a(-b + c) = -ab + ac$
    $=$ **ac - ab**

(c) $a(b + c) =$ **ab + ac**

(d) $a(-b - c) =$ **-ab - ac**

(e) $-a(-b + c) =$ **ab - ac**

(f) $-a(-b - c) =$ **ab + ac**

(g) $a + (b - c) =$ **a + b - c**

(h) $a - (b + c) =$ **a - b - c**

(i) $a + (-b + c) =$ **a - b + c**

(j) $a + (-b - c) =$ **a - b - c**

(k) $a - (-b + c) =$ **a + b - c**

(l) $a - (-b - c) =$ **a + b + c**

2. (a) $x + (2b - c) =$ **x + 2b - c**

(b) $2x + (4a - 2b) =$ **2x + 4a - 2b**

(c) $3a + (-2b + 3c) =$ **3a - 2b + 3c**

(d) $2y + (-3x + 2w) =$ **2y - 3x + 2w**

(e) $g + (-4b - 3c) = g$ **- 4b - 3c**

(f) $4m + (-3n - 4p) =$ **4m - 3n - 4p**

(g) $2n - (-5t + 3u) =$ **2n + 5t - 3u**

(h) $6p - (-2q + 5r) =$ **6p + 2q - 5r**

(i) $-(2x + 7y) =$ **-2x -7y**

(j) $-(10r + 35) =$ **-10r - 35**

(k) $-(2m - 3n) = -2m + 3n =$ **3n - 2m**

(l) $-(6p - 7q) =$ **-6p + 7q**

(m) $3x - (3t + 8u) =$ **3x - 3t - 8u**

(n) $4r - (10s + 7t) =$ **4r - 10s - 7t**

(o) $6z - (3y - 5w) =$ **6z - 3y + 5w**

(p) $2w - (4x - 9y) =$ **2w - 4x + 9y**

(q) $-x - (-3y - 4z) = -x + 3y + 4z$
    $=$ **3y - x + 4z**

(r) $-a - (-3b - 5c) = -a + 3b + 5c$
    $=$ **3b + 5c - a**

3. (a) $3a(4b - 5c) =$ **12ab - 15ac**

(b) $6x(2y - 3z) =$ **12xy - 18xz**

(c) $3n(5m + 6p) =$ **15mn + 18np**

(d) $-4p(3q - 7r) = -12pq + 28pr$
    $=$ **28pr - 12pq**

(e) $(5x + 7y)4z =$ **20xz + 28yz**

(f) $(9t + 8u)4v =$ **36tv + 32uv**

(g) $(7m - 3n)5p =$ **35mp - 15np**

(h) $(6p - q)7r =$ **42pr - 7qr**

4. (a) $4x + 3xy =$ **x(4 + 3y)**

(b) $15m + 6n + 9mn =$ **3(5m + 2n + 3mn)**

(c) $7p + 8pq - 5p = 2p + 8pq$
    $=$ **2p(1 + 4q)**

(d) $4a + 8ab =$ **4a(1 + 2b)**

(e) $3x + 6xy + 9yx = 3x + 15xy$
    $=$ **3x(1 + 5y)**

(f) $2ab + 3abc + 5cba = 2ab + 8abc$
    $=$ **2ab(1 + 4c)**

(g) $5rst + 3st - 2rt =$ **t(5rs + 3s - 2r)**

(h) $6ab + 3bc - ba + b = 5ab + 3bc + b$
    $=$ **b(5a + 3c + 1)**

Exercise 5.5 (pp. 147-148)

1. (a) $2a + 3b - 2b + a$
    $= (2 + 1)a + (3 - 2)b$
    $= \mathbf{3a + b}$

   (b) $2a - 3b + c - b + 2a$
    $= (2 + 2)a + (-3 - 1)b + c$
    $= \mathbf{4a - 4b} + c$

   (c) $3d + e - f + 4e - 3f + d$
    $= (3 + 1)d + (1 + 4)e + (-1 - 3)f$
    $= \mathbf{4d + 5e \text{ -}4f}$

   (d) $4a^2 + b - c + a + 2c + 2b$
    $= 4a^2 + a + (1 + 2)b + (-1 + 2)c$
    $= \mathbf{4a^2 + a + 3b + c}$

   (e) $5a + c - b - a - b - c^2 - 4a$
    $= (5 - 1 - 4)a + (-1 - 1)b + c - c^2$
    $= \mathbf{-2b + c - c^2}$

   (f) $2a + b^2 + a - 7b + 3b^2$
    $= (2 + 1)a + (1 + 3)b^2 - 7b$
    $= \mathbf{3a + 4b^2 - 7b}$

   (g) $b - 7a + 3b + 8a + 3c - a^2$
    $= (-7 + 8)a - a^2 + (1 + 3)b + 3c$
    $= \mathbf{a - a^2 + 4b + 3c}$

   (h) $-7b - 7a - 6b - 6a + c^2 - 2b + c$
    $= (-7 - 6)a + (-7 - 6 - 2)b + c^2 + c$
    $= \mathbf{-13a - 15b + c^2 + c}$

2. (a) $(a - b) + (b - a)$
    $= (1 - 1)a + (-1 + 1)b$
    $= \mathbf{0}$

   (b) $(-a + b) + (b - a)$
    $= (-1 - 1)a + (1 + 1)b$
    $= \mathbf{-2a + 2b}$

   (c) $(-a - b) - (-b - a)$
    $= -a - b + b + a$
    $= (-1 + 1)a + (-1 + 1)b$
    $= \mathbf{0}$

   (d) $(a - b) - (b - c) - (c - a)$
    $= a - b - b + c - c + a$
    $= (1 + 1)a + (-1 + -1)b + (1 + -1)c$
    $= \mathbf{2a - 2b}$

   (e) $(a - b) + (b - c) + (c - a)$
    $= (a - 1)a + (-1 + 1)b + (-1 + 1)c$
    $= \mathbf{0}$

   (f) $3(6b - 9a) + 7(6a - 5b)$
    $= 18b - 27a + 42a - 35b$
    $= (-27 + 42)a + (18 - 35)b$
    $= \mathbf{15a - 17b}$

   (g) $3(a - b) + 7(2a + 2b)$
    $= 3a - 3b + 14a + 14b$
    $= (3 + 14)a + (-3 + 14)b$
    $= \mathbf{17a + 11b}$

   (h) $17(1 - 3c) + 3(c + c^2)$
    $= 17 - 51c + 3c - 3c^2$
    $= 17 + (-51 + 3)c - 3c^2$
    $= \mathbf{17 - 48c - 3c^2}$

3. (a) $a(a - b) + b(b - c) + c(c - a)$
    $= \mathbf{a^2 - ab + b^2 - bc + c^2 - ac}$

   (b) $a(a - b) + b(b - a) + c(a - b)$
    $= a^2 - ab + b^2 - ab + ac - bc$
    $= a^2 + (-1 - 1)ab + b^2 + ac - bc$
    $= \mathbf{a^2 - 2ab + b^2 + ac - bc}$

   (c) $a(a - b) + [3(c + a^2) - ab]$
    $= a^2 - ab + 3c + 3a^2 - ab$
    $= (1 + 3)a^2 + (-1 - 1)ab + 3c$
    $= \mathbf{4a^2 - 2ab + 3c}$

   (d) $[(2a + 2b)c + d]c - 4ac^2 + bc^2$
    $= [2ac + 2bc + d]c - 4ac^2 + bc^2$
    $= 2ac^2 + 2bc^2 + dc - 4ac^2 + bc^2$
    $= (2 - 4)ac^2 + (2 + 1)bc^2 + dc$
    $= \mathbf{-2ac^2 + 3bc^2 + dc}$

   (e) $c[a + b(a^2 + 2bc) - 3a^3] - a^2bc + b^2c^2 - ac$
    $= c[a + ba^2 + 2b^2c - 3a^3] - a^2bc + b^2c^2 - ac$
    $= ac + a^2bc + 2b^2c^2 - 3a^3c - a^2bc + b^2c^2 - ac$
    $= (1 - 1)ac + (1 - 1)a^2bc + (2 + 1)b^2c^2 - 3a^3c$
    $= \mathbf{3b^2c^2 - 3a^3c}$

(f) $a(b^2 + 3c) - [b^2(a - 2c) - b(2ab + 1)]$
$= ab^2 + 3ac - (ab^2 - 2b^2c - 2ab^2 - b)$
$= ab^2 + 3ac - ab^2 + 2b^2c + 2ab^2 + b)$
$= (1 - 1 + 2)ab^2 + 3ac + 2b^2c + b$
$= \mathbf{2ab^2 + 3ac + 2b^2c + b}$

(g) $x(y - 3z) - y(z - 3x) - z(x - 3y)$
$= xy - 3xz - yz + 3xy - xz + 3yz$
$= (1 + 3)xy + (-3 - 1)xz + (-1 + 3)yz$
$= \mathbf{4xy - 4xz + 2yz}$

(h) $3xy + [x(3z - 2y) - xy] - y(x - 2z)$
$= 3xy + 3xz - 2xy - xy - xy + 2yz$
$= (3 - 2 - 1 - 1)xy + 3xz + 2yz$
$= \mathbf{-xy + 3xz + 2yz}$

4. (a) $\dfrac{1}{4}(8x + 4) - 3 = 2x + 1 - 3$
$\qquad\qquad\qquad = \mathbf{2x - 2}$

(b) $\dfrac{1}{3}(3x + 9) - 2x = x + 3 - 2x$
$\qquad\qquad\qquad = (1 - 2)x + 3$
$\qquad\qquad\qquad = -x + 3$
$\qquad\qquad\qquad = \mathbf{3 - x}$

(c) $\dfrac{y}{2} - \dfrac{4y}{5} - 3 = \left(\dfrac{1}{2} - \dfrac{4}{5}\right)y - 3$
$\qquad\qquad\quad = \left(\dfrac{5 - 8}{10}\right)y - 3$
$\qquad\qquad\quad = -\dfrac{\mathbf{3y}}{\mathbf{10}} - \mathbf{3}$

(d) $\dfrac{1}{3}(x + 3) + \dfrac{5}{6}(x - 1) = \dfrac{x}{3} + 1 + \dfrac{5x}{6} - \dfrac{5}{6}$
$\qquad\qquad\qquad\qquad = \left(\dfrac{1}{3} + \dfrac{5}{6}\right)x + 1 - \dfrac{5}{6}$
$\qquad\qquad\qquad\qquad = \left(\dfrac{2 + 5}{6}\right)x + \dfrac{1}{6}$
$\qquad\qquad\qquad\qquad = \dfrac{\mathbf{7x}}{\mathbf{6}} + \dfrac{\mathbf{1}}{\mathbf{6}}$

(e) $\dfrac{5}{6}(x + 1) + \dfrac{1}{4}(x - 3) = \dfrac{5x}{6} + \dfrac{5}{6} + \dfrac{x}{4} - \dfrac{3}{4}$
$\qquad\qquad\qquad\qquad = \left(\dfrac{5}{6} + \dfrac{1}{4}\right)x + \dfrac{5}{6} - \dfrac{3}{4}$
$\qquad\qquad\qquad\qquad = \left(\dfrac{10 + 3}{12}\right)x + \dfrac{10 - 9}{12}$
$\qquad\qquad\qquad\qquad = \dfrac{\mathbf{13x}}{\mathbf{12}} + \dfrac{\mathbf{1}}{\mathbf{12}}$

(f) $\dfrac{7}{8}(x - 1) - \dfrac{1}{6}(2x + 1) = \dfrac{7x}{8} - \dfrac{7}{8} - \dfrac{2x}{6} - \dfrac{1}{6}$
$\qquad\qquad\qquad\qquad = \left(\dfrac{7}{8} - \dfrac{2}{6}\right)x + \left(-\dfrac{7}{8} - \dfrac{1}{6}\right)$
$\qquad\qquad\qquad\qquad = \left(\dfrac{21 - 8}{24}\right)x + \left(\dfrac{-21 - 4}{24}\right)$
$\qquad\qquad\qquad\qquad = \dfrac{\mathbf{13x}}{\mathbf{24}} - \dfrac{\mathbf{25}}{\mathbf{24}}$

(g) $\dfrac{7x - 6}{8} + \dfrac{5x + 3}{4} = \dfrac{7x}{8} - \dfrac{6}{8} + \dfrac{5x}{4} + \dfrac{3}{4}$
$\qquad\qquad\qquad\quad = \left(\dfrac{7}{8} + \dfrac{5}{4}\right)x + \left(-\dfrac{6}{8} + \dfrac{3}{4}\right)$
$\qquad\qquad\qquad\quad = \left(\dfrac{7 + 10}{8}\right)x + \left(\dfrac{-6 + 6}{8}\right)$
$\qquad\qquad\qquad\quad = \dfrac{\mathbf{17x}}{\mathbf{8}}$

(h) $\dfrac{3(5x - 1)}{4} - \dfrac{3x + 7}{6} = \dfrac{15x}{4} - \dfrac{3}{4} - \dfrac{3x}{6} - \dfrac{7}{6}$
$\qquad\qquad\qquad\qquad = \left(\dfrac{15}{4} - \dfrac{3}{6}\right)x + \left(-\dfrac{3}{4} - \dfrac{7}{6}\right)$
$\qquad\qquad\qquad\qquad = \left(\dfrac{45 - 6}{12}\right)x + \left(\dfrac{-9 - 14}{12}\right)$
$\qquad\qquad\qquad\qquad = \dfrac{\mathbf{39x}}{\mathbf{12}} - \dfrac{\mathbf{23}}{\mathbf{12}}$

Chapter 6

Exercise 6.1 (pp. 153-154)

1. (a) $7 + 5 = 12$

    $12 = 12$

    true

   (b) $-2 + 4 = -2$

    $2 = -2$

    false

   (c) $\mathbf{1} + (-3) = 2$

    $-2 = 2$

    false

   (d) $-2 + 9 = 11$

    $7 = 11$

    false

   (e) $5 + (-2) = -3$

    $3 = -3$

    false

   (f) $1\frac{2}{3} - \frac{2}{3} = 0$

    $1 = 0$

    false

2. (a) $\mathbf{5} + 4 = 9$

   (b) $\mathbf{15} - 5 = 10$

   (c) $\frac{\mathbf{6}}{\mathbf{4}} + \frac{1}{4} = \frac{7}{4}$

    $1\frac{\mathbf{1}}{\mathbf{2}} + \frac{1}{4} = \frac{7}{4}$

   (d) $\frac{\mathbf{5}}{\mathbf{5}} - \frac{4}{5} = \frac{1}{5}$

    $\mathbf{1} - \frac{4}{5} = \frac{1}{5}$

   (e) $3 - (\mathbf{-7}) = 10$

   (f) $3 - \mathbf{3} = 0$

Natural numbers are positive integers

3. (a) $\mathbf{1} < 3$

    $\mathbf{2} < 3$

   (b) $\mathbf{1} \leq 3$

    $\mathbf{2} \leq 3$

    $\mathbf{3} \leq 3$

   (c) $\mathbf{1} + 2 < 4$

   (d) $4 > \mathbf{1}$

    $4 > \mathbf{2}$

    $4 > \mathbf{3}$

   (e) $4 \geq \mathbf{1}$

    $4 \geq \mathbf{2}$

    $4 \geq \mathbf{3}$

    $4 \geq \mathbf{4}$

   (f) $4 > \mathbf{1} - 1$

    $4 > \mathbf{2} - 1$

    $4 > \mathbf{3} - 1$

    $4 > \mathbf{4} - 1$

4. (a) $2 < \mathbf{3} < 7$

    $2 < \mathbf{4} < 7$

    $2 < \mathbf{5} < 7$

    $2 < \mathbf{6} < 7$

   (b) $15 < \mathbf{16} < 20$

    $15 < \mathbf{17} < 20$

    $15 < \mathbf{18} < 20$

    $15 < \mathbf{19} < 20$

   (c) $9 \leq \mathbf{9} \leq 15$

    $9 \leq \mathbf{10} \leq 15$

    $9 \leq \mathbf{11} \leq 15$

    $9 \leq \mathbf{12} \leq 15$

    $9 \leq \mathbf{13} \leq 15$

    $9 \leq \mathbf{14} \leq 15$

    $9 \leq \mathbf{15} \leq 15$

   (d) $15 \leq \mathbf{15} \leq 20$

    $15 \leq \mathbf{16} \leq 20$

    $15 \leq \mathbf{17} \leq 20$

    $15 \leq \mathbf{18} \leq 20$

    $15 \leq \mathbf{19} \leq 20$

    $15 \leq \mathbf{20} \leq 20$

   (e) $\mathbf{21} - 7 = 14$

    $\therefore$ solutions for

    $x - 7 \neq 14$

    are all natural numbers

    except 21.

   (f) $\mathbf{7} + 3 = 10$

    $\therefore$ solutions for

    $x + 3 \neq 10$

    are all natural numbers

    except 7.

(g) **35** - 15 = 20
∴ solutions for
x - 15 < 20
are 1, 2, 3,..., 34

(h) **12** + 3 = 15
∴ solutions for
x + 3 ≤ 15
are 1, 2, 3,..., 12

(i) 10 - **8** = 2
∴ solutions for
10 - x > 2
are 1, 2, 3, ..., 7

(j) 7 - **5** = 2
∴ solutions for
7 - x ≥ 2
are 1, 2, 3, 4, 5

(k) $\dfrac{\mathbf{9}}{3}$ = 3
∴ solutions for
$\dfrac{x}{3}$ < 3
are 1, 2, 3,..., 8

(l) 3 - $\dfrac{\mathbf{6}}{3}$ = 1
∴ solutions for
3 - $\dfrac{x}{3}$ > 1
are 1, 2, 3, 4, 5

5. (a) **True**. Positive integers are greater than 0.

(b) **True**. Positive integers are greater than -4.

(c) **True**. Positive integers don't include 0.

(d) **True**. Positive integers are not equal to -1.

(e) **False**. 4 is a natural number (positive integer).

(f) **True**. Positive integers are all greater than or equal to 1.

6. (a) $(\mathbf{\pm 3})^2 = 9$

(b) $4 - (\mathbf{\pm 2})^2 = 0$

(c) **No solution**. Square numbers are always positive.

(d) $\dfrac{1}{(\mathbf{\pm 5})^2} = \dfrac{1}{25}$

(e) $\dfrac{1}{2} \times (\mathbf{\pm 2})^2 = 2$

(f) $\left(\pm \dfrac{\mathbf{2}}{\mathbf{3}}\right)^2 = \dfrac{4}{9}$

Exercise 6.2 (pp. 158 - 159)

The terms "from both sides", "to both sides" and "both sides" are implied in the explanation of steps.

1. (a)
$6x + 3 = 5x + x$
$5x + 3 = 5$ subtract x
$5x = 2$ subtract 3

(b)
$3x - 4 = 14 - 3x$
$6x - 4 = 14$ add $3x$
$6x = 18$ add 4

(c)
$3(2x - 5) = 12$
$2x - 5 = 4$ divide by 3
$2x = 9$ add 5

(d)
$3[(x - 5) + 2x] = 0$
$x - 5 + 2x = 0$ divide by 3
$x + 2x = 5$ add 5

2. (a)
$3x - 13 = 26$
$3x - 13 + 13 = 26 + 13$ add 13
$3x = 39$
$\dfrac{3x}{3} = \dfrac{39}{3}$ divide by 3
$x = \mathbf{13}$

(b)
$3x - 7 = 32$
$3x - 7 + 7 = 32 + 7$ add 7
$3x = 39$
$\dfrac{3x}{3} = \dfrac{39}{3}$ divide by 3
$x = \mathbf{13}$

(c)
$4y - 9 = -5$
$4y - 9 + 9 = -5 + 9$ add 9
$4y = 4$
$\dfrac{4y}{4} = \dfrac{4}{4}$ divide by 4
$y = \mathbf{1}$

(d)
$8 + 3a = 11$
$8 + 3a - 8 = 11 - 8$ subtract 8
$3a = 3$
$\dfrac{3a}{3} = \dfrac{3}{3}$ divide by 3
$a = \mathbf{1}$

(e)
$$8 + 2x = 14$$
$$8 + 2x - 8 = 14 - 8 \qquad \text{subtract 8}$$
$$2x = 6$$
$$\frac{2x}{2} = \frac{6}{2} \qquad \text{divide by 2}$$
$$x = \mathbf{3}$$

(f)
$$y + 6 = 18$$
$$y + 6 - 6 = 18 - 6 \qquad \text{subtract 6}$$
$$y = \mathbf{12}$$

(g)
$$8x + 4 = 12$$
$$8x + 4 - 4 = 12 - 4 \qquad \text{subtract 4}$$
$$8x = 8$$
$$\frac{8x}{8} = \frac{8}{8} \qquad \text{divide by 8}$$
$$x = \mathbf{1}$$

(h)
$$2x - 10 = 8$$
$$2x - 10 + 10 = 8 + 10 \qquad \text{add 10}$$
$$2x = 18$$
$$\frac{2x}{2} = \frac{18}{2} \qquad \text{divide by 2}$$
$$x = \mathbf{9}$$

(i)
$$3x + 6 = 1$$
$$3x + 6 - 6 = 1 - 6 \qquad \text{subtract 6}$$
$$3x = -5$$
$$\frac{3x}{3} = -\frac{5}{3} \qquad \text{divide by 3}$$
$$x = \mathbf{-1\frac{2}{3}}$$

(j)
$$x + 4 = 60$$
$$x + 4 - 4 = 60 - 4 \qquad \text{subtract 4}$$
$$x = \mathbf{56}$$

(k)
$$2a + 45 = 0$$
$$2a + 45 - 45 = 0 - 45 \qquad \text{subtract 45}$$
$$2a = -45$$
$$\frac{2a}{2} = -\frac{45}{2} \qquad \text{divide by 2}$$
$$a = \mathbf{-22\frac{1}{2}}$$

(l)
$$7y + 3 = y + 18$$
$$7y + 3 - y = y + 18 - y \qquad \text{subtract } y$$
$$6y + 3 = 18$$
$$6y + 3 - 3 = 18 - 3 \qquad \text{subtract 3}$$
$$6y = 15$$
$$\frac{6y}{6} = \frac{15}{6} \qquad \text{divide by 6}$$
$$y = \mathbf{2\frac{1}{2}}$$

(m)
$$x + 3 = 18 - 3x$$
$$x + 3 + 3x = 18 - 3x + 3x \qquad \text{add } 3x$$
$$4x + 3 = 18$$
$$4x + 3 - 3 = 18 - 3 \qquad \text{subtract 3}$$
$$4x = 15$$
$$\frac{4x}{4} = \frac{15}{4} \qquad \text{divide by 4}$$
$$x = \mathbf{3\frac{3}{4}}$$

(n)
$$2y - 2 = 4 - y$$
$$2y - 2 + y = 4 - y + y \qquad \text{add } y$$
$$3y - 2 = 4$$
$$3y - 2 + 2 = 4 + 2 \qquad \text{add 2}$$
$$3y = 6$$
$$\frac{3y}{3} = \frac{6}{3} \qquad \text{divide by 3}$$
$$y = \mathbf{2}$$

(o)
$$5x - 4 = 2x + 11$$
$$5x - 4 - 2x = 2x + 11 - 2x \qquad \text{subtract } 2x$$
$$3x - 4 = 11$$
$$3x - 4 + 4 = 11 + 4 \qquad \text{add 4}$$
$$3x = 15$$
$$\frac{3x}{3} = \frac{15}{3} \qquad \text{divide by 3}$$
$$x = \mathbf{5}$$

(p)
$$4x = 7 + 3x$$
$$4x - 3x = 7 + 3x - 3x \qquad \text{subtract } 3x$$
$$x = \mathbf{7}$$

3. (a) $3(x + 2) + 7(x - 1) = 12$
$3x + 6 + 7x - 7 = 12$
$10x - 1 = 12$
$10x - 1 + 1 = 12 + 1$ add 1
$10x = 13$
$\dfrac{10x}{10} = \dfrac{13}{10}$ divide by 10
$x = \mathbf{1\dfrac{3}{10}}$

(b) $5(x + 1) + 3(x - 1) = 5$
$5x + 5 + 3x - 3 = 5$
$8x + 2 = 5$
$8x + 2 - 2 = 5 - 2$ subtract 2
$8x = 3$
$\dfrac{8x}{8} = \dfrac{3}{8}$ divide by 8
$x = \mathbf{\dfrac{3}{8}}$

(c) $4(x - 1) - (x + 3) = 0$
$4x - 4 - x - 3 = 0$
$3x - 7 = 0$
$3x - 7 + 7 = 0 + 7$ add 7
$3x = 7$
$\dfrac{3x}{3} = \dfrac{7}{3}$ divide by 3
$x = \mathbf{2\dfrac{1}{3}}$

(d) $3(1 - x) + 4(x - 5) = 10$
$3 - 3x + 4x - 20 = 10$
$x - 17 = 10$
$x - 17 + 17 = 10 + 17$ add 17
$x = \mathbf{27}$

(e) $28(x - 3) - (x - 3) = 0$
$28x - 84 - x + 3 = 0$
$27x - 81 = 0$
$27x - 81 + 81 = 0 + 81$ add 81
$27x = 81$
$\dfrac{27x}{27} = \dfrac{81}{27}$ divide by 27
$x = \mathbf{3}$

(f) $9(x - 4) + (2 + 8x) = 0$
$9x - 36 + 2 + 8x = 0$
$17x - 34 = 0$
$17x - 34 + 34 = 0 + 34$ add 34
$17x = 34$
$\dfrac{17x}{17} = \dfrac{34}{17}$ divide by 17
$x = \mathbf{2}$

(g) $3x + 3(x - 3) - (4 - 4x) = 0$
$3x + 3x - 9 - 4 + 4x = 0$
$10x - 13 = 0$
$10x - 13 + 13 = 0 + 13$ add 13
$10x = 13$
$\dfrac{10x}{10} = \dfrac{13}{10}$ divide by 10
$x = \mathbf{1\dfrac{3}{10}}$

(h) $3(2x - 3) - (2x + 2) = x - 3$
$6x - 9 - 2x - 2 = x - 3$
$4x - 11 = x - 3$
$4x - 11 - x = x - 3 - x$ subtract x
$3x - 11 = -3$
$3x - 11 + 11 = -3 + 11$ add 11
$3x = 8$
$\dfrac{3x}{3} = \dfrac{8}{3}$ divide by 3
$x = \mathbf{2\dfrac{2}{3}}$

(i) $3y + 6(y + 3) - (8y - 16) = 60$
$3y + 6y + 18 - 8y + 16 = 60$
$y + 34 = 60$
$y + 34 - 34 = 60 - 34$ subtract 34
$y = \mathbf{26}$

(j) $3 + (4 + 4p) = 6(4 - p)$
$7 + 4p = 24 - 6p$
$7 + 4p + 6p = 24 - 6p + 6p$ add $6p$
$7 + 10p = 24$
$7 + 10p - 7 = 24 - 7$ subtract 7
$10p = 17$
$\dfrac{10p}{10} = \dfrac{17}{10}$ divide by 10
$p = \mathbf{1\dfrac{7}{10}}$

(k) $3(u - 3) - 3(4 + u) = 5 + u$
     $3u - 9 - 12 - 3u = 5 + u$
     $-21 = 5 + u$
     $-21 - 5 = 5 + u - 5$ subtract 5
     $\mathbf{-26} = u$

(l) $5 - 3(q - 7) = 2(2 - q) - 8$
     $5 - 3q + 21 = 4 - 2q - 8$
     $26 - 3q = -4 - 2q$
     $26 - 3q + 2q = -4 - 2q + 2q$ add $2q$
     $26 - q = -4$
     $26 - q - 26 = -4 - 26$ subtract 26
     $-q = -30$
     $q = \mathbf{30}$

(m) $5(3 - s) - 4(s - 3) = 5 - 4s$
     $15 - 5s - 4s + 12 = 5 - 4s$
     $27 - 9s = 5 - 4s$
     $27 - 9s + 4s = 5 - 4s + 4s$ add $4s$
     $27 - 5s = 5$
     $27 - 5s - 27 = 5 - 27$ subtract 27
     $-5s = -22$
     $s = \dfrac{-22}{-5}$ divide by -5
     $s = \mathbf{4\dfrac{2}{5}}$

(n) $x(3 + x) - 3(1 + 2x) = 3 + x^2$
     $3x + x^2 - 3 - 6x = 3 + x^2$
     $-3x + x^2 - 3 = 3 + x^2$
     $-3x + x^2 - 3 - x^2 = 3 + x^2 - x^2$
                                   subtract x^2
     $-3x - 3 = 3$
     $-3x - 3 + 3 = 3 + 3$ add 3
     $\dfrac{-3x}{-3} = \dfrac{6}{-3}$ divide by -3
     $x = \mathbf{-2}$

(o) $n(3n - 3) - 5(3 + n) = 3n^2 + 2n + 3$
     $3n^2 - 3n - 15 - 5n = 3n^2 + 2n + 3$
     $3n^2 - 8n - 15 = 3n^2 + 2n + 3$
     $3n^2 - 8n - 15 - 3n^2 = 3n^2 + 2n + 3 - 3n^2$
                                   subtract $3n^2$
     $-8n - 15 = 2n + 3$
     $-8n - 15 + 15 = 2n + 3 + 15$
                                   add 15
     $-8n = 2n + 18$
     $-8n - 2n = 2n - 2n + 18$
                                   subtract $2n$
     $-10n = 18$
     $\dfrac{-10n}{-10} = \dfrac{18}{-10}$ divide by -10
     $n = \mathbf{-1\dfrac{4}{5}}$

(p) $w^2 - w(w - 3) = 12(1 + w)$
     $w^2 - w^2 + 3w = 12 + 12w$
     $3w = 12 + 12w$
     $3w - 12w = 12 + 12w - 12w$
                                   subtract $12w$
     $-9w = 12$
     $\dfrac{-9w}{-9} = \dfrac{12}{-9}$ divide by -9
     $w = \mathbf{-1\dfrac{1}{3}}$

4. (a) $x^2 - 3 = 1$
        $x^2 - 3 + 3 = 1 + 3$ add 3
        $x^2 = 4$
        $x = \mathbf{\pm 2}$

(b) $2x^2 + 5 = 23$
     $2x^2 + 5 - 5 = 23 - 5$ subtract 5
     $2x^2 = 18$
     $\dfrac{2x^2}{2} = \dfrac{18}{2}$ divide by 2
     $x^2 = 9$
     $x = \mathbf{\pm 3}$

(c)
$$2x^2 + 7 = 55 - x^2$$
$$2x^2 + 7 + x^2 = 55 - x^2 + x^2 \quad \text{add } x^2$$
$$3x^2 + 7 = 55$$
$$3x^2 + 7 - 7 = 55 - 7 \qquad \text{subtract } 7$$
$$\frac{3x^2}{3} = \frac{48}{3} \qquad \text{divide by 3}$$
$$3x^2 = 48$$
$$x^2 = 16$$
$$x = \mathbf{\pm 4}$$

(d)
$$2(x^2 + 1) = 52$$
$$2x^2 + 2 = 52$$
$$2x^2 + 2 - 2 = 52 - 2 \qquad \text{subtract 2}$$
$$2x^2 = 50$$
$$\frac{2x^2}{2} = \frac{50}{2} \qquad \text{divide by 2}$$
$$x^2 = 25$$
$$x = \mathbf{\pm 5}$$

(e)
$$2(x^2 - 9) = 90 - x^2$$
$$2x^2 - 18 = 90 - x^2$$
$$2x^2 - 18 + x^2 = 90 - x^2 + x^2 \quad \text{add } x^2$$
$$3x^2 - 18 = 90$$
$$3x^2 - 18 + 18 = 90 + 18 \qquad \text{add 18}$$
$$3x^2 = 108$$
$$\frac{3x^2}{3} = \frac{108}{3} \qquad \text{divide by 3}$$
$$x = \mathbf{\pm 6}$$

(f)
$$(x - 1)^2 = 4$$
$$x - 1 = 2 \text{ or } x - 1 = -2$$
$$x = \mathbf{3 \text{ or }} \quad x = \mathbf{-1}$$

Exercise 6.3 (pp. 161)

The alternative solutions given in this section are explained more fully in New Elementary Math 2 and therefore will not be used here.

1.
$$\frac{1}{2}y + 3 = 9$$
$$\frac{1}{2}y + 3 - 3 = 9 - 3 \qquad \text{subtract 3}$$
$$\frac{1}{2}y = 6$$
$$2\left(\frac{1}{2}y\right) = 2(6) \qquad \text{multiply by 2}$$
$$y = \mathbf{12}$$

2.
$$\frac{1}{4}(8x + 4) = 3$$
$$2x + 1 = 3$$
$$2x + 1 - 1 = 3 - 1 \qquad \text{subtract 1}$$
$$2x = 2$$
$$\frac{2x}{2} = \frac{2}{2} \qquad \text{divide by 2}$$
$$x = \mathbf{1}$$

3.
$$\frac{1}{3}(3x + 9) = 2x + 3$$
$$x + 3 = 2x + 3$$
$$x + 3 - x = 2x + 3 - x \quad \text{subtract } x$$
$$3 = x + 3$$
$$3 - 3 = x + 3 - 3 \qquad \text{subtract 3}$$
$$\mathbf{0} = x$$

4.
$$\frac{2}{5}(2x + 3) = x + 1$$
$$\frac{4}{5}x + \frac{6}{5} = x + 1$$
$$\frac{4}{5}x - \frac{4}{5}x + \frac{6}{5} = x - \frac{4}{5}x + 1 \qquad \text{subtract } \frac{4}{5}x$$
$$\frac{6}{5} = \frac{1}{5}x + 1$$
$$\frac{6}{5} - 1 = \frac{1}{5}x + 1 - 1 \qquad \text{subtract 1}$$
$$\frac{1}{5} = \frac{1}{5}x$$
$$5\left(\frac{1}{5}\right) = 5\left(\frac{1}{5}x\right) \qquad \text{multiply by 5}$$
$$\mathbf{1} = x$$

5.

$$\frac{1}{3}(x+4)=20$$

$$\frac{x}{3}+\frac{4}{3}=20$$

$$\frac{x}{3}+\frac{4}{3}-\frac{4}{3}=20-\frac{4}{3}\qquad\text{subtract }\frac{4}{3}$$

$$\frac{x}{3}=\frac{56}{3}$$

$$3\left(\frac{x}{3}\right)=3\left(\frac{56}{3}\right)\qquad\text{multiply by }3$$

$$x=\mathbf{56}$$

6.

$$\frac{2}{5}a+9=0$$

$$\frac{2}{5}a+9-9=0-9\qquad\text{subtract }9$$

$$\frac{2}{5}a=-9$$

$$\frac{5}{2}\left(\frac{2}{5}a\right)=\frac{5}{2}(-9)\qquad\text{multiply by }\frac{5}{2}$$

$$a=-\frac{45}{2}$$

$$a=\mathbf{-22\frac{1}{2}}$$

7.

$$\frac{3}{5}y-\frac{2}{5}=\frac{4}{5}$$

$$\frac{3}{5}y-\frac{2}{5}+\frac{2}{5}=\frac{4}{5}+\frac{2}{5}\qquad\text{add }\frac{2}{5}$$

$$\frac{3}{5}y=\frac{6}{5}$$

$$\frac{5}{3}\left(\frac{3}{5}y\right)=\frac{5}{3}\left(\frac{6}{5}\right)\qquad\text{multiply by }\frac{5}{3}$$

$$y=\mathbf{2}$$

8.

$$\frac{1}{2}(5x-4)=x+\frac{11}{2}$$

$$\frac{5x}{2}-2=\frac{2x}{2}+\frac{11}{2}\qquad x=\frac{2x}{2}$$

$$\frac{5x}{2}-2-\frac{2x}{2}=\frac{2x}{2}+\frac{11}{2}-\frac{2x}{2}\qquad\text{subtract }\frac{2x}{2}$$

$$\frac{3x}{2}-2=\frac{11}{2}$$

$$\frac{3x}{2}-2+2=\frac{11}{2}+2\qquad\text{add }2$$

$$\frac{3x}{2}=\frac{15}{2}$$

$$\frac{2}{3}\left(\frac{3x}{2}\right)=\frac{2}{3}\left(\frac{15}{2}\right)\qquad\text{divide by }\frac{2}{3}$$

$$x=\mathbf{5}$$

9.

$$\frac{4}{3}x=\frac{7}{3}+x$$

$$\frac{4}{3}x-x=\frac{7}{3}+x-x\qquad\text{subtract }x$$

$$\frac{1}{3}x=\frac{7}{3}$$

$$3\left(\frac{1}{3}x\right)=3\left(\frac{7}{3}\right)\qquad\text{multiply by }3$$

$$x=\mathbf{7}$$

10.

$$\frac{y}{2}-\frac{4y}{5}=3$$

$$\frac{5y-8y}{10}=3$$

$$\frac{-3}{10}y=3$$

$$\frac{-10}{3}\left(\frac{-3}{10}y\right)=\frac{-10}{3}(3)\qquad\text{multiply by }\frac{-10}{3}$$

$$y=\mathbf{-10}$$

11.
$$\frac{9}{10}a + 7 = \frac{4}{5}a$$

$$\frac{9}{10}a + 7 - \frac{4}{5}a = \frac{4}{5}a - \frac{4}{5}a \qquad \text{subtract } \frac{4}{5}a$$

$$\frac{1}{10}a + 7 = 0$$

$$\frac{1}{10}a + 7 - 7 = 0 - 7 \qquad \text{subtract } 7$$

$$\frac{1}{10}a = -7$$

$$10\left(\frac{1}{10}a\right) = 10(-7) \qquad \text{multiply by } 10$$

$$a = \mathbf{-70}$$

12.
$$\frac{m}{6} - \frac{m}{4} + \frac{m}{5} = 2$$

$$\frac{10m - 15m + 12m}{60} = 2$$

$$\frac{7m}{60} = 2$$

$$\frac{60}{7}\left(\frac{7m}{60}\right) = \frac{60}{7}(2) \qquad \text{multiply by } \frac{60}{7}$$

$$m = \frac{120}{7}$$

$$m = \mathbf{17\frac{1}{7}}$$

13.
$$\frac{1}{2}(x - 1) + \frac{3}{4}(x + 3) = 0$$

$$\frac{x}{2} - \frac{1}{2} + \frac{3x}{4} + \frac{9}{4} = 0$$

$$\frac{2x + 3x}{4} + \frac{-2 + 9}{4} = 0$$

$$\frac{5x}{4} + \frac{7}{4} = 0$$

$$\frac{5x}{4} + \frac{7}{4} - \frac{7}{4} = 0 - \frac{7}{4} \qquad \text{subtract } \frac{7}{4}$$

$$\frac{5x}{4} = -\frac{7}{4}$$

$$\frac{4}{5}\left(\frac{5x}{4}\right) = \frac{4}{5}\left(-\frac{7}{4}\right) \qquad \begin{array}{l}\text{multiply by}\\ \frac{4}{5}\end{array}$$

$$x = \mathbf{-1\frac{2}{5}}$$

14.
$$\frac{2}{3}(7 - x) + \frac{1}{4}(x + 2) = 0$$

$$\frac{14}{3} - \frac{2x}{3} + \frac{x}{4} + \frac{1}{2} = 0$$

$$\frac{-8x + 3x}{12} + \frac{28 + 3}{6} = 0$$

$$\frac{-5x}{12} + \frac{31}{6} = 0$$

$$\frac{-5x}{12} + \frac{31}{6} - \frac{31}{6} = 0 - \frac{31}{6} \qquad \text{subtract } \frac{31}{6}$$

$$\frac{-5x}{12} = \frac{-31}{6}$$

$$\frac{-12}{5}\left(\frac{-5x}{12}\right) = \frac{-12}{5}\left(\frac{-31}{6}\right) \qquad \begin{array}{l}\text{multiply by}\\ \frac{-12}{5}\end{array}$$

$$x = \mathbf{12\frac{2}{5}}$$

15.

$$\frac{3}{4}(x+4) - \frac{5}{6}\left(\frac{1}{4} - x\right) = 0$$

$$\frac{3x}{4} + 3 - \frac{5}{24} + \frac{5x}{6} = 0$$

$$\frac{9x+10x}{12} + \frac{72-5}{24} = 0$$

$$\frac{19x}{12} + \frac{67}{24} = 0$$

$$\frac{19x}{12} + \frac{67}{24} - \frac{67}{24} = 0 - \frac{67}{24} \qquad \text{subtract } \frac{67}{24}$$

$$\frac{19x}{12} = \frac{-67}{24}$$

$$\frac{12}{19}\left(\frac{19x}{12}\right) = \frac{12}{19}\left(\frac{-67}{24}\right) \qquad \text{multiply by } \frac{12}{19}$$

$$x = -\frac{67}{38}$$

16.

$$\frac{1}{6}(4-p) - \frac{3}{4}(1+p) = \frac{1}{4}$$

$$\frac{2}{3} - \frac{p}{6} - \frac{3}{4} - \frac{3p}{4} = \frac{1}{4}$$

$$\frac{-2p-9p}{12} + \frac{8-9}{12} = \frac{1}{4}$$

$$\frac{-11p}{12} - \frac{1}{12} = \frac{3}{12}$$

$$\frac{-11p}{12} - \frac{1}{12} + \frac{1}{12} = \frac{3}{12} + \frac{1}{12} \qquad \text{add } \frac{1}{12}$$

$$\frac{-11p}{12} = \frac{4}{12}$$

$$\frac{-12}{11}\left(\frac{-11p}{12}\right) = \frac{-12}{11}\left(\frac{4}{12}\right) \qquad \text{multiply by } \frac{-12}{11}$$

$$p = -\frac{4}{11}$$

17.

$$6.2x - 1.3 = 5.2$$
$$6.2x - 1.3 + 1.3 = 5.2 + 1.3 \qquad \text{add } 1.3$$
$$6.2x = 6.5$$
$$\frac{6.2x}{6.2} = \frac{6.5}{6.2} \qquad \text{divide by } 6.2$$
$$x \approx \mathbf{1.048}$$

18.

$$4.7y - 3 = 0.2$$
$$4.7y - 3 + 3 = 0.2 + 3 \qquad \text{add } 3$$
$$4.7y = 3.2$$
$$\frac{4.7y}{4.7} = \frac{3.2}{4.7} \qquad \text{divide by } 4.7$$
$$y \approx \mathbf{0.681}$$

19.

$$1.41 - 1.2x = 1.02$$
$$1.41 - 1.2x - 1.41 = 1.02 - 1.41 \qquad \text{subtract } 1.41$$
$$-1.2x = -0.39$$
$$\frac{1.2x}{-1.2} = -\frac{0.39}{-1.2} \qquad \text{divide by } -1.2$$
$$x = \mathbf{0.325}$$

20.

$$1.12x - 4.1 = 0.12$$
$$1.12x - 4.1 + 4.1 = 0.12 + 4.1 \qquad \text{add } 4.1$$
$$1.12x = 4.22$$
$$\frac{1.12x}{1.12} = \frac{4.22}{1.12} \qquad \text{divide by } 1.12$$
$$x \approx \mathbf{3.768}$$

21.

$$6.4z - 3 = z + 1.2$$
$$6.4z - 3 - z = z + 1.2 - z \qquad \text{subtract } z$$
$$5.4z - 3 = 1.2$$
$$5.4z - 3 + 3 = 1.2 + 3 \qquad \text{add } 3$$
$$5.4z = 4.2$$
$$\frac{5.4z}{5.4} = \frac{4.2}{5.4} \qquad \text{divide by } 5.4$$
$$z \approx \mathbf{0.778}$$

22.

$$6.1x = 6 + 1.3x$$
$$6.1x - 1.3x = 6 + 1.3x - 1.3x \qquad \text{subtract } 1.3x$$
$$4.8x = 6$$
$$\frac{4.8x}{4.8} = \frac{6}{4.8} \qquad \text{divide by } 4.8$$
$$x = \mathbf{1.25}$$

23.
$$3(1.4x - 1) = 3.3x + 1.2$$
$$4.2x - 3 = 3.3x + 1.2$$
$$4.2x - 3 - 3.3x = 3.3x + 1.2 - 3.3x$$
subtract 3.3x
$$0.9x - 3 = 1.2$$
$$0.9x - 3 + 3 = 1.2 + 3 \quad \text{add 3}$$
$$0.9x = 4.2$$
$$\frac{0.9x}{0.9} = \frac{4.2}{0.9} \quad \text{divide by 0.9}$$
$$x \approx \mathbf{4.667}$$

24.
$$1.2(1 - x) = 8.1 + 3.5x$$
$$1.2 - 1.2x = 8.1 + 3.5x$$
$$1.2 - 1.2x - 3.5x = 8.1 + 3.5x - 3.5x$$
subtract 3.5x
$$1.2 - 4.7x = 8.1$$
$$1.2 - 4.7x - 1.2 = 8.1 - 1.2$$
subtract 1.2
$$-4.7x = 6.9$$
$$\frac{-4.7x}{-4.7} = \frac{6.9}{-4.7} \quad \text{divide by -4.7}$$
$$x = \mathbf{-1.468}$$

25.
$$\frac{3x - 1}{4} + \frac{x + 3}{8} = 0$$
$$\frac{6x - 2 + x + 3}{8} = 0$$
$$8\left(\frac{7x + 1}{8}\right) = 8(0) \quad \text{multiply by 8}$$
$$7x + 1 = 0$$
$$7x + 1 - 1 = 0 - 1 \quad \text{subtract 1}$$
$$7x = -1$$
$$\frac{7x}{7} = -\frac{1}{7} \quad \text{divide by 7}$$
$$x = -\frac{\mathbf{1}}{\mathbf{7}}$$

26.
$$\frac{x + 2}{6} - \frac{3x - 5}{4} = 0$$
$$\frac{2x + 4 - 9x + 15}{12} = 0$$
$$12\left(\frac{-7x + 19}{12}\right) = 12(0) \quad \text{multiply by 12}$$
$$-7x + 19 = 0$$
$$-7x + 19 - 19 = 0 - 19 \quad \text{subtract 19}$$
$$-7x = -19$$
$$\frac{-7x}{-7} = \frac{-19}{-7} \quad \text{divide by -7}$$
$$x = \mathbf{2}\frac{\mathbf{5}}{\mathbf{7}}$$

27.
$$\frac{2 - y}{8} - \frac{3(2 + y)}{4} = 0$$
$$\frac{2 - y - 6(2 + y)}{8} = 0$$
$$8\left(\frac{2 - y - 12 - 6y}{8}\right) = 8(0) \quad \text{multiply by 8}$$
$$-7y - 10 = 0$$
$$-7y - 10 + 10 = 0 + 10 \quad \text{add 10}$$
$$-7y = 10$$
$$\frac{-7y}{-7} = \frac{10}{-7} \quad \text{divide by -7}$$
$$y = -\mathbf{1}\frac{\mathbf{3}}{\mathbf{7}}$$

28.
$$\frac{3(x + 2)}{4} - \frac{5(1 - x)}{6} = 1$$
$$\frac{9(x + 2) - 10(1 - x)}{12} = 1$$
$$12\left(\frac{9x + 18 - 10 + 10x}{12}\right) = 12(1) \quad \text{multiply by 12}$$
$$19x + 8 = 12$$
$$19x + 8 - 8 = 12 - 8$$
$$19x = 4 \quad \text{subtract 8}$$
$$\frac{19x}{19} = \frac{4}{19}$$
divide by 19
$$x = \frac{\mathbf{4}}{\mathbf{19}}$$

29.
$$\frac{1}{x} - 1 = \frac{1}{3}$$
$$\frac{1}{x} - 1 + 1 = \frac{1}{3} + 1 \qquad \text{add 1}$$
$$\frac{1}{x} = \frac{4}{3}$$
$$x\left(\frac{1}{x}\right) = x\left(\frac{4}{3}\right) \qquad \text{multiply by } x$$
$$1 = \frac{4x}{3}$$
$$\frac{3}{4} = \frac{3}{4}\left(\frac{4x}{3}\right) \qquad \text{multiply by } \frac{3}{4}$$
$$\mathbf{\frac{3}{4}} = x$$

30.
$$\frac{1}{x} + 1 = \frac{3}{x} + \frac{1}{2}$$
$$\frac{1 + x}{x} = \frac{6 + x}{2x}$$
$$\frac{2 + 2x}{2x} = \frac{6 + x}{2x}$$
$$2x\left(\frac{2 + 2x}{2x}\right) = 2x\left(\frac{6 + x}{2x}\right) \qquad \text{multiply by } 2x$$
$$2 + 2x = 6 + x$$
$$2 + 2x - x = 6 + x - x \qquad \text{subtract } x$$
$$2 + x = 6$$
$$2 + x - 2 = 6 - 2 \qquad \text{subtract 2}$$
$$x = \mathbf{4}$$

Exercise 6.4 (p.163)

1.
$$a = \frac{t - q}{qr}$$
$$a = \frac{120 - 20}{(20)(10)}$$
$$a = \frac{100}{200}$$
$$a = \mathbf{\frac{1}{2}}$$

2.
$$A = h\left(R^2 - r^2\right)$$
$$A = 2\left(13^2 - 5^2\right)$$
$$A = 2(169 - 25)$$
$$A = 2(144)$$
$$A = \mathbf{288}$$

3.
$$s = ut + \frac{1}{2}ft^2$$
$$s = (20)(10) + \frac{1}{2}(15)(10)^2$$
$$s = 200 + \frac{1}{2}(1500)$$
$$s = 200 + 750$$
$$s = \mathbf{950}$$

4.
$$A = LB$$
$$450 = L(18)$$
$$\frac{450}{18} = L$$
$$\mathbf{25} = L$$

5.
$$A = 2\pi rh$$
$$33 = 2\left(\frac{22}{7}\right)\left(\frac{7}{4}\right)h$$
$$33 = 11h$$
$$\mathbf{3} = h$$

6.
$$E = \frac{1}{2}mV^2$$
$$180 = \frac{1}{2}(10)V^2$$
$$180 = 5V^2$$
$$36 = V^2$$
$$\pm\mathbf{6} = V$$

7.
$$v = u + ft$$
$$80 = 14 + 16f$$
$$66 = 16f$$
$$\frac{66}{16} = f$$
$$\mathbf{4\frac{1}{8}} = f$$

8.
$$v^2 = u^2 + 2fs$$
$$120^2 = 10^2 + 2(64)s$$
$$14{,}400 = 100 + 128s$$
$$14{,}300 = 128s$$
$$\frac{14{,}300}{128} = s$$
$$\mathbf{111\frac{23}{32}} = s$$

9.
$$\frac{t}{100} = \frac{w - v}{u - v}$$
$$\frac{t}{100} = \frac{5 - 4}{10 - 4}$$
$$\frac{t}{100} = \frac{1}{6}$$
$$t = \frac{100}{6}$$
$$t = \mathbf{16\frac{2}{3}}$$

10.
$$\frac{a^2 - b^2}{c^2 - b^2} = \frac{p}{q}$$
$$\frac{2^2 - 3^2}{4^2 - 3^2} = \frac{p}{5}$$
$$\frac{4 - 9}{16 - 9} = \frac{p}{5}$$
$$\frac{-5}{7} = \frac{p}{5}$$
$$\frac{-25}{7} = p$$
$$-3\frac{4}{7} = p$$

11.
$$\frac{b}{h} = r\left(1 + \frac{k}{h}\right)$$
$$\frac{3}{4} = r\left(1 + \frac{12}{4}\right)$$
$$\frac{3}{4} = 4r$$
$$\frac{3}{16} = r$$

12.
$$A = \frac{1}{2}(a + b)h$$
$$225 = \frac{1}{2}(a + 12)10$$
$$225 = 5(a + 12)$$
$$225 = 5a + 60$$
$$165 = 5a$$
$$33 = a$$

13.
$$v = \frac{1}{3}\pi r^2 h$$
$$660 = \frac{1}{3}\left(\frac{22}{7}\right)(70)r^2$$
$$660 = \frac{220}{3}r^2$$
$$\frac{(660)(3)}{220} = r^2$$
$$9 = r^2$$
$$\pm 3 = r$$

14
$$\frac{1}{t} = (u - 1)\left(\frac{1}{r_1} + \frac{1}{r_2}\right)$$
$$\frac{1}{t} = \left(\frac{3}{2} - 1\right)\left(\frac{1}{20} + \frac{1}{10}\right)$$
$$\frac{1}{t} = \left(\frac{1}{2}\right)\left(\frac{1 + 2}{20}\right)$$
$$\frac{1}{t} = \frac{3}{40}$$
$$1 = \frac{3}{40}t$$
$$\frac{40}{3} = t$$
$$13\frac{1}{3} = t$$

Exercise 6.5 (pp. 168-167)

1. Let m be the number of mangoes Arthur has. Arthur has 12 more mangoes than Margaret, so the number of mangoes Margaret has is 12 less than Arthur's, or (m - 12). Together they have 28 mangoes:
$$m + (m - 12) = 28$$
$$2m - 12 = 28$$
$$2m = 40$$
$$m = 20$$
Arthur has **20** mangoes.

2. Let p be the number of pineapples Michael has. Hassan has 3 pineapples less than Michael, so he has (p - 3) pineapples. Together they have 19 pineapples:
$$p + (p - 3) = 19$$
$$2p - 3 = 19$$
$$2p = 22$$
$$p = 11$$
Michael has **11** pineapples.

3.   Let n be the first number. Since it is one third of the second number, the second number must be three times the first number, or $3n$. Their difference is 38:

$$3n - n = 38$$
$$2n = 38$$
$$n = 19$$
$$3n = 57$$

The numbers are **19** and **57**.

4.   Let n be the number. If it is less than another by $\dfrac{3}{4}$, the other must be $\dfrac{3}{4}$ larger, or $\left(n + \dfrac{3}{4}\right)$. Their sum is $9\dfrac{1}{4}$:

$$n + \left(n + \frac{3}{4}\right) = \frac{37}{4}$$
$$2n = \frac{34}{4}$$
$$n = \frac{34}{8}$$
$$n = 4\frac{1}{4}$$
$$n + \frac{3}{4} = 4\frac{1}{4} + \frac{3}{4}$$
$$= 5$$

The numbers are $\mathbf{4\dfrac{1}{4}}$ and **5**.

5.   A number is greater than half of another by 15. Illustrating this can help with forming an equation:

```
[--------]   15   |
[--------|--------]   n
```

Let n be the second number, then the first number is $\left(\dfrac{1}{2}n + 15\right)$ Their sum is 48:

$$n + \left(\frac{1}{2}n + 15\right) = 48$$
$$\frac{3}{2}n = 33$$
$$n = 33\left(\frac{2}{3}\right)$$
$$n = 22$$
$$\frac{1}{2}n + 15 = \frac{1}{2}(22) + 15$$
$$= 26$$

The two numbers are **22** and **26**.
(The first number ends up being larger than the second but the illustration is still valid, since the amount between the bars is unknown.)

6. Let x be the son's age. The father's age is $4x$. Two years ago the father was 46:
$4x - 2 = 46$
$\quad 4x = 48$
$\quad\quad x = 12$
The son is **12** years old.

7. Let x be the number of weeks for the plant to be 27.5 cm. It needs to grow
(27.5 - 10) cm. In one week it grows 3.5 cm. In x weeks it grows $3.5x$ cm.
$3.5x = 27.5 - 10$
$3.5x = 17.5$
$\quad\boldsymbol{x = 5}$
It grows to 27.5 cm in **5 weeks**.

8. Let n be one number. The consecutive even number is $(n + 2)$. Their sum is 54:
$n + (n + 2) = 54$
$\quad\quad\quad 2n = 52$
$\quad\quad\quad\ n = 26$
$\quad\ n + 2 = 28$
The two numbers are **26** and **28**.

9. Let n be one number. The consecutive odd number is $(n + 2)$. Their sum is 208:
$n + (n + 2) = 208$
$\quad\quad\quad 2n = 206$
$\quad\quad\quad\ n = 103$
$\quad\ n + 2 = 105$
The two numbers are **103** and **105**.

10. The next three consecutive odd numbers after m are $m + 2$, $m + 4$, $m + 6$. The sum of
the 4 numbers is 32:
$32 = m + m + 2 + m + 4 + m + 6$
$32 = 4m + 12$
$20 = 4m$
$\boldsymbol{m = 5}$

11. Let n be the number.
$$n + \frac{3}{8}n + \frac{5}{16}n = 7\frac{1}{2}$$
$$\frac{16n + 6n + 5n}{16} = \frac{120}{16}$$
$$27n = 120$$
$$n = \frac{120}{27}$$
$$n = \frac{40}{9}$$
$$n = \boldsymbol{4\frac{4}{9}}$$

12.   Let *n* be the number. Multiply it by 6: 6*n*. Add -18 to the product: 6*n* - 18.

Take away one-third of the sum: 6*n* - 18 - $\frac{1}{3}(6n - 18)$. The answer is -2:

$$6n - 18 - \frac{1}{3}(6n - 18) = -2$$
$$6n - 18 - 2n + 6 = -2$$
$$4n - 12 = -2$$
$$4n = 10$$
$$n = \frac{10}{4}$$
$$n = \mathbf{2\frac{1}{2}}$$

13.   The sum of 2 numbers is 2.
<-------2------>
[--------][------]
Let *n* be one number. The other is (2 - *n*). Their difference is 10:
n - (2 - *n*) = 10
n - 2 + *n* = 10
2*n* = 12
n = 6
2 - *n* = -4
The two numbers are **-4** and **6**.

14.   Let *n* be the number of 50¢ pieces. If there are twice as many 50¢ pieces as dollar coins,

then there are half as many dollar coins as 50¢ pieces, or $\frac{1}{2}n$. The value of the 50¢ pieces

is $0.50*n* and the value of the dollar coins is 1\left(\frac{1}{2}n\right)$. The total value of the money in the

box is $154:
$$0.50n + \frac{1}{2}n = 154$$
$$n = 154$$
There are **154** 50¢ pieces.

15.   A gets twice as much as B and C gets one and a half times as much as A:
A: [------|------]
B: [------]
C: [------|------|------]
Let *n* be the amount B gets. A gets 2*n*, and C gets 3*n*. The total amount of money is
$102.
2*n* + *n* + 3*n* = 102
6*n* = 102
n = 17
2*n* = 2 x 17 = 34
3*n* = 3 x 17 = 51
A gets $34, B gets $17, C gets $51.

16.   Let m be the cost of one mug. The cost of the plate is $(m + 0.30)$. He spent $\$3m$ on the mugs and $\$3(m + 0.30)$ on the plates. He spent $\$2.40$:
$$3m + 3(m + 0.30) = 2.40$$
$$6m + 0.90 = 2.40$$
$$6m = 1.50$$
$$m = 0.25$$
Each mug costs **25¢**.

17.   Let x be the age of the son. The age of the father is $4x$. Ten years ago the son was $(x - 10)$ years and the father was $(4x - 10)$ years old. The sum of their ages then was 60:
$$(x - 10) + (4x - 10) = 60$$
$$5x - 20 = 60$$
$$5x = 80$$
$$x = 16$$
$$4x = 64$$
The son is **16** years old and the father is **64** years old.

18.   The total amount spent was $210.
Let x be how many book he buys at $3. The cost $\$3x$. He buys $(20 - x)$ at $18, so they cost a total of $\$18(20 - x)$. Together they cost $210:
$$3x + 18(20 - x) = 210$$
$$3x + 360 - 18x = 210$$
$$-15x = -150$$
$$x = 10$$
He bought **10** 3-dollar books.

19.   Let x be the age of the sister. The age of the boy is $(x - 3)$. His age 3 years ago was $(x - 3 - 3) = (x - 6)$. Her age 3 years ago was $x - 3$. His age then was two thirds of hers:
$$x - 6 = \frac{2}{3}(x - 3)$$
$$3(x - 6) = 2(x - 3)$$
$$3x - 18 = 2x - 6$$
$$x - 18 = -6$$
$$x = 12$$
$$x - 3 = 12 - 3 = 9$$
The **sister is 12** years old, and the **boy is 9** years old.

20.   Let x be the number of apples John can buy. His total money is the amount he would pay for 30 apples plus the amount he has left, or $(30x + 300)$¢. To buy 40 apples he needs another $1, or 100¢. So his total money is the amount he would pay for 40 apples minus the amount he still needs, or $(40x - 100)$¢.
$$30x + 300 = 40x - 100$$
$$400 = 10x$$
$$40 = x$$
He buys **40** apples.

21.   Let m be the number of pupils who took the mathematics test. Since 50 more pupils took the math test than the geography test, 50 less pupils took the geography test than the math test, and (m - 50) is the number of students who took the geography test. The number of girls who took the mathematics test is $\frac{1}{5}m$ and the number of girls who took the geography test is $\frac{1}{4}(m - 50)$. 6 more girls took the math test than the geography test, so 6 needs to be added to the number of girls that took the geography test to equal the number of girls that took the math test.

$$\frac{1}{5}m = \frac{1}{4}(m-50)+6$$
$$\frac{1}{5}m = \frac{m}{4} - \frac{50}{4} + 6$$
$$20\left(\frac{1}{5}m\right) = 20\left(\frac{m}{4} - \frac{50}{4} + 6\right)$$
$$4m = 5m - 250 + 120$$
$$130 = m$$

130 students took the mathematics test.

22.   Each packet has the same number of meatballs and fishballs. Let n be this number. Meatballs cost 4 pieces for $1, so the price of one meatball is $\$\frac{1}{4}$. Fishballs cost 6 pieces for $1, so the price of one fishball is $\$\frac{1}{6}$. The price of one packet of n meatballs is $\$\frac{1}{4}n$ and the price of one packet of n fishballs is $\$\frac{1}{6}n$. The man can buy 2 packets of meatballs and 1 of fishballs with the amount of money he has, but is short one dollar to buy 3 packets of meatballs.

$$2\left(\frac{1}{4}n\right) + \frac{1}{6}n = 3\left(\frac{1}{4}n\right) - 1$$
$$12\left(\frac{2n}{4} + \frac{n}{6}\right) = 12\left(\frac{3n}{4} - 1\right)$$
$$6n + 2n = 9n - 12$$
$$12 = n$$

There are **12** meatballs or fishballs in a packet.

23. Let n be the number of each type he can buy. Represent the total money by the unit 1. He can buy 20 mangoes so each mango costs $\frac{1}{20}$. He can buy 30 oranges so each orange costs $\frac{1}{30}$. He buys the same number of each.

$$\frac{1}{20}n + \frac{1}{30}n = 1$$
$$\frac{3n + 2n}{60} = 1$$
$$3n + 2n = 60$$
$$5n = 60$$
$$n = 12$$

He buys **12** of each.

Chapter 7

Exercise 7.1 (pp. 174-175)

1. (a) 4 hours = 100 km

   1 hour = $\dfrac{100}{4}$ km = 25 km

   Rate = **25 km/h**

   (b) 12 eggs = $2.40

   1 egg = $\$\dfrac{2.40}{12}$ = $0.20/egg

   Rate = **20¢/egg**

   (c) 1 h = 450 ℓ

   60 min = 450 ℓ

   1 min = $\dfrac{450}{60}$ ℓ = 7.5 ℓ

   Rate = **7.5 ℓ/min**

   (d) 120 kWh = $24.00

   120 kWh = 2400¢

   1 kWh = $\dfrac{2400}{120}$ ¢ = 20¢

   Rate = **20 ¢/kWh**

2. (a) 10:00 to 12:00 = 2 h

   2 h = 4°C

   1 h = $\dfrac{4}{2}$ °C = 2°C

   Rate of rise = **2°C/h**

   (b) 15:00 to 17:00 = 2 h

   2 h = 6°C

   1 h = $\dfrac{6}{2}$ °C = 3°C

   Rate of fall = **3°C/h**

3. 15 ℓ = 150 km   150 km = 15 ℓ

    1 ℓ = $\dfrac{150}{15}$ km = 10 km   100 km = $\dfrac{15}{150}$ x 100 ℓ = 10 ℓ

    Rate = **10 km/ℓ**   Rate = **10 ℓ/100 km**

4. (a) 6 m² = 150 g

   1 m² = $\dfrac{150}{6}$ g = 25 g

   Rate = **25 g/m²**

   (b) 1 g = 0.001 kg

   25 g = 0.001 x 25 = 0.025 kg

   1 m² = 25 g = 0.025 kg

   Rate = **0.025 kg/m²**

5.   1 h = 450 km   1 h = 3,600 s

   3,600 s = 450 km

   1 s = $\dfrac{450}{3,600}$ km

                                    1 km = 1,000 m

   10 s = $\dfrac{450}{360}$ km   450 km = 450 x 1,000 m

   10 s = $\dfrac{450 \times 1,000}{360}$ m

   10 s = 1,250 m

   It will travel **1,250 m** in 10 s.

6.   1 week = 300 s

   2 weeks = 2 x 300 s   2 weeks = 14 days

   14 days = 600 s

   In 14 days it will lose **600 s**.

7. (a)   1 h = 30 km   1 h = 3,600 s
     3,600 s = 30 km   1 km = 100,000 cm
     3,600 s = 30 x 100,000 cm   30 km = 30 x 100,000 cm

$$1 \text{ s} = \frac{30 \times 100,000}{3,600} \text{ cm}$$

$$1 \text{ s} = 833\frac{1}{3} \text{ cm}$$

30 km/h = $\mathbf{833\frac{1}{3}}$ cm/s

   (b)   1 km = $100   1 km = 1,000 m
     1,000 m = 10,000¢ $1 = 100¢

$$1 \text{ m} = \frac{10,000}{1,000} \text{ ¢}$$ $100 = 100 x 100 ¢ = 10,000¢

     1 m = 10¢
     $100 per km = **10**¢ per m

   (c)   1 L = $2.50   1 ℓ = 1,000 ml
     1,000 ml = 250¢ $2.50 = 250¢

$$1 \text{ ml} = \frac{250}{1,000} \text{ ¢}$$

     1 ml = 0.25¢
     $2.50 per liter = **0.25**¢ per ml

8.   Total distance = 143 km + 97 km = 240 km

Total time = $1\frac{1}{2}$ h + $1\frac{1}{2}$ h = 3 h

Average speed = $\frac{240 \text{ km}}{3 \text{ h}}$ = **80 km/h**

P   R
|<--------------->|<------------>|
143 km; $1\frac{1}{2}$ h   97 km; $1\frac{1}{2}$ h

9. (a)   1 s = 1.5 m   3,600 s = 1 h

$$\frac{1}{3,600} \text{ h} = \frac{1.5}{1,000} \text{ km}$$ $1 \text{ s} = \frac{1}{3,600} \text{ h}$

$$1 \text{ h} = \frac{1.5}{1,000}(3,600) \text{ km}$$ 1,000 m = 1 km

     1 h = 5.4 km $1 \text{ m} = \frac{1}{1,000} \text{ km}$
     Its speed is **5.4 km/h**.

   (b)   1 h = 30 km
     3,600 s = 30,000 m

$$1 \text{ s} = \frac{30,000}{3,600} \text{ m}$$

$$1 \text{ s} = 8\frac{1}{3} \text{ m}$$

Its speed is $\mathbf{8\frac{1}{3}}$ **m/s**.

(c) 1 s = 200 cm

$\dfrac{1}{60}$ min = $\dfrac{200}{100}$ m

1 min = 60 x 2 m

1 min = 120 m

The water flows at **120 m/min**.

60 s = 1 min

1 s = $\dfrac{1}{60}$ min

100 cm = 1 m

1 cm = $\dfrac{1}{100}$ m

10.

Distance for last $\dfrac{2}{3}$ = 120 km

Distance for $\dfrac{1}{3}$ = $\dfrac{120}{2}$ = 60 km

Total distance = 60 x 3 = 180 km

Total time = $\dfrac{180 \text{ km}}{90 \text{ km/h}}$ = 2 h

Time for last $\dfrac{2}{3}$ = 2 h - 45 min

$\quad$ = 2 - $\dfrac{3}{4}$ h = $\dfrac{5}{4}$ h

Speed for last $\dfrac{2}{3}$ = $\dfrac{120}{\frac{5}{4}}$ km/h

$\quad$ = 120 x $\dfrac{4}{5}$ km/h = **96 km/h**

```
X                               Y
|---------|---------|------->|
|          90 km/h           |
| 45 min |                   |
|          120 km           |
```

or: 90 m = 1 h

$\quad$ 1 km = $\dfrac{1}{90}$ h

$\quad$ 180 km = $\dfrac{180}{80}$ h = 2 h

Speed = $\dfrac{\text{Distance}}{\text{Time}}$

Time = $\dfrac{\text{Distance}}{\text{Speed}}$

45 min = $\dfrac{45}{60}$ h

$\quad$ = $\dfrac{3}{4}$ h

11. They passed each other after 2 h

(14:00 - 12:00).

Distance for car = 80 km/h x 2 h

$\quad$ = 160 km

(Or: 1 h = 80 km

$\quad$ 2 h = 2 x 80 km = 160 km)

Distance for bus = 250 km - 160 km

$\quad$ = 90 km

Speed of bus = $\dfrac{90}{2}$ km/h

$\quad$ = **45 km/h**

```
|---------250 km----------|
|------ car--->|<---bus---|
    2 hr            2 hr
  80 km/h         ? km/h
```

Speed = $\dfrac{\text{Distance}}{\text{Time}}$

Distance = Speed x Time

12.

Speed = $\dfrac{42,000}{\frac{3}{2}}$ km/h = 42,000 x $\dfrac{2}{3}$ km/h = 28,000 km/h

1 h = 28,000 km

24 h = 24 x 28,000 km

1 day = 672,000 km

Speed = **672,000 km/day**

13. First Route:

time = 13:00 - 8:30 = $4\frac{1}{2}$ h = $\frac{9}{2}$ h

speed = $\dfrac{243}{\frac{9}{2}}$ = 243 x $\dfrac{2}{9}$ = 54 km/h

Shortcut:
speed = 54 - 4 = 50 km/h
distance = 243 - 13 = 230 km

time = $\dfrac{230}{50}$ h

= $4\frac{3}{5}$ h

= 4 h 36 min
8:30 + 4 h 36 min = 13:06
He would arrive at town B at **13:06**.

first route:

8:30   13:00
|-------------------->|
        243 km
        speed = s km/h

shortcut:
|------------------->|
   (243 - 13) km
   speed = s - 4 km/h

Time = $\dfrac{\text{Distance}}{\text{Speed}}$

1 h = 60 min

$\dfrac{3}{5}$ h = $\dfrac{3}{5}$ x 60 min = 36 min

14. Distances for both cases is equal:

$\dfrac{9s}{2} = \dfrac{15s + 45}{4}$

$\dfrac{18s}{4} = \dfrac{15s + 45}{4}$

$18s = 15s + 45$

$3s = 45$

$s = 15$

∴ speed for case 1 = 15 km/h
Distance for case 1

= 15 km/h x $\dfrac{9}{2}$ h

= 67.5 km

The distance from his hometown to his destination is **67.5 km**.

Distance = Speed x Time
case 1
|----------------->|
  speed = s km/h

  time = $4\frac{1}{2}$ h

  distance = s x $4\frac{1}{2}$ = $\dfrac{9s}{2}$ km

case 2
|----------------->|
  speed = (s + 3) km/h

  time = $4\frac{1}{2}$ h - 45 min

  = $4\frac{1}{2} - \frac{3}{4} = 3\frac{3}{4} = \dfrac{15}{4}$ h

distance = (s + 3) x $\dfrac{15}{4}$ km

= $\dfrac{15s + 45}{4}$ km

15. They pass after 1 h 45 min

= $1\frac{3}{4}$ h = $\dfrac{7}{4}$ h

Car's distance = 65 km/h x $\dfrac{7}{4}$ h

= 113.75

Motorcycle's distance

= 50 km/h x $\dfrac{7}{4}$ h

= 87.5 km

Total distance = 113.75 + 87.5 km

= **201.25 km**

|---------------------------|
|--car---->|<-motorcycle-|
 65 km/h   50 km/h

45 min = $\dfrac{3}{4}$ h

Distance = Speed x Time

16.   Car B leaves 1.5 h after car A   A: 9:30   65 km/h
        Car B catches up with car A after 5 h |---------------------->|
        So car A has been traveling   B: 11:00
            5 + 1.5 = 6.5 h
        Distance for car A: 65 km/h x 6.5 h   Distance = Speed x Time
                = 422.5 km
        Distance for car B is the same.   Speed = $\dfrac{\text{Distance}}{\text{Time}}$
        Speed for car B = $\dfrac{422.5}{5}$ km/h
                = **84.5 km/h**

Exercise 7.2 (pp. 180-182)

1. (a) $10 : 6 = \mathbf{5 : 3}$ (b) $24 : 8 = \mathbf{3 : 1}$

   (c) $3.5 : 2.1 = 35 : 21 = \mathbf{5 : 3}$ (d)

$$\frac{2}{3} : \frac{1}{4} = \frac{\frac{2}{3}}{\frac{1}{4}} = \left(\frac{2}{3}\right)\left(\frac{4}{1}\right) = \frac{8}{3} = \mathbf{8 : 3}$$

   (e) $2.4 : 3.6 = 24 : 36 = \mathbf{2 : 3}$ (f)

$$3\frac{1}{2} : 1\frac{1}{7} = \frac{3\frac{1}{2}}{1\frac{1}{7}} = \frac{\frac{7}{2}}{\frac{8}{7}} = \left(\frac{7}{2}\right)\left(\frac{7}{8}\right) = \frac{49}{16} = \mathbf{49 : 16}$$

2. (a) $\dfrac{20\text{ cm}}{1\text{ m}} = \dfrac{20\text{ cm}}{100\text{ cm}} = \dfrac{1}{5} = \mathbf{1 : 5}$ (b) $\dfrac{1\text{ kg}}{70\text{ g}} = \dfrac{1{,}000\text{ g}}{70\text{ g}} = \dfrac{100}{7} = \mathbf{100 : 7}$

   (c) $\dfrac{80\text{ m}}{1\text{ km}} = \dfrac{80\text{ m}}{1{,}000\text{ m}} = \dfrac{8}{100} = \dfrac{2}{25} = \mathbf{2 : 25}$ (d) $\dfrac{40\text{ cm}^2}{1\text{ m}^2} = \dfrac{40\text{ cm}^2}{10{,}000\text{ cm}^2} = \dfrac{1}{240} = \mathbf{1 : 250}$
   note: $1\text{ m}^2 = 100^2\text{ cm}^2 = 10{,}000\text{ cm}^2$

   (e) $\dfrac{2\text{ h}}{45\text{ min}} = \dfrac{2\text{ h}}{0.75\text{ h}} = \dfrac{200}{75} = \dfrac{8}{3} = \mathbf{8 : 3}$ (f) $\dfrac{\frac{1}{2}\text{ m}^3}{20{,}000\text{ cm}^3} = \dfrac{500{,}000\text{ cm}^3}{20{,}000\text{ cm}^3} = \dfrac{50}{2} = \mathbf{25 : 1}$
   note: $1\text{ m}^3 = (100)^3\text{ cm}^3 = 1{,}000{,}000\text{ cm}^3$
   $\dfrac{1}{2}\text{ m}^3 = \dfrac{1}{2} \times 1{,}000{,}000\text{ cm}^3$
   $= 500{,}000\text{ cm}^3$

3. (a) $A : B = 24 : 64 = \mathbf{3 : 8}$ (b) $\dfrac{A}{B} = \dfrac{3}{8}$ $\boldsymbol{A = \dfrac{3}{8}B}$

4. $A = \dfrac{3}{4}B$ $\dfrac{A}{B} = \dfrac{3}{4}$ $A : B = \mathbf{3 : 4}$

5.

Let p = one part
boys = $5p$; girls = $6p$
$5p + 6p = 44$
$\quad 11p = 44$
$\quad\quad p = 4$
$\quad\quad 5p = 20$
There are **20** boys.

Alternative solution:
Let b = the number of boys

girls = $\dfrac{6}{5}$ boys

boys + girls = 44

$b + \dfrac{6}{5}b = 44$

$\dfrac{11}{5}b = 44$

$\quad\quad b = 20$

6. (a) $\dfrac{\text{teachers}}{\text{pupils}} = \dfrac{64}{2560}$

$\quad\quad = \dfrac{1}{40}$

teachers : pupils
$\quad = \mathbf{1 : 40}$

(b) $\dfrac{\text{girls}}{\text{pupils}} = \dfrac{1024}{2560}$

$\quad\quad = \dfrac{2}{5}$

girls : pupils = **2 : 5**

(c) $\dfrac{\text{teachers}}{\text{boys}} = \dfrac{64}{1536}$

$\quad\quad = \dfrac{1}{24}$

teachers = $\dfrac{\mathbf{1}}{\mathbf{24}}$ boys

7. $\dfrac{\text{side of square 1}}{\text{side of square 2}} = \dfrac{2}{3}$

side of square 1 = $\dfrac{2}{3}$ side of square 2

Let s = side of square 2
area of square 2 = s^2

side of square 1 = $\dfrac{2}{3}s$

area of square 1 = $\left(\dfrac{2}{3}s\right)^2$

$\quad\quad\quad\quad\quad = \dfrac{4}{9}s^2$

ratio of areas = **4 : 9**

8. $\dfrac{\text{side of cube 1}}{\text{side of cube 2}} = \dfrac{1}{3}$

side of cube 1 = $\dfrac{1}{3}$ side of cube 2

Let s = side cube 2

side of cube 1 = $\dfrac{1}{3}s$

volume of cube 1 = $\left(\dfrac{1}{3}s\right)^3$

$\quad\quad\quad\quad\quad = \dfrac{1}{27}s^3$

Ratio of volumes = **1 : 27**

9. (a) $\dfrac{\text{expenses}}{\text{income}} = \dfrac{2}{5}$

  expenses $= \dfrac{2}{5}$ income

  $= \dfrac{2}{5}(\$3,500)$

  $= \mathbf{\$1,400}$

(b) savings $= \$3,500 - \$1,400$

  $= \$2,100$

  $\dfrac{\text{savings}}{\text{income}} = \dfrac{\$2100}{\$3500}$

  $= \dfrac{3}{5}$

  savings : income $= \mathbf{3 : 5}$

10.(a)

Let p = one part
$15p = 24,000$

  $p = \dfrac{24,000}{15}$

  $p = 1,600$

Largest share $= 7p$

  $= 7(1,600)$

  $= \mathbf{\$11,200}$

Alternative solution:
Let x = largest share

smallest share $= \dfrac{3}{7}x$

middle share $= \dfrac{5}{7}x$

$x + \dfrac{3}{7}x + \dfrac{5}{7}x = 24,000$

  $\dfrac{15}{7}x = 24,000$

  $x = 11,200$

The largest share $= \$11,200$

(b)

Let p be one part
$4p + 5p + 6p = 45$

  $15p = 45$

  $p = 3$

Side 1 $= 4p = 4 \times 3 = \mathbf{12\ cm}$
Side 2 $= 5p = 5 \times 3 = \mathbf{15\ cm}$
Side 3 $= 6p = 6 \times 3 = \mathbf{18\ cm}$

Alternative solution:

Side 1 $= \dfrac{4}{15} \times 45$ cm = 12 cm

Side 2 $= \dfrac{5}{15} \times 45$ cm = 15 cm

Side 3 $= \dfrac{6}{15} \times 45$ cm = 18 cm

11.(a) $\dfrac{\text{income}}{\text{expenses}} = \dfrac{\$2,500}{\$1,750}$

  $= \dfrac{10}{7}$

income : expenses
  $= \mathbf{10 : 7}$

(b) savings $= \$2,500 - \$1,750$

  $= \$750$

  $\dfrac{\text{savings}}{\text{income}} = \dfrac{\$750}{\$2,500}$

  $= \dfrac{3}{10}$

savings : income
  $= \mathbf{3 : 10}$

(c) $\dfrac{\text{savings}}{\text{expenses}} = \dfrac{\$750}{\$1,750}$

  $= \dfrac{3}{7}$

savings : expenses
  $= \mathbf{3 : 7}$

12.(a) $A : B : C$

3 : 4		(1)
2 : 3		(2)
4 : 6		(2) x 2
3 : 4 : 6		

(b) $X : Y : Z$

5 : 4		(1)
6 : 1		(2)
15 : 12		(1) x 3
12 : 2		(2) x 2
15 : 12 : 2		

13. $\dfrac{\text{new price}}{\text{old price}} = \dfrac{\$1.50}{\$1.20} = \dfrac{15}{20} = \dfrac{5}{4}$

The price increases in the ratio **5 : 4**.

14. $\dfrac{\text{new price}}{\text{old price}} = \dfrac{6}{5}$ new price $= \dfrac{6}{5}$ old price $= \dfrac{6}{5}(\$15) =$ **$18**

15.(a) new price $= \dfrac{4}{5}$ old price   (b) $\dfrac{4}{5}(\$1.50) =$ **$1.20**   (c) $\dfrac{4}{5}(\$3.75) =$ **$3.00**

$\dfrac{4}{5}(\$25) =$ **$20**

16. new dimensions $= \dfrac{7}{5}$ old dimensions

new length $= \dfrac{7}{5}(8.5 \text{ cm}) = 11.9 \text{ cm}$

new width $= \dfrac{7}{5}(5.5 \text{ cm}) = 7.7 \text{ cm}$

The dimensions of the new picture are **11.9 cm by 7.7 cm**.

17. Original expense for petrol = 200 L x $1.50 /ℓ = $300
New expense for petrol = 300 ℓ x $1.20 = $360

$\dfrac{\text{New expense}}{\text{Original expense}} = \dfrac{360}{300} = \dfrac{6}{5}$

His petrol bill increases in the ratio **6 : 5**.

18. New number of girls $= \dfrac{4}{5}$ old number $= \dfrac{4}{5}(175) = 140$

New number of boys $= \dfrac{6}{5}$ old number of boys $= \dfrac{6}{5}(250) = 300$

$\dfrac{\text{boys}}{\text{girls}} = \dfrac{300}{140} = \dfrac{15}{7}$

Ratio of boys to girls is **15 : 7**.

19. March
     April

Let p = one part.
He saved one part.
$p = \$120$.
March expenses = $5p$
$= 5(\$120)$
= **$600**

Alternative solution:
Let x be his March expenses. April expenses $= \dfrac{4}{5}x$. The difference between the two months' expenses is his savings.

$x - \dfrac{4}{5}x = \$120$

$\dfrac{1}{5}x = \$120$

$x = \$600$

20.

Let p = one part.
C is longer than B by 8 cm
$2p = 8$ cm
$p = 4$ cm
$10p = 10 \times 4$ cm $= 40$ cm
The stick is **40 cm** long.

Alternative solutions:
Let x be the length of the stick.

The length of C is $\dfrac{5}{10}x$.

The length of B is $\dfrac{3}{10}x$.

C is longer than B by 8 cm.
$$\frac{5}{10}x - \frac{3}{10}x = 8$$
$$\frac{2}{10}x = 8$$
$$x = 40$$

21.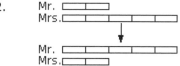

The shaded part represents the
number of pupils that wear glasses.
The ratio of the number of girls who wear
glasses to the number of boys
who wear glasses is **2 : 1**.

Alternative solution:
Let p = one part

$$\frac{\text{girls with glasses}}{\text{boys with glasses}} = \frac{\frac{1}{3}(3p)}{\frac{1}{4}(2p)} = \frac{\frac{1}{1}}{\frac{1}{2}} = \frac{2}{1}$$

22. Mr.
Mrs.

Mr.
Mrs.

Let p = one part.
If Mr. Lin got 5 parts rather than 2, he
would have $600 more
$3p = 600$
$p = 200$
Total $= 7p = 7 \times 200 = 1,400$
The sum of money is **$1,400**.

Alternative solution:
Let x be the total amount of money.

Mr. Lin receives $\dfrac{2}{7}x$

Had he received $\dfrac{5}{7}x$, he would have

received $600 more.
$$\frac{5}{7}x - \frac{2}{7}x = \$600$$
$$\frac{3}{7}x = \$600$$
$$x = \$1,400$$

23.   A woman's subscription is $\dfrac{3}{4}$ of a man's subscription.

Let x be a man's subscription.
2 men and 5 women pay $460.
$$2x + 5\left(\frac{3}{4}x\right) = 460$$
$$\frac{8+15}{4}x = 460$$
$$\frac{23}{4}x = 460$$
$$x = \frac{4}{23}(460)$$
$$x = 80$$
The subscription fee for a man is **$80**.

24.

A : B : C = **5 : 9 : 6**

3 parts for B and C

5 parts for B and C

LCM of 3 and 5 is 15

$A = 1 \times 5 = 5$

$B = 3 \times 3 = 9$

$C = 2 \times 3 = 6$

Exercise 7.3 (pp. 186-187)

1. Let x be the amount of petrol used for
600 km. Use of petrol is directly proportional to the distance.

$$\frac{x}{35.5} = \frac{600}{426}$$

$$x = \frac{(600)(35.5)}{426}$$

$$x = \frac{(100)(6)(5)(7.1)}{(71)(6)}$$

$$x = 50$$

He uses **50 ℓ** of petrol.

2. Time for first part of journey = 3 h.
Let x be the time for the second part.
Time is directly proportional to distance if the speed is constant.

$$\frac{x}{3} = \frac{600}{150}$$

$$x = \frac{(600)(3)}{(150)}$$

$$x = \frac{(12)(50)(3)}{(50)(3)}$$

$$x = 12$$

It takes him 12 h to go 600 km. 12 h after noon is **12 midnight**.

3. Regular pay rate = $\frac{\$630}{42 \, h}$ = \$15/h

Double rate = \$15 × 2 = \$30
He works 48 - 42 = 6 hours of overtime.
Earnings for overtime = \$30 × 6 = \$180
Total earnings = \$180 + \$630 = **\$810**

4. Area of first carpet = 4 × 2.5 = 10 m^2
Area of second carpet = 5 × 3 = 15 m^2
Let x be the cost of the second carpet.
The area of the carpet is directly proportional to the cost.

$$\frac{x}{86} = \frac{15}{10}$$

$$x = \frac{(15)(86)}{10}$$

$$x = 129$$

The carpet would cost **\$129**

5.   3 men x 2 h = 6 man-hours. In each case, let x be the number of hours needed.
   (a) $6x = 6$ (b) $5x = 6$ (c) $2x = 6$
          $x = \mathbf{1\ h}$ $x = \mathbf{3\ h}$
                                              $x = \mathbf{1\dfrac{1}{5}\ h}$

6.   Let x be the time needed. The time needed is inversely proportional to the number of men.
        $$\dfrac{x}{2} = \dfrac{5}{10}$$
        $$x = \dfrac{(5)(2)}{10}$$
        $$x = 1$$
                        It takes **1 week** for 10 men.

7.   If the work is to be completed 5 days earlier, it must be completed in 30 - 5 = 25 days.
        Let x be the number of men needed. The number of men needed is inversely proportional to
        the time.
        $$\dfrac{x}{10} = \dfrac{30}{25}$$
        $$x = \dfrac{(30)(10)}{25}$$
        $$x = \dfrac{(6)(5)(5)(2)}{(5)(5)}$$
        $$x = 12$$ 12 men are needed. There are already 10, so **2 more** are needed.

8.   Let x be the number of days needed.
        The number of men is inversely proportional to the time.
        $$\dfrac{x}{4} = \dfrac{9}{8}$$
        $$x = \dfrac{(9)(4)}{8}$$
        $$x = \dfrac{9}{2}$$
        $$x = 4\dfrac{1}{2}$$ It will take **$4\dfrac{1}{2}$ days**.

9.   6 men working 5 hours = 6 x 5 = 30 man-hours
        10 men working 8 hours = 10 x 8 = 80 man-hours.
        Let x be the amount paid in the second case. Man-hours is directly proportional to wages.
        $$\dfrac{x}{480} = \dfrac{80}{30}$$
        $$x = \dfrac{(8)(480)}{3}$$
        $$x = 1,280$$
                        The wages will be **$1,280**.

10. 7 days x 8 hours/days = 56 hours
     16 days x 6 hours/day = 96 hours
     48 men can do the job in 56 hours
     Let x be the number of men needed for 96 hours. The number of men needed is inversely proportional to the number of days.

$$\frac{x}{48} = \frac{56}{96}$$

$$x = \frac{(56)(48)}{96}$$

$$x = \frac{(28)(2)(48)}{(2)(48)}$$

$$x = 28 \qquad\qquad \textbf{28} \text{ men are needed.}$$

11. Let x be the number of days the food lasts. The number of days the food lasts is inversely proportional to the number of men - more men, fewer days.

$$\frac{x}{5} = \frac{24}{30}$$

$$x = \frac{(24)(5)}{30}$$

$$x = \frac{(4)(6)(5)}{(6)(5)}$$

$$x = 4 \qquad\qquad \text{The food will last } \textbf{4 days.}$$

12. Time for car A = 3 h. Time for car B = $3 - 1\frac{1}{2} = \frac{3}{2}$

Let x be the distance car A travels.
Car B travels (60 - x) km.
Speed is the same for both cars.

$$\frac{\text{distance}}{\text{time}} = \text{speed}$$

$$\frac{x}{3} = \frac{60 - x}{\frac{3}{2}}$$

$$\frac{x}{3} = \frac{(60 - x)2}{3}$$

$$x = 120 - 2x$$

$$3x = 120$$

$$x = 40$$

distance for car **A = 40 km**
distance for car **B** = 60 - 40 = **20 km**.

13. Let x be his speed up hill.
     His speed downhill is $(x + 4)$ km/h
     Distance is the same both uphill and downhill.
     distance = speed x time
     Both times are equally proportional to hours, so it is not necessary to convert to hours.
     $45x = 30(x + 4)$
     $45x = 30x + 120$
     $15x = 120$
     $x = 8$ He cycled uphill at **8 km/h**.

14. Distance when using 9 ℓ = (3)(60) km (Distance = Speed x Time)
     Distance in case 2 = (4)(40) km. Let x be the amount of petrol needed. Petrol needed is directly proportional to the distance.

     $$\frac{x}{9} = \frac{(4)(40)}{(3)(60)}$$

     $$\frac{x}{9} = \frac{(4)(2)}{(3)(3)}$$

     $$x = \frac{(8)(9)}{9}$$

     $x = 8$ **8 ℓ** of petrol is needed.

15. (a) Let x be the time needed for 8 men.
         Time needed is inversely proportional to the number of men.

         $40 \text{ min} = \frac{2}{3}$ h

         $6 \text{ h } 40 \text{ min} = 6\frac{2}{3} = \frac{20}{3}$ hr

         $$\frac{x}{\frac{20}{3}} = \frac{14}{8}$$

         $$x = \frac{(14)(20)}{(8)(3)}$$

         $$x = \frac{35}{3}$$

         $$x = 11\frac{2}{3}$$

         It takes 8 men **11 h 40 min**.

    (b) 8 men x $\frac{35}{3}$ h = $\frac{280}{3}$ man hours.

         The job takes $\frac{280}{3}$ man hours.

         After 1 hour, 8 men have done 8 man hours of the job
         Amount of job left

         $= \frac{280}{3} - 8 = \frac{280}{3} - \frac{24}{3} = \frac{256}{3}$ man hours

         Time required for 6 men =

         $$\frac{\frac{256}{3}}{6} = \frac{256}{(3)(6)} = \frac{128}{9} = 14\frac{2}{9}$$ h

         It will take the remaining 6 men

         14 h 13$\frac{1}{3}$ min to finish.

Exercise 7.4 (p. 190)

1. (a) $\dfrac{3}{4} = \dfrac{3}{4} \times 100\%$

$\quad = \dfrac{(3)(4)(25)}{4}\%$

$\quad = \textbf{75\%}$

(b) $\dfrac{4}{125} = \dfrac{4}{125} \times 100\%$

$\quad = \dfrac{16}{5}\%$

$\quad = \textbf{3.2\%}$

(c) $\dfrac{5}{5} = 1$

$\quad = \textbf{100\%}$

(d) $2\dfrac{1}{2} = 2\dfrac{1}{2} \times 100\%$

$\quad = (2 \times 100) + \left(\dfrac{1}{2} \times 100\right)\%$

$\quad = (200 + 50)\%$

$\quad = \textbf{250\%}$

(e) $\dfrac{110}{100} = \dfrac{110}{100} \times 100\%$

$\quad = \textbf{110\%}$

(f) $\dfrac{1}{50} = \dfrac{1}{50} \times 100\%$

$\quad = \dfrac{(50)(2)}{(50)}\%$

$\quad = \textbf{2\%}$

2. (a) $0.325 = 0.325 \times 100\%$
$\quad = \textbf{32.5\%}$

(b) $0.05 = 0.05 \times 100\%$
$\quad = \textbf{5\%}$

(c) $2.3 = 2.3 \times 100\%$
$\quad = \textbf{230\%}$

(d) $1.25 = 1.25 \times 100\%$
$\quad = \textbf{125\%}$

(e) $0.225 = 0.225 \times 100\%$
$\quad = \textbf{22.5\%}$

(f) $0.015 = 0.015 \times 100\%$
$\quad = \textbf{1.5\%}$

3. (a) $4\% = 4 \times \dfrac{1}{100} = \dfrac{\textbf{1}}{\textbf{25}}$

(b) $5\% = 5 \times \dfrac{1}{100} = \dfrac{\textbf{1}}{\textbf{20}}$

(c) $55\dfrac{1}{2}\% = \dfrac{111}{2} \times \dfrac{1}{100}$

$\quad = \dfrac{\textbf{111}}{\textbf{200}}$

(d) $0.2\% = \dfrac{2}{10} \times \dfrac{1}{100}$

$\quad = \dfrac{1}{5} \times \dfrac{1}{100}$

$\quad = \dfrac{\textbf{1}}{\textbf{500}}$

(e) $7\dfrac{1}{3}\% = \dfrac{22}{3} \times \dfrac{1}{100}$

$\quad = \dfrac{\textbf{11}}{\textbf{150}}$

(f) $7\dfrac{1}{5}\% = \dfrac{36}{5} \times \dfrac{1}{100}$

$\quad = \dfrac{\textbf{9}}{\textbf{125}}$

4. (a) $33\% = 33 \times \dfrac{1}{100}$

$\quad = \textbf{0.33}$

(b) $\dfrac{1}{2}\% = 0.5 \times \dfrac{1}{100}$

$\quad = \textbf{0.005}$

(c)
$$1.5\% = 1.5 \times \frac{1}{100}$$
$$= \mathbf{0.015}$$

(d)
$$12\frac{1}{2}\% = 12.5 \times \frac{1}{100}$$
$$= \mathbf{0.125}$$

(e)
$$250\% = 250 \times \frac{1}{100}$$
$$= \mathbf{2.5}$$

(f)
$$75\% = 75 \times \frac{1}{100}$$
$$= \mathbf{0.75}$$

5. (a)
$$5\frac{1}{5}\% \text{ of } \$74 = \frac{26}{5} \times \frac{1}{100} \times \$74$$
$$= \$\frac{481}{125}$$
$$\approx \mathbf{\$3.85}$$

(b)
$$10\% \text{ of } \$230 = \frac{10}{100} \times \$230$$
$$= \mathbf{\$23}$$

(c)
$$25\% \text{ of } \$750.28 = \frac{25}{100} \times \$750.28$$
$$= \$\frac{750.28}{4}$$
$$= \mathbf{\$187.57}$$

(d)
$$5\% \text{ of } \$130 = \frac{5}{100} \times \$130$$
$$= \$\frac{13}{2}$$
$$= \mathbf{\$6.50}$$

(e)
$$7\frac{1}{5}\% \text{ of } \$100 = 7\frac{1}{5} \times \frac{1}{100} \times \$100$$
$$= \mathbf{\$7.50}$$

(f)
$$110\% \text{ of } \$220 = \frac{110}{100} \times \$220$$
$$= \$11 \times 22$$
$$= \mathbf{\$242}$$

6. (a)
$$\frac{10m}{1km} = \frac{10m}{1,000m} \times 100\%$$
$$= \mathbf{1\%}$$

(b)
$$\frac{5 \text{ mm}}{1 \text{ m}} = \frac{5 \text{ mm}}{1,000 \text{ mm}} \times 100\%$$
$$= \mathbf{0.5\%}$$

(c)
$$\frac{120^{o}}{360^{o}} = \frac{1}{3} \times 100\%$$
$$= \mathbf{33\frac{1}{3}\%}$$

(d)
$$\frac{20 \text{ min}}{1 \text{ h}} = \frac{20 \text{ min}}{60 \text{ min}} \times 100\%$$
$$= \frac{200}{6}\%$$
$$= \mathbf{33\frac{1}{3}\%}$$

(e)
$$\frac{3 \text{ months}}{1 \text{ year}} = \frac{3 \text{ months}}{12 \text{ months}} \times 100\%$$
$$= \frac{100}{4}\%$$
$$= \mathbf{25\%}$$

(f)
$$\frac{33¢}{\$3} = \frac{33¢}{300¢} \times 100\%$$
$$= \frac{33}{3}\%$$
$$= \mathbf{11\%}$$

Exercise 7.5 (pp. 193-195)

1. (a) $100\% + 15\% = \mathbf{115\%}$ (b) $105\% - 100\% = \mathbf{5\%}$

   (c) $100\% - 16\% = \mathbf{84\%}$ (d) $100\% - 96\% = \mathbf{4\%}$

2.   Increase = $81{,}000 - 72{,}000 = 9{,}000$

         % increase = $\dfrac{9{,}000}{72{,}000}$ x $100\% = \mathbf{12.5\%}$

3.   Decrease = $1{,}275 - 1{,}020 = 255$

         % decrease = $\dfrac{255}{1{,}275}$ x $100\% = \mathbf{20\%}$

4. (a)   Increase 2nd month = $810 - 750 = 60$

         Percent increase = $\dfrac{60}{750}$ x $100\% = \mathbf{8\%}$

   (b)   Decrease 3rd month = $810 - 729 = 81$

         Percent decrease = $\dfrac{81}{810}$ x $100\% = \mathbf{10\%}$

5.   Increased number = 116% of original.
         100% of original = 450
           1% of original = 4.5
         116% of original = 4.5 x 116 = 522
         The enrollment in 1990 was **522**.

         Alternative solution:

         116% of $450 = \dfrac{116}{100}$ x 450

         $= 522$

6.   Increased price = 125% of original
         125% of original = 95

           1% of original = $\dfrac{95}{125} = \dfrac{19}{25}$

         100% of original = $\dfrac{(19)(100)}{25} = 19$ x $4 = 76$

         Original price was **$76**.

         Alternative solution:
         Let x be the original price.
         125% of $x = 95$

         $x = \dfrac{95}{125}(100)$

         $= 76$

7.   Decreased price = 95% of original
         95% of original = 19

           1% of original = $\dfrac{19}{95}$

         100% of original = $\dfrac{(19)(100)}{95} = \dfrac{(19)(20)}{19} = 20$

         Original price was **$20**.

         Alternative solution:
         Let x be the original price.
         95% of $x = 19$

         $x = \dfrac{19}{95}(100)$

         $x = 20$

8.   Increased price = 120% of original
      120% of original = 150

      $$1\% \text{ of original} = \frac{150}{120} = \frac{5}{4}$$

      $$100\% \text{ of original} = \frac{5}{4}(100) = 5 \times 25 = 125$$

      Original price was **$125**.

Alternative solution:
Let x be the original price.
120% of x = 150

$$x = \frac{150}{120}(100)$$

$x = 125$

9.   Decreased price = 95% of original
      95% of original = 285

      $$1\% \text{ of original} = \frac{285}{95} = 3$$

      100% of original = 3 x 100 = 300
      Original price was **$300**.

Alternative solution:
Let x be the original price.
95% of x = 285

$$x = \frac{285}{95}(100)$$

$x = 300$

10.   70 → 100%

      $$1 \to \frac{100}{70} = \frac{10}{7}\%$$

      $$55 \to \frac{10}{7}(55)\% \approx 78.6\%$$

      He got **78.6%**
      100% of the exam = 70
      10% of the exam = 7
      40% of the exam = 7 x 4 = 28
      The least number of correct answers to pass is **28**.

Alternative solutions:

$$\frac{55}{70} = \frac{55}{70}(100)\%$$

$$\approx 78.6\%$$

answers = 40% of 70

$$= \frac{40}{100}(70)$$

$$= 28$$

11.   His math score was 120% of his geography score.
      120% of score = 90

      $$1\% \text{ of score} = \frac{90}{120} = \frac{3}{4}$$

      $$100\% \text{ of score} = \frac{3}{4}(100) = 3 \times 25 = 75$$

      He got **75 marks** in geography.

Alternative solutions:
Let x be the geog. score.
120% of x = 90

$$x = \frac{90}{120}(100)$$

$x = 75$

12.   If one of them received 65%, the other received 100 - 65 = 35%.
      The first candidate received 65 - 35 = 30% more votes.
      30% of the votes = 1,500

      $$100\% \text{ of the votes} = \frac{1,500}{30}(100)$$

      $$= 5,000$$

      5,000 people voted.

13.   The amount of alcohol = 8% of 40 ℓ = $\dfrac{8}{100}$ x 40 = 3.2 ℓ

If 10 ℓ is drawn off, $\dfrac{1}{4}$ of the total liquid is removed, and $\dfrac{3}{4}$ remains.

$\dfrac{3}{4}$ of the alcohol = $\dfrac{3}{4}$ x 3.2 ℓ = 2.4 ℓ

10 ℓ of water is added back in, bringing the total volume to 40 ℓ again.

2.4 ℓ in 40 ℓ = $\dfrac{2.4}{40}$ x 100% = 6%

The mixture has **6%** alcohol.

14.   Let Henry's weight be 100%
James is 10% lighter, or 90%
Peter is 8% heavier, or 108%
Peter is 108 - 90 = 18% heavier than James.

$\dfrac{18}{90}$ x 100% = **20%**

100	Henry
108	Peter
90 |18| James

15.   The company's capital is one whole. Divide that whole into 15 parts.

$\dfrac{1}{3}$ of the capital = $\dfrac{1}{3}$ of 15 = 5.

This increases by 4%. 4% of 5 = $\dfrac{4}{100}$ x 5 = 0.2

$\dfrac{1}{5}$ of the capital = $\dfrac{1}{5}$ of 15 = 3.

This decreases by 5%. 5% of 3 = $\dfrac{5}{100}$ x 3 = 0.15

The remainder is 15 - 5 - 3 = 7.
This increases by 10%. 10% of 7 = 0.7
Total increase = 0.2 - 0.15 + 0.7 = 0.75

$\dfrac{0.75}{15}$ x 100% = 5%

The total percentage increase is **5%**.

16.   In 10 weeks they would work 70 days. They plan to produce 10 tonnes, or 10,000 kg.
During the firs 10 days, they produce 10 kg less than 10%:

(10% x 10,000) - 10 = $\dfrac{10}{100}$ x 10,000 - 10 = 1,000 - 10 = 990 kg

In the next 10 days they produce 10% more than in the first 10 days, or 110%:

110% x 990 = $\dfrac{10}{100}$ x 990 = 1,089 kg.

Remaining amount = 10,000 - 990 - 1,089 = 7,921 kg
They want to finish in 60 days total, or 40 more days.
10 hours/day for 40 days is 400 hours

$\dfrac{7,921 \text{ kg}}{400 \text{ hours x 10 men}}$ = 1.98025 kg/h/man ≈ **1,980 g/h/man**

17.   The amount of money he still needs after saving for two weeks is $\frac{1}{4}$ of the

remainder, or $\frac{1}{4}$ of 60% = 15% of the original price.

The price went up 5%, so he needs an additional 5% of the original price.
15% + 5% = 20%. He needs $12.
20% of the original price = $12

original price = $\$\frac{12}{20}(100) = \$60$.

The original price of the racket was **$60**.

18.   This final solution is 7% of $(840 + x)$ cm³. The amount of acid in both solutions is the same.

10%	7%
840 cm³	$(840 + x)$ cm³

$$\frac{10}{100}(840) = \frac{7}{100}(840 + x)$$

$$8{,}400 = 5{,}880 + 7x$$
$$2{,}520 = 7x$$
$$360 = x$$

360 cm³ of water needs to be added.

19.   Let x be the amount of sugar to be added. The final amount of sugar is 40% of the final total solution.

30 g sugar	$(30 + x)$ g sugar
500 g water	500 g water
530 g total	500 + 30 + x g total

$$30 + x = \frac{40}{100}(530 + x)$$

$$100(30 + x) = 40(530 + x)$$
$$3{,}000 + 100x = 21{,}200 + 40x$$
$$60x = 18{,}200$$

$$x = 303\frac{1}{3}$$

$303\frac{1}{3}$ g of sugar must be added.

20.   Let x be the amount of the 60% alloy needed. Then $1{,}200 - x$ is the amount of 65% alloy needed. The final amount of silver is the sum of the silver in the two alloys.

60%	65%	62%
x g	$(1{,}200 - x)$ g	1,200 g

$$\frac{60}{100}x + \frac{65}{100}(1{,}200 - x) = \frac{62}{100}(1{,}200)$$

$$60x + 78{,}000 - 65x = 74{,}400$$
$$-5x = -3{,}600$$
$$x = 720$$

720 g of the 60% alloy and 480 g of the **65%** alloy is needed.

Revision Exercise 2

Revision 2A (p. 200)

1.   Tap A:
     1 min = 95 ℓ
     30 min = 30 x 95 ℓ = 2,850 ℓ one half hour = 30 min.
     Tap B:
      1 min = 105 ℓ
     30 min = 30 x 105 ℓ = 3,150 ℓ
     Total water = 2,850 ℓ + 3,150 ℓ = 6,000 ℓ
     6,000 ℓ flows from both taps in half an hour.

2. (a) $-8x^4 - 2x + 8 + (3x^2 + 2x - 5) = -8x^4 + 3x^2 + (2 - 2)x - 5 + 8$
                                    $= \mathbf{-8x^4 + 3x^2 + 3}$
   (b) $18x^5 - 7x^3 - x^2 - 15 - (2x^4 + 3x^2 - 10) = 18x^5 - 2x^4 - 7x^3 + [(-1) - 3]x^2 - 15 + 10$
                                           $= \mathbf{18x^5 - 2x^4 - 7x^3 - 4x^2 - 5}$

3. (a) $7 + 4x \le 15$
         $7 + 4(2) \le 15$
         $7 + 8 \le 15$
         $15 \le 15$
         true for $x = 2$

   (b) $3x - 2\left(\dfrac{4}{5}x\right) \ge 23$

         $3(-5) - 2\left(\dfrac{4}{5}(-5)\right) \ge 23$

         $-15 - (-8) \ge 23$

         $-7 \ge 23$

         false for $x = -5$

   (c) $\dfrac{6x}{5} + 4 \le \dfrac{23}{5}$

         $\dfrac{6\left(\dfrac{1}{2}\right)}{5} + 4 \le \dfrac{23}{5}$

         $\dfrac{3}{5} + 4 \le \dfrac{23}{5}$

         $\dfrac{23}{5} \le \dfrac{23}{5}$

         true for $x = \dfrac{1}{2}$

4. $a^2 - 3ab = b + 2$; $a = 3$
         $3^2 - (3)(3b) = b + 2$
         $9 - 9b = b + 2$
         $9 = 10b + 2$ add $9b$ to both sides
         $7 = 10b$ subtract 2 from both sides
         $\dfrac{\mathbf{7}}{\mathbf{10}} = b$

5. (a)   The tank is $\dfrac{3}{4}$ full.

         $\dfrac{3}{4}$ x 36 ℓ = 27 ℓ

         The tank has **27 ℓ** of petrol.

   (b)   1 ℓ = 8 km
         27 ℓ = 27 x 8 km
         27 ℓ = 216 km
         It can go **216 km**.

6.   The final cost is 100 + 25 = 125% of the original cost.
         125% x $72.80 = $\dfrac{125}{100}$ ($72.80) = $91
         The new price is **$91**.

7.   Let x be the number.
      $2x$ double it
      $6x$ multiply result by 3
      $6x = 138$ product is 138
         $x = \textbf{23}$

8.   Total is $7 + 11 = 18$
      $\dfrac{7}{18} \times 100\% \approx \textbf{38.9\%}$

9.   Let x be one number.
      The other number is $3 - x$.
      Their difference is 7.
      $3 - x - x = 7$
      $3 - 2x = 7$
      $-2x = 4$
      $x = -2$
      $3 - x = 3 - (-2) = 3 + 2 = 5$
      The two numbers are **-2** and **5**.

10.   Let m be Mabel's mass.
      Mary's mass is $\dfrac{2}{5}m$.
      Their total mass is 84 kg.
      $m + \dfrac{2}{5}m = 84$ kg
      $\dfrac{7}{5}m = 84$
      $m = \dfrac{(84)(5)}{7}$
      $m = (12)(5)$
      $m = 60$
      Mabel's mass is **60 kg**.

Revision 2B (pp. 200 - 201)

1.   For 5 people, $\dfrac{5}{3}$ of the recipe would be needed.

      $\dfrac{5}{3} \times 300$ g sweet corn = **500 g sweet corn**

      $\dfrac{5}{3} \times 120$ g sugar = **200 g sugar**

      $\dfrac{5}{3} \times 105$ g cream = **175 g cream**

      $\dfrac{5}{3} \times 60$ g water = **100 g water**

2. (a) $5 + x > 2$
        $5 + 4 > 2$
        $9 > 2$
        true for $x = 4$

   (b) $2x - 5\left(\dfrac{2}{3}x\right) > 2$
        $2\left(-\dfrac{3}{4}\right) - 5\left(\dfrac{2}{3}\right)\left(-\dfrac{3}{4}\right) > 2$
        $-\dfrac{3}{2} + \dfrac{5}{2} > 2$
        $2 > 2$
        false for $x = -\dfrac{3}{4}$

3. (a) $\dfrac{al}{bcd} \times \dfrac{bm}{ac} \div \dfrac{cm}{dp} = \dfrac{albm}{bcdac} \times \dfrac{dp}{cm}$

$= \dfrac{lp}{c^3}$

(b) $\dfrac{\dfrac{st}{pq}}{\dfrac{rs}{p}} = \dfrac{st}{pq} \times \dfrac{p}{rs}$

$= \dfrac{t}{rq}$

(c) $\dfrac{\dfrac{mn}{a} \div \dfrac{ap}{m}}{\dfrac{m}{n}} = \dfrac{mn}{a} \times \dfrac{m}{ap} \times \dfrac{n}{m}$

$= \dfrac{mn^2}{a^2 P}$

4. $2x + \dfrac{1}{8} = \dfrac{4}{3}x - 7$

$\dfrac{16x + 1}{8} = \dfrac{4x - 21}{3}$

$3(16x + 1) = 8(4x - 21)$ multiply both sides by 3 and by 8

$48x + 3 = 32x - 168$ distributive property

$16x = -171$ subtract 32x and 3 from both sides

$x = -\dfrac{171}{16}$ divide both sides by 16

$x = -10\dfrac{11}{16}$

5. (a) $F = \dfrac{9}{5}(C + 25) - 20$

$= \dfrac{9}{5}(15 + 25) - 20$

$= \dfrac{9}{5}(40) - 20$

$= (9)(8) - 20$

$= 72 - 20$

$= \mathbf{52}$

(b) $(x - y)^2 - w^2 = \left(\dfrac{1}{2} - \dfrac{1}{4}\right)^2 - \left(\dfrac{3}{4}\right)^2$

$= \left(\dfrac{1}{4}\right)^2 - \dfrac{9}{16}$

$= \dfrac{1}{16} - \dfrac{9}{16}$

$= -\dfrac{8}{16}$

$= -\dfrac{1}{2}$

6. Total of the 5 bills = $50 - $1.55 = $48.45
Total of 4 bills = $10.20 + $9.40 + $11.45 + $8.50 = $39.55
Lost bill = $48.45 - $39.55 = **$8.90**

7.   Candidate B got 100% - 65% = 35%
        Difference between A's and B's votes = 65% - 35% = 30%
        30% of total votes = 2,400
        100% of total votes = $\dfrac{2,400}{30}$ x 100 = 80 x 100 = 8,000
        8,000 people voted.

8.
        Let p = one part
        $15p$ = \$300,000
          p = 20,000
        $3p$ = 3 x 20,000 = 60,000
        $5p$ = 5 x 20,000 = 100,000
        $7p$ = 7 x 20,000 = 140,000
        Their shares were **\$60,000, \$100,000, and \$140,000**.

9.   Let x be the number of sweets Ali's sister gets.
        Ali gets $x + 5$ sweets.
        Altogether there are 19 sweets.
        $x + x + 5 = 19$
            $2x + 5 = 19$
                $2x = 14$
                  $x = 7$
            $x + 5 = 12$
        Ali gets **12** sweets, and his sister gets **7**.

10.   Let x be one number.
        $28 - x$ = other number.
        Three times the first plus the second is 40.
        $3x + (28 - x) = 40$
        $2x + 28 = 40$
        $2x = 12$
        $x = 6$
        $28 - x = 28 - 6 = 22$
        The numbers are **6** and **22**.

Revision 2C (pp. 201-202)

1. $\dfrac{360 \text{ tonnes}}{12 \text{ men} \times 5 \text{ hours}}$ = **6 tonnes/man hour**
        In 4 hours 4 x 6 = 24 tonnes can be unloaded.
        Let x be the amount of men needed $\dfrac{x}{1} = \dfrac{72}{24}$
        $x = 3$ The number of men needed is
        3 men are needed.   inversely proportional to the
                                                    amount.

2. (a) $\dfrac{5x}{3} + 6 \neq -\dfrac{11}{3}$

$\dfrac{(5)(1)}{3} + 6 \neq -\dfrac{11}{3}$

This will be **true** for $x = 1$, since one side stays positive and the other negative.

(b) $5 + 2x \geq 11$
$5 + (2)(3) \geq 11$
$5 + 6 \geq 11$
$11 \geq 11$
True for $x = 3$
(Answer in text is wrong.)

3. $0.4(2x - 1) = 0.6$
$0.8x - 0.4 = 0.6$ distributive law
$0.8x = 1.0$ add 0.4 to both sides
$x = \mathbf{1.25}$ divide both sides by 0.8

4. (a)
$$(p + q)^2 - (p - q - 2r)^2 = \left(\dfrac{1}{3} + \dfrac{1}{6}\right)^2 - \left(\dfrac{1}{3} - \dfrac{1}{6} - \dfrac{2}{9}\right)^2$$
$$= \left(\dfrac{2+1}{6}\right)^2 - \left(\dfrac{6-3-4}{18}\right)^2$$
$$= \left(\dfrac{1}{2}\right)^2 - \left(\dfrac{-1}{18}\right)^2$$
$$= \dfrac{1}{4} - \dfrac{1}{324}$$
$$= \dfrac{81 - 1}{324}$$
$$= \dfrac{80}{324}$$
$$= \mathbf{\dfrac{20}{81}}$$

(b)
$$\sqrt{5\left(\dfrac{x^2 - y^2}{x}\right)} = \sqrt{5\left(\dfrac{5^2 - 4^2}{5}\right)}$$
$$= \sqrt{25 - 16}$$
$$= \sqrt{9}$$
$$= \mathbf{\pm 3}$$

5. (a) $23{:}00 + 7\dfrac{1}{2}$ h $= 06{:}30$

He finishes work at **06:30**.

(b) $\dfrac{\$41.25}{7.5 \text{ h}} = \$5.50$

He is paid **$5.50** per hour.

6. Hourly pay $= \dfrac{\$264}{44 \text{ hours}} = \$6$

Overtime rate $= \$6 \times 1\dfrac{1}{4} = \$7.50$

Hours overtime $= 52 - 44 = 8$
Pay for overtime $= 8 \times \$7.50 = \$60.00$
Total pay $= \$264 + \$60 = \mathbf{\$324}$

7.   Let x be the amount of time needed.

$$\frac{x}{14} = \frac{10}{4}$$ Time needed is inversely proportional to the number of men.

$$x = \frac{10}{4}(14)$$

$$x = 35$$

35 days are needed.

8.   Let x be one number.
Second number $= 3x$ Three times the first number
Third number $= 4x - 3$ 3 less than 4 times the first number
$x + 3x + 4x - 3 = 37$ Sum is 37
$8x - 3 = 37$
$8x = 40$ Add 3 to both sides.
$x = 5$ Divide both sides by 8
$3x = (3)(5) = 15$ Second number
$4x - 3 = (4)(5) - 3 = 17$ Third number
The three numbers are **5, 15, and 17**.

9.   Let $p =$ one part $= \$25.70$
Henry has $2p$
Thomas has $3(p + 2p) = 9p$.
He has $9p - 2p = 7p$ more than Henry.
$7p = 7 \times \$25.70 = \$179.90$
Thomas has **\$179.90** more than Henry.

10.   Let x be the number of the big books.
The number of small books $= 50 - x$
Amount spent on big books $= \$4x$

Each small book costs $\$\frac{1}{4}$

She spent $\$\frac{1}{4}(50 - x)$

$$4x + \frac{1}{4}(50 - x) = 50$$ Total cost is \$50

$$4x + \frac{50}{4} - \frac{x}{4} = 50$$ Distributive property

$$\frac{16x - x}{4} = 50 - \frac{50}{4}$$

$$\frac{15x}{4} = \frac{150}{4}$$ Subtract $\frac{50}{4}$ from both sides

$$15x = 150$$

$$x = 10$$ Multiply both sides by 4
$50 - x = 50 - 10 = 40$
She bought **10 big and 40 small** books.   Number of smaller books

Revision 2D (pp. 202-203)

1. (a) $3x^2 + 6xy - 3y^2 + 4x^2 - 8xy + 2y^2 = (3 + 4)x^2 + (6 - 8)xy + (-3 + 2)y^2$
$$= \mathbf{7x^2 - 2xy - y^2}$$

(b) $6a^2 + 5ab - 6b^2 - 6a^2 + ab + 2b^2 = (6 - 6)a^2 + (5 + 1)ab + (-6 + 2)b^2$
$$= \mathbf{6ab - 4b^2}$$

(c) $3(a + 3b) + 4(a - 3b) = 3a + 9b + 4a - 12b$
$$= (3 + 4)a + (9 - 12)b$$
$$= \mathbf{7a - 3b}$$

2.
$$7 - \frac{3}{4}(p - 5) = \frac{1}{2}(p + 1)$$
$$7 - \frac{3}{4}p + \frac{15}{4} = \frac{1}{2}p + \frac{1}{2}$$ Distributive property, distribute negative too
$$7 + \frac{15}{4} - \frac{1}{2} = \frac{1}{2}p + \frac{3}{4}p$$ Add $\frac{3}{4}p$ and subtract $\frac{1}{2}$ from both sides
$$\frac{28 + 15 - 2}{4} = \frac{2p + 3p}{4}$$
$$41 = 5p$$
$$\frac{41}{5} = p$$ Divide both sides by 5
$$\mathbf{8\frac{1}{5}} = p$$

3. (a)
$$x = \frac{a}{b} - \left(\frac{c - d}{e}\right)$$
$$1 = \frac{2}{3} - \left(\frac{4 - 5}{e}\right)$$
$$1 = \frac{2}{3} - \frac{-1}{e}$$
$$1 = \frac{2e + 3}{3e}$$
$$3e = 2e + 3$$ multiply by 3e
$$e = \mathbf{3}$$ subtract 2e

(b)
$$\frac{1}{a} + \frac{1}{b} = 1$$ Alternative approach: express a in terms of b first.
$$\frac{b + a}{ab} = 1$$
$$b + a = ab$$ multiply by ab
$$a - ab = b$$ add ab
$$a(1 - b) = b$$ extract a on LHS
$$a = \frac{b}{1 - b}$$ divide by 1 - b
$$a = \frac{1\frac{1}{2}}{1 - \frac{1}{2}}$$ substitute $1\frac{1}{2}$ for b
$$a = \frac{\frac{3}{2}}{\frac{1}{2}}$$
$$a = \left(\frac{3}{2}\right)(2)$$
$$= \mathbf{3}$$

4.   cost of apples = 8 x $95 = $760
         cost of transport = 8 x $3 = $24
         total cost = $760 + $24 = $784
         sale = cost + profit = $784 + $152 = $936
         cost for each box = $\dfrac{\$936}{8}$ = **$117**

5.   Total distance bus travels in the 3 minutes is the length of the bus plus the length of the
         tunnel. Let x be the length of the tunnel in m. Then distance traveled = (8 + x) m =
         $\dfrac{8 + x}{1{,}000}$ km. 3 minutes = $\dfrac{3}{60} = \dfrac{1}{20}$ h
         Distance = Speed x Time
         $\dfrac{8 + x}{1{,}000} = 30\left(\dfrac{1}{20}\right)$

         $\dfrac{8 + x}{1{,}000} = \dfrac{1{,}500}{1{,}000}$

         $8 + x = 1{,}500$

         $x = 1{,}492$
         The tunnel is **1,492 m** long.

6. (a)   Amount increase = $627 - $550   (b)   New cost = 95% original cost
                          = $77   95% of 78¢ = $\dfrac{95}{100}$ x 78
         Percentage increase = $\dfrac{77}{550}$ x 100%   = 74.1
                             = **14%**   New cost = **74¢ per kg**

7.   Let s be the speed of the car. Then 16s is the speed of the plane.
         distance of car = s km/h x 1 h = s km
         distance for plane = 16s km/h x 1 h = 16s km
         Total distance = 850 km
         s + 16s = 850
             17s = 850
               s = 50
         Speed of car is 50 km/hr. Since it traveled 1 h, it went **50 km**.

8.   Let y = the number of years ago that Mary's mother's age was 4 times Mary's age.
         Mary's age then was 12 - y and her mother's age then was 42 - y. Her mother's age
         then was 4 times Mary's age:
         42 - y = 4(12 - y)
         42 - y = 48 - 4y
             3y = 6
              y = 2
         2 years ago Mary was **10 years old**.

9.   Total mass of boys = 24 x 35.5 kg = 852 kg
Total mass of girls = 15 x 29 kg = 435 kg
Total mass of class = 852 kg + 435 kg = 1,287 kg
Average mass of class = $\dfrac{1{,}287\text{kg}}{39}$ = 33 kg
Mass of new boy = 33 kg + 1.4 kg = 34.4 kg
New total mass of class = 1,287 kg + 34.4 kg = 1,321.4 kg
New average mass of class = $\dfrac{1{,}321.4}{40}$ = **33.035 kg**

10.   Let s be the number of Singapore stamps. Then 16 - s is the number of Malaysian stamps. If she trades her Singapore stamps for 2 Malaysian stamps, she will have an additional 2s Malaysian stamps and a total of 21 stamps:
$2s + 16 - s = 21$
$s + 16 = 21$
$s = 5$
$16 - s = 16 - 5 = 11$
She has 5 Singapore stamps and **11 Malaysian stamps**.

Revision 2E (pp. 203-204)

1. (a) $2(4 - b) + 3(b - 2b) = 8 - 2b + 3b - 6b$
$= 8 + (-2 + 3 - 6)b$
$= \mathbf{8 - 5b}$

   (b) $2x(x - 3y) + y(3x - y) = 2x^2 - 6xy + 3xy - y^2$
$= \mathbf{2x^2 - 3xy - y^2}$

   (c) $2a(1 - a) + 3a^2(1 + a) = 2a - 2a^2 + 3a^2 + 3a^3$
$= \mathbf{3a^3 + a^2 + 2a}$

2. $2.1t - 1.4 = 1.6t + 1.2$
$0.5t - 1.4 = 1.2$ subtract 1.6t from both sides
$0.5t = 2.6$ add 1.4 to both sides
$t = \mathbf{5.2}$ divide both sides by 0.5

3. (a) $\dfrac{a + c}{2} - 8d \times b = \dfrac{4 + 3}{2} - 8(7) \times (-2)$

$= \dfrac{7}{2} - (-112)$

$= \dfrac{7 + 224}{2}$

$= \dfrac{231}{2}$

$= \mathbf{115\dfrac{1}{2}}$

   (b) $[2c(b + d) + a]b + 5c$
$= [2(3)(-2 + 7) + 4](-2) + 5(3)$
$= [6(5) + 4](-2) + 15$
$= (34)(-2) + 15$
$= -68 + 15$
$= \mathbf{-53}$

4. (a) $m^4 + 3m^3 - 10m^2 + 8$
         $- (45m^2 + 3m - 2)$

$$\begin{array}{l} \; m^4 + 3m^3 \;-\; 10m^2 + 8 \\ +\; \underline{ - 45m^2 - 3m + 2} \\ \; \mathbf{m^4 + 3m^3 - 55m^2 - 3m + 10} \end{array}$$

   (b) $12t^6 - 8t^3 - 4t^2 + 2t - 8$
         $- (t^4 - 5t^5 - 10t^3 - 4)$

$$\begin{array}{l} \; 12t^6 - 8t^3 - 4t^2 + 2t - 8 \\ +\; \underline{ 5t^5 - t^4 + 10t^3 + 4} \\ \; \mathbf{12t^6 + 5t^5 - t^4 + 2t^3 - 4t^2 + 2t - 4} \end{array}$$

   (c)
$$[2(a-b)] - \left[\left(\frac{a}{3} + \frac{b}{4}\right) + \left(\frac{a}{6} - \frac{3b}{4}\right)\right] = 2a - 2b - \left[\frac{4a + 3b}{12} + \frac{2a - 9b}{12}\right]$$

$$= \frac{24a - 24b - 4a - 3b - 2a + 9b}{12}$$

$$= \frac{18a - 18b}{12}$$

$$= \frac{18}{12}(a - b)$$

$$= \mathbf{\frac{3}{2}(a - b)}$$

To subtract, you can line up terms vertically, change all the signs in the second row, and add.

5.   Let p be one part.
     $7p = 42$
     $p = 6$
     6 boys left the class.

before
□□□□□ boys
□□□ girls
after
□□□ boys
□□□ girls

6. (a)   Total savings = 12 x $150
                     = **$1,800**

   (b)   Percent savings $= \dfrac{1{,}800}{11{,}250} \times 100\%$

                     = **16%**

7.   Let x be the number of points scored by school B.

     School A scored $\frac{1}{2}x + 21$. Total score is 120.

     $x + \frac{1}{2}x + 21 = 120$

     $\frac{3}{2}x = 99$

     $x = 66$

     School B's score = **66**

     School A's score $= \frac{1}{2}x + 21 = \frac{1}{2}(66) + 21 =$ **54**

Alternate solution:

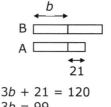

$3b + 21 = 120$
$3b = 99$
$b = 33$
B's score = $2b = 66$
A's score = $33 + 21 = 54$

8.   Let y be the number of years required.
        In y years the son will be $3 + y$ and the father will be $27 + y$.
        The father will be 3 times as old as the son.
        $27 + y = 3(3 + y)$
        $27 + y = 9 + 3y$
        $\quad\;\; 18 = 2y$
        $\quad\;\;\; 9 = y$
        In **9 years** the father will be 3 times as old as the son.

9.   Let x be the amount of money Peter has.
        Paul has $\$340 - x$.

        Peter spends $\dfrac{3}{4}$ of his money; he has $\dfrac{1}{4}$ of it, or $\dfrac{1}{4}x$ left.

        Paul spends $\dfrac{2}{5}$ of his money; he has $\dfrac{3}{5}$ of it, or $\dfrac{3}{5}(340 - x)$ left.

        They now have the same amount of money.

$$\frac{1}{4}x = \frac{3}{5}(340 - x)$$

$$\frac{1}{4}x = 204 - \frac{3}{5}x$$

$$\frac{1}{4}x + \frac{3}{5}x = 204$$

$$\frac{5 + 12}{20}x = 204$$

$$17x = 4{,}080$$

$$x = 240$$

        Peter's money = **$240**
        Paul's money = $\$340 - x = \$340 - \$240 = $**$100**

        Alternate Solution:

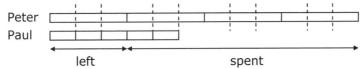

        Peter
        Paul
        left   spent

        17 units = $340
        1 unit = $20
        Peter started with 12 units = 12 x $20 = $240
        Paul started with 5 units = 5 x $20 = $100

10.   Tom and Jerry have some money.

       ⌧⌧⌧⌧⌧⌧⌧⌧⌧⌧   Tom
       ⫻⫻⫻⫻⫻⫻⫻⫻⫻⫻⫻⫻   Jerry

       If Jerry gives Tom $5, they will have the same amount of money.

       ⌧⌧⌧⌧⌧⌧⌧⌧⌧⌧⌧⫻⫻   Tom
       ⫻⫻⫻⫻⫻⫻⫻⫻⫻⫻⫻⫻$5| Jerry

       So Jerry has $10 more than Tom.
       Let t be the amount of money Tom has. Jerry has t + 10.
       If Tom gives Jerry $5, Jerry will have twice as much as Tom.

       ⌧⌧⌧⌧⌧⌧⌧⌧⌧ |$5| Tom
       ⫻⫻⫻⫻⫻⫻⫻⫻⫻⫻⫻⫻⫻⫻⌧⌧   Jerry

       So two times Tom's money - 5 equals Jerry's money + 5.
       $2(t - 5) = t + 10 + 5$
       $2t - 10 = t + 15$
       $t - 10 = 15$
       $t = 25$
       Tom has **$25**.
       Jerry has $t + 10 = 25 + 10 =$ **$35**

Miscellaneous Exercise 2 (pp. 205-207)

1. (a)

n	0	1	2	3	4
# of dots	1	4	7	10	13
	0+1	3+1	6+1	9+1	12+1

   (b) Each new pattern of the sequence adds a dot on the bottom and two along the top, or 3 new dots. The 5th pattern would have $13 + 3 = \mathbf{16}$ dots.

   (c) Let n represent the term in the sequence. If the pattern is extended down to the 0th pattern, there would be $4 - 3 = 1$ dot. From this, each term can be taken to be a multiple of $n + 1$. Represent each number of dots as a value + 1. Then it can be seen that the multiple of n is 3. So the nth pattern has $3n + 1$ dots. The 10th pattern has $3n + 1 = 3 \times 10 + 1 = \mathbf{31}$ dots.

2. Let n be the number.
   The other number is $n + a$.
   The larger number plus b is c times the smaller:
   $n + a + b = cn$
   Find n in terms of a, b, and c.
   $n + a + b = cn$

   $a + b = cn - n$

   $a + b = n(c - 1)$

   $\dfrac{a + b}{c - 1} = n$

   The sum of the two numbers is $n + n + a = 2n + a$. Substitute for n:

   $2n + a = 2\left(\dfrac{a + b}{c - 1}\right) + a$

   $= \dfrac{2a + 2b + a(c - 1)}{c - 1}$

   $= \dfrac{2a + 2b + ca - a}{c - 1}$

   $= \dfrac{a + ca + 2b}{c - 1}$

   $= \dfrac{\mathbf{a(1 + c) + 2b}}{\mathbf{c - 1}}$

3. Let w be the number of workbooks.
   5 less than twice the number of workbooks $= 2w - 5$
   $2w - 5 = 15$

   $2w = 20$

   $w = 10$
   There are **10** workbooks.

4.
$$\frac{d_1}{d_2} = \frac{2}{3} \qquad \frac{v_1}{v_2} = \frac{3}{2}$$

Express the ratios as fractions.

$$t_1 = \frac{d_1}{v_1} \qquad t_2 = \frac{d_2}{v_2}$$

$$\text{Time} = \frac{\text{Distance}}{\text{Speed}}$$

$$\frac{t_1}{t_2} = \frac{\dfrac{d_1}{v_1}}{\dfrac{d_2}{v_2}}$$

Find the ratio of t_1 to t_2 as a fraction.

$$= \frac{d_1}{v_1} \times \frac{v_2}{d_2}$$

$$= \frac{d_1}{d_2} \times \frac{v_2}{v_1}$$

$$= \frac{2}{3} \times \frac{2}{3}$$

Substitute in the ratios. Invert the one for speed.

$$= \frac{4}{9}$$

$$t_1 : t_2 = \mathbf{4 : 9}$$

5.   The ratio of their perimeters is 5 : 4

[bar diagram] perimeter of A
[bar diagram] perimeter of B

Let a be a unit of length for rectangle A. Since the ratio of the length to the breadth is 3
: 2, then the length is 3a and the breadth is 2a and the perimeter is
2(3a + 2a) = 10a
Let b be a unit of length for rectangle B. Since the ratio of the length to the breadth is 5
: 3, then the length is 5b and the breadth is 3b and the perimeter is
2(5b + 3b) = 16b
Divide the perimeter of A into 10 units, and the perimeter of B into 16 units.

[bar diagram] perimeter of A
[bar diagram] perimeter of B

∴ the unit a is twice the unit b.
Express the length and breadth of rectangle A in terms of b.
The length of rectangle A = 6b and the breadth is 4b.
The area of rectangle A = 6b x 4b = 24b
The area of rectangle B = 5b x 3b = 15b

$$\frac{\text{area of } A}{\text{area of } B} = \frac{24b}{15b} = \frac{8}{5}$$

area of rectangle A : area of rectangle B = **8 : 5**

6. (a) A = 110% of B
        B = 110% of C
        A = 110% of 110% of C
        $= \dfrac{110}{100}$ x 110% of C
        $= 121\%$ of C
        121% - 100% = 21%
        So A costs **21%** more than C.

(b) $A = \dfrac{110}{100} \times B$

   $\dfrac{100}{110} \times A = B$

   $0.909 \times A = B$
   $\therefore B$ = 90.9% of A
   Similarly, C = 90.9% of B
   C = 90.9% of 90.9% of A

   $= \dfrac{90.9}{100}$ x 90.9% of A

   $= 82.6\%$ of A
   100% - 82.6% = 17.4%
   C costs **17.4%** less than A.

7. Let x be his original rent 2 years ago.
    His increase in rent after 1 year is 10% of x = $0.10x$
    His total rent after 1 year is 110% of x = $1.10x$
    His increase in rent the next year is 10% of $1.10x$ = $0.10(1.10x) = 0.11x$
    His total increase in rent, \$168, is the increase at the end of year 1 + the increase at
    the end of year 2, or $0.10x + 0.11x$.
    $0.10x + 0.11x = 168$
    $\qquad 0.21x = 168$
    $\qquad\quad x = 800$
    $\therefore$ his original rent was \$800.
    His new rent is \$800 + \$168 = **\$968**.

8. (a) He gives his parents $\dfrac{1}{6}$ x \$2,400 = **\$400**

   (b) (i) Amount of increase = 6% of \$2,400 = $\dfrac{6}{100}$ x \$2,400 = **\$144**

        (ii) Increased amount he gives his parents = $\dfrac{1}{6}$ x \$144 = **\$24**

   (c) Although it is not evident from the wording of this problem, in order to get the same
        answer as in the text you need to assume he saves 15% of his remaining pay after
        giving some to his parents.

        (i) First month's savings = 15% of (2,400 - 400) $= \dfrac{15}{100}$ x 2,000 = 300

        Second month's earnings = \$2,400 + \$144 = \$2,544

        Second month's savings = 15 % of (2,544 - 424) $= \dfrac{15}{100}$ x 2,120 = 318

        $\dfrac{300}{318} = \dfrac{\mathbf{50}}{\mathbf{53}}$

        (ii) Percent increase $= \dfrac{318 - 300}{300} x100\% = \dfrac{18}{3}\% =$ **6%**

9. (a)

Fraction of yellow marbles = $1 - \dfrac{3}{5} - \dfrac{3}{8} = \dfrac{40}{40} - \dfrac{24}{40} - \dfrac{15}{40} = \dfrac{1}{40}$

(b)

Percentage of blue marbles = $\dfrac{3}{8}$ x 100% = **37.5%**

(c)

Since $\dfrac{1}{40}$ are blue, the smallest possible number of marbles is **40**.

(d)

$\dfrac{red}{blue} = \dfrac{\frac{3}{5}}{\frac{3}{8}} = \dfrac{3}{5} \times \dfrac{8}{3} = \dfrac{8}{5}$ red : blue = **8 : 5**

10. (a)

Let p be the number of parts. Since there are 18 more women than men,

$p = 18$

Number of men = $2p$ = 2 x 18 = **36**.

men
women

(b)

Number of young men = $(1 - \dfrac{2}{3})$ of the men = $\dfrac{1}{3}$ x 36 = 12

Number of women = $3p$ = 3 x 18 = 54

Number of young women = $(1 - \dfrac{5}{9})$ of the women = $\dfrac{4}{9}$ x 54 = 24

Total young adults = 12 + 24 = **36**

(c)

Total number of retirees = $5p$ - 36 = (5 x 18) - 36 = 54

Cost for retiree = (100% - 15%) x \$350 = $\dfrac{85}{100}$ x \$350 = \$297.50

Amount of money company collects = (36 x \$350) + (54 x \$297.50) = **\$28,665**

11. (a)

$1\,\ell = 90¢$

$\dfrac{1}{90}$ (100) ℓ = \$1.00

$\dfrac{45}{90}$ (100) ℓ = \$45.00

$50\,\ell$ = \$45

50 ℓ can be bought for \$45.

Or: \$45 x $\dfrac{1\,\ell}{\$0.90}$ = 50 ℓ

(b)

(i) Price per liter = 120% x 0.90 = $\dfrac{120}{100}$ x 0.90 = \$1.08

(ii) \$17.28 x $\dfrac{1}{1.08}$ = **16 ℓ**

(c)

(i) $\dfrac{0.27}{1.08}$ x 100% = **25%**

(ii) 1995 price = \$1.08 + \$0.27 = \$1.35

\$37.80 x $\dfrac{1}{\$1.35}$ = **28 ℓ**

12.(a)　　$\dfrac{0.54}{1.2} = \dfrac{54}{120} = \dfrac{9}{20}$　　Mass of can : mass of case = **9 : 20**

　(b)　　Mass of all cans = 150 x 12 x 0.54 kg = **972 kg**

　(c)　　Mass of cases = 150 x 1.2 = 180 kg

　　　　$\dfrac{180}{972} = \dfrac{5}{27}$

　　　　Mass of cases = $\dfrac{\mathbf{5}}{\mathbf{27}}$ of mass of all cans

　(d)　　Total mass = 972 kg + 180 kg = 1152 kg
　　　　Cost of transport = 1152 x $0.25 = **$288**

13.　　The players names will be represented by letters. Start with G, who has played 7 games. He has played every other player, including H. F has played 6 games, but not with A, since A has only played 1 game already with G, so F has played a game with H. E has played 5 games, but not with A or B, since A already has 1 game now and B already has 2 games, so has played with H. D has played 4 games, but not with A, B, or C, so played one with H. H has played 4 games, one each with G, F, E, and D.

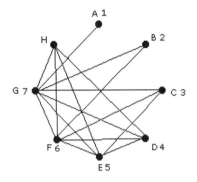

　　　　Henry has already played **4** games.

14.　　This problem supplies insufficient information to arrive at a solution.

15.　　For explanation purposes, a is the divisor, w, x, y and z are digits in the quotient, and b, c, d, e, f, g, and h are the remaining lines of the problem.

```
               p 7 q r s
a    * * * ) * * * * * * * *
b          * * * *
c            * * *
d            * * *
e            * * * *
f              * * *
g            * * * *
h            * * * *
                     0
```

c - d is a 3 digit number. The smallest the first three digits of d can be is 100, and the largest c can be is 999, so the largest c can be is 899.

899 ÷ 7 = 128.4, so the largest a can be is 128. The largest p can be is 9. 9 times the largest a can be is 9 x 128 = 1,152 so 1,000 ≤ b ≤ 1,152. Similarly, 1,000 ≤ g ≤ 1,152, and since g = h then 1,000 ≤ g ≤ 1,152. The smallest a can be when p is largest is 112, since 9 x 111 gives a three digit number. So 112 ≤ a ≤ 128. c - d cannot be greater than a, so the first three digits of e have to be less than 128. So 1,000 ≤ e ≤ 1,279

```
                                    p 7 q  r s
112 to 128       a   1 * * ) * * * * * * * *
1,000 to 1,152   b          1 * * *
                 c            * * *
784 to 896       d            * * *
1,000 to 1,279   e          1 * * *
                 f            * * *
1,000 to 1,152   g            1 * * *
1,000 to 1,152   h            1 * * *
                                    0
```

e - f is a 2 digit number, the first 2 digits of g. Since $1{,}000 \le g \le 1{,}152$ then e - f = 10 or 11. The maximum f can be is 999, $999 + 10 = 1{,}009$. The smallest f can be and still get a four digit number (e) when added to 10 or 11 is 990. So $990 \le f \le 999$. $990 + 11 = 1{,}001$ and $999 + 11 = 1{,}010$, so $1{,}001 \le e \le 1{,}010$.

```
                                    p 7 q  r s
112 to 128       a   1 * * ) * * * * * * * *
1,000 to 1,152   b          1 * * *
                 c            * * *
784 to 896       d            * * *
1,000 to 1,010   e          1 0 * *
990 to 999       f            9 9 *
1,001 to 1,152   g            1 * * *
1,001 to 1,152   h            1 * * *
                                    0
```

Now q can be found. Since $128 \times 7 = 896$ is too small ($f \ge 990$) and 112×9 is too large, q must be 8. But if q is 8, then $990 \div 8$ is 123.8 and $999 \div 8$ is 124.8, a must be 124. If f is 124, then $f = 124 \times 8 = 992$, and $d = 124 \times 7 = 868$. Since b and h are 4 digits, then p and s are 9, which makes b and h 1,116, and also g. r has to be 0.

```
                            9 7 8 0 9
              a   1 2 4 ) * * * * * * 1 6
              b          1 1 1 6
              c            * * *
              d            8 6 8
              e          1 0 * *
              f            9 9 2
              g              1 1 1 6
              h              1 1 1 6
                                    0
```

Now e must be 1,003 ($992 + 11$) so c must be 968 ($100 + 868$). The first 4 digits of the dividend must be 1,212 ($1{,}116 + 96$) and the rest are known from the values of the digits in c, e, and g.

```
                            9 7 8 0 9
              a   1 2 4 ) 1 2 1 2 8 3 1 6
              b          1 1 1 6
              c            9 6 8
              d            8 6 8
              e          1 0 0 3
              f            9 9 2
              g              1 1 1 6
              h              1 1 1 6
                                    0
```

Chapter 8

Exercise 8.1 (pp. 215-216)

1. Let x be his annual income.
    20% of $x = \$500$
    $$x = \frac{\$500}{0.20} = \$2,500$$
    His annual income is **$2,500**.

2. If his increment is 8% his new salary is 108% of his old salary.
    New salary = 108% of $2,580 = $\frac{108}{100}$ x $2,580 = **$2,786.40**

3. Increase = $1,805.50 - $1,570 = $235.50
    Percent increase $= \frac{235.50}{1,570}$ x 100 = 15%
    His salary increased by **15%**.

4. He saves 100% - 70.5% = 29.5%. Let x be his monthly income.
    29.5% of $x = \$885$
    $$x = \$\frac{885}{29.5}(100)$$
    $$x = 3,000$$
    His monthly income is **$3,000**.

5. Peter saves 100% - 87.5% = 12.5%. Let x be his monthly income.
    12.5% of $x = \$240$
    $$x = \$\frac{240}{12.5}(100)$$
    $$x = \$1,920$$
    Peter earns $1,920.
    Let y be Paul's monthly income.
    15% of $y = \$330$
    $$y = \frac{\$330}{15}(100)$$
    $$y = \$2,200$$
    Paul earns $2,200.
    Paul earns 2,200 - 1,920 = **$280 more**.

6. Let x be the original wage.
    115% of $x = \$59,800$
    $$x = \frac{\$59,800}{115}(100)$$
    $$x = \$52,000$$
    Original wage = $52,000
    Increase = final - original = $59,800 - $52,000 = $7,800
    The amount of increase was **$7,800**.

7.   Let x be the original yearly bill.
       112.5% of x = $51,300
$$x = \$\frac{51,300}{112.5}(100)$$
       x = $45,600
       Original yearly bill = $45,600
       Increase = final - original = 51,300 - 45,600 = 5,700
       Monthly increase = $\dfrac{\$5,700}{12}$ = **$475**

8.   Amount loss = $87,500 - $75,000 = $12,500
       Percent loss = $\dfrac{\$12,500}{\$87,500}$ x 100% = **14.29%**

9.   Profit = Selling Price - Cost Price = 10 - 8 = 2
       Percent profit = $\dfrac{2}{8}$ x 100% = **25%**

10.   Let x be the original cost.
       117% of x = $175.50
$$x = \$\frac{175.5}{117}(100)$$
       x = $150
       The original cost was **$150**.

11.   Let x be the outlay. He lost 25%, so he sold at 100% - 25% = 75%
       75% of x = $250
$$x = \$\frac{250}{75}(100)$$
       x = 333.333
       Outlay was $333.33.
       Gain of 10% is 110% outlay.
       110% of $333.333 = $\dfrac{110}{100}$ x $333.333 = $366.67
       He would have to sell at **$366.67**.

12.   Let x be the cost price.
       120% of x = $8.50
$$x = \frac{\$8.50}{120}(100)$$
       x = $7.083
       To make a profit of 30%, the selling price must be 130% of cost price.
       130% of 7.083 = $\dfrac{130}{100}$ x 7.083 = 9.208
       The selling price should be **$9.21**.

13.   12 handkerchiefs = $1.80
       96 = 12 x 8
       96 handkerchiefs = $1.80 x 8 = $144
       He sold 780 at 3 for $1.

       $\frac{780}{3}$ = 260

       He made $260 from them.
       He had 960 - 780 = 180 left, which he sold at 4 for $1.

       $\frac{180}{4}$ = 45

       He made $45 from them.
       Total price = $260 + $45 = $305
       Profit = selling price - cost price = 305 - 144 = 161

       Percent profit = $\frac{161}{144}$ x 100% = 111.8%

       His profit was **112%.**

14.   4% of 100, or 4 eggs were broken.
       96 eggs remain.
       Profit of 80% means selling price must be 180% of original.

       180% of $8.50 = $\frac{180}{100}$ x $8.5 = $15.30

       The number of sets he must sell at 80¢ = $\frac{\$15.30}{0.80}$ = 19.12 = 19

       96 eggs have to be put into 19 sets.

       $\frac{96}{19}$ = 5.05

       Each set would get 5 eggs. So he should sell **5 eggs** at 80¢ to get a profit of 80%.

15.
       Gain in volume = 110% of 100 ℓ = $\frac{110}{100}$ x 100 ℓ = 110 ℓ

       He added 10 ℓ sugar syrup.
       He spills 10%, and is left with 90%.

       Amount remaining = 90% of 110 ℓ = $\frac{90}{100}$ x 110 ℓ = 99 ℓ

         1 ℓ sells at $2.10
       99 ℓ sells at 99 x $2.10 = $207.90
       Cost of syrup = $86
       Cost of sugar syrup = 10 x $0.13 = $1.30
       Total cost = $86 + $1.30 = $87.30
       Profit = $207.90 - $87.30 = $120.60

       Percent profit = $\frac{120.60}{87.30}$ x 100% = 138.14%

       Percent profit is **138%.**

16. $\frac{1}{2}$% of $62,500 = $\frac{1}{200}$0.05 x 62,500 = 3,125

       His commission is **$3,125**.

17. Let x be his sales.
     12.5% of x = $250
     $$x = \frac{\$250}{12.5}(100)$$
     $$x = \$2,000$$
     His sales are **$2,000**.

18. Percent commission = $\dfrac{90}{2,000}$ x 100% = 4.5%
     His commission is **4.5%** of his sales.

19. For two of the weeks he made sales over $5,000.
     So commission = $3\frac{1}{2}$% of $(4,800 + 3,200) + 6$ % of $(5,600 + 8,200)
     $$= \frac{3.5}{100} \times \$8,000 + \frac{6}{100} \times \$13,800$$
     $$= \mathbf{\$1,108}$$
     His total commission is $1,108.
     Total sales = $8,000 + $13,800 = $21,800
     Percent commission = $\dfrac{1,108}{21,800}$ x 100% = 5.08%
     Average commission is **5.08%.**

20. The discount is 15% of the selling price, so the new price is 85% of the selling price.
     85% of $260 = $\dfrac{85}{100}$ x $260 = $221
     Profit = new price - cost price = $221 - $160 = **$61**

21. If the discount is 20%, then the cost is 80% of price. Let x be the price.
     80% of $$x$ = $45
     $$x = \$\frac{45}{80}(100)$$
     $$x = \$56.25$$
     The marked price was **$56.25**.

22. If the rebate is 5%, the final price is (100% - 5%) = 95%
     95% of $1,200 = $\dfrac{95}{100}$ x $1,200 = $1,140
     He must pay **$1,140**.

23. With a discount of 15%, the final price is 85% of the marked price.
     Let x be the marked price.
     85% of x = $29.75
     $$x = \frac{\$29.75}{85}(100)$$
     $$x = \$35$$
     The marked price is **$35**.

24. A 25% discount on list price is 75% of list price to give the selling price. The selling price gave a profit of 15%, which is 115% of his cost. Let x be the list price.
75% of x = 115% of $300

$$x = \$\frac{(115)(300)(100)}{(100)(75)}$$

$$x = \$460$$

The list price is **$460**.

25. A gain of 40% is 140% of cost.

$$140\% \text{ of } \$374 = \frac{140}{100} \times \$374 = \$523.60$$

Marked price = $523.60
A 25% discount is 75% of price.

$$75\% \text{ of } \$523.60 = \frac{75}{100} \times \$523.60 = \$392.70$$

Sales price = $392.70
Profit = selling price - cost = $392.70 - $374 = 18.70

$$\text{Percent profit} = \frac{18.70}{374} \times 100\% = 5\%$$

Percent profit is **5%**.

Or Percent Profit $= \dfrac{\text{selling price} - \text{cost}}{\text{cost}} \times 100\%$

$$= \frac{75\% \text{ of marked price} - \text{cost}}{\text{cost}} \times 100\%$$

$$= \frac{75\% \text{ of } (140\% \text{ of cost}) - \text{cost}}{\text{cost}} \times 100\%$$

$$= \frac{0.75(1.40)\$374 - \$374}{\$374} \times 100\%$$

$$= \big((0.75)(1.40) - 1\big) \times 100\%$$

$$= 5\%$$

Exercise 8.2 (pp. 219-222)

1. (a) $I = \dfrac{5}{100} \times \$300 \times 3$

   $= \mathbf{\$45}$

(b) $I = \dfrac{3.5}{100} \times \$500.50 \times 4$

   $= \mathbf{\$70.07}$

(c) $I = \dfrac{2.5}{100} \times \$1{,}000 \times 3$

   $= \mathbf{\$75}$

(d) $I = \dfrac{3}{100} \times \$750 \times 2.5$

   $= \mathbf{\$56.25}$

(e) $I = \dfrac{5}{100} \times \$500 \times 4$

   $= \mathbf{\$100}$

(f) $I = \dfrac{3.5}{100} \times \$525 \times 4$

   $= \mathbf{\$73.50}$

2.
$$\$35 = \frac{4}{100} \times \$500 \times T$$
$$\$35 = \$20T$$
$$T = \frac{35}{20}$$
$$T = 1.75 \text{ years}$$
The period is **1 year 9 months**.

3.
$$\$43.75 = \frac{R}{100} \times \$250 \times 5$$
$$\$43.75 = \$\frac{25}{2} R$$
$$R = \frac{(43.75)(2)}{25}$$
$$R = 3.5$$
The rate is **3.5%** p.a.

4.
$$I = \$385 - \$350 = \$35$$
$$\$35 = \frac{2.5}{100} \times \$350 \times T$$
$$\$35 = \$\frac{35}{4} T$$
$$T = 4$$
The duration is **4 years**.

5.
$$\$100 = \frac{3.5}{100} \times P \times 4$$
$$\$100 = \frac{7}{50} P$$
$$P = \frac{\$5,000}{7}$$
$$P = \$714.29$$
The principal is **$714.29**.

6.
$$\text{Interest} = \text{Total} - \text{Principal}$$
$$= \$729 - P$$
$$\$729 - P = \frac{2}{100} \times P \times 4$$
$$\$729 - P = \frac{2}{25} P$$
$$\$18,225 - 25P = 2P$$
$$\$18,225 = 27P$$
$$P = \$675$$
The principal is **$675**.

7.
$$I = \frac{2.5}{100} \times \$840 \times 1$$
$$= \$21 \text{ per year}$$
$$\text{Interest per quarter} = \frac{21}{4}$$
$$= \mathbf{\$5.25}$$

8.
$$I = \$750 - \$500 = \$250$$
$$\$250 = \frac{R}{100} \times \$500 \times 4$$
$$250 = 20R$$
$$R = \frac{250}{20}$$
$$R = 12.5$$
The rate is **12.5%** p.a.

9.
$$9 = \frac{3}{100} \times P \times 1$$
$$P = \frac{\$900}{3}$$
$$P = \$300$$
The principal is **$300**.

10. Difference in interest = $67.50 - $63
     0.5% of P = $4.50
       1% of P = $4.50 x 2
             = $9.00
     100% of P = $900
     He loaned $900.

     $67.5 = \dfrac{R}{100} \times 900$

          $R = 7.5$
     The new interest rate is **7.5%** p.a.

11. $I = \dfrac{5.5}{100} \times 5{,}000 \times 1$

        $= 275
     Wife's interest is $275.
     Husband's interest = $1,000 - $275
                       = 725

     $\$725 = \dfrac{8}{100} \times P \times 1$

     $\$725 = \dfrac{2}{25} P$

          $P = \$9{,}062.50$

12. Increase in rate = 7% - 6.5%
                   = 0.5%
     0.5% of P = $330
       1% of P = $330 x 2
             = $660
     100% of P = $66,000
     The loan was **$66,000**.

13. $\$252 = \dfrac{R}{100} \times \$3{,}200 \times 1\dfrac{1}{2}$

     $\$252 = \$48R$
         $R = 5.25$
     The rate is 5.25% p.a.

     4 months = $\dfrac{1}{3}$ yr

     $I = \dfrac{5.25}{100} \times \$12{,}000 \times \dfrac{1}{3}$

        $= 210
     The interest is **$210**.

14. The difference in amount between year 1 and year 3 is the interest for 2 years.
     2 year interest = $34,720 - $30,240 = $4,480

     1 year interest = $\$\dfrac{4{,}480}{2}$ = $2,240$

     The amount after 2 years is the amount after one year + a year's interest.
     So a = $30,240 + $2,240 = $32,480
     The amount after 4 years is the amount after 3 years + a year's interest.
     So b = $34,720 + $2,240 = $36,960
     Amount for 1 year - interest for 1 year = principal
     So x = $30,240 - $2,240 = $28,000

     $\$2{,}240 = \dfrac{R}{100} \times \$28{,}000$

     $\$2{,}240 = \$280R$
          $R = 8$
     a = $32,480, b = $36,960, x = $28,000, r = 8%

15. P for year 1 = $4,500

I for year 1 = $\dfrac{10}{100}$ x $4,500

= $450

P for year 2 = $4,500 + $450

= $4,950

I for year 2 = $\dfrac{10}{100}$ x $4,950

= $495

I for both years = $450 + $495

= $945

Compound interest is **$945**.

16. P for year 1 = $2,500

I for year 1 = $\dfrac{12}{100}$ x $2,500

= $300

P for year 2 = $2,500 + $300

= $2,800

I for year 2 = $\dfrac{12}{100}$ x $2,800

= $336

P for year 3 = $2,800 + $336

= $3,136

I for year 3 = $\dfrac{12}{100}$ x $3,136

= $376.32

I for 3 years = $300 + $336 + $376

= $1,012

Compound interest is **$1,012**.

17. P for year 1 = $3,000

I for year 1 = $\dfrac{8}{100}$ x $3,000

= $240

P for year 2 = $3,000 + $240

= $3,240

I for year 2 = $\dfrac{8}{100}$ x $3,240

= $259.20

P for year 3 = $3,240 + $259.20

= $3,499.20

I for year 3 = $\dfrac{8}{100}$ x $3,499.20

= $279.94

I for 3 years = $240 + $259 + $280

= $779

Amount to be repaid is the principal plus the compound interest.

Amount = $3,000 + $779

= $3,779

He must repay **$3,779**.

18.(a)(i)   hire purchase price = $10 + 12($12.50) = $160

difference = $160 - $120 = **$40**

(ii)   percent difference = $\dfrac{40}{120}$ x 100% = $\mathbf{33\dfrac{1}{3}}$%

(b)(i)   hire purchase price = $600 + 24($90) = $2,760

difference = $2,760 - $2,400 = **$360**

(ii)   percent difference = $\dfrac{360}{2,400}$ x 100% = **15%**

(c)(i)   hire purchase price = $200 + 24($55) = $1,520

difference = $1,520 - $1,200 = **$320**

(ii)   percent difference = $\dfrac{320}{1,200}$ x 100% = $\mathbf{26\dfrac{2}{3}}$%

(d)(i) hire purchase price = $200 + 24($140) = $3,560
        difference = $3,560 - $3,200 = **$360**

(ii)   percent difference = $\frac{360}{3,200}$ x 100% = **11.25%**

(e)(i) hire purchase price = $625 + 12($190) = $2905
        difference = $2,905 - $2,600 = **$305**

(ii)   percent difference = $\frac{305}{2,950}$ x 100% = **11.73%**

19.(a) Let x be the installment.
        $27,000 = $9,000 + 12$x$
        12x = $18,000
        x = $1,500
        His installments are **$1,500**.

(b)   100$ - 10.5% = 89.5%
        89.5% of $27,000 = $\frac{895}{100}$ x $27,000
                         = $24,165
        He would pay **$24,165**.

20.(a) Interest = 6.5% of $336
                  = $\frac{65}{100}$ x $336
                  = $21.84
        Amount = Principal + Interest
                = $336 + $21.84
                = 357.84
        Paid already = 12($13.75)
                     = $165
        Owed = $357.84 - $165
             = **$192.84**

(b)   Interest yr. 2 = 6.5% of $193.84
                       = $\frac{65}{100}$ x $192.84
                       = $12.53
        Amount yr. 2 = $192.84 + $12.53
                     = $205.37
        He still owes **$205.37**.

21.   difference = hire purchase price - cash price
                   = [deposit + (months x installment)] - cash price
        Shop A:
        deposit = 15% of $2,256 = $\frac{15}{100}$ x $2,256 = $338.40
        difference = [$338.40 + 12($183.77)] - $2,256 = $2,543.64 - $2,256 = $287.64
        Shop B:
        deposit = 10% of $2,256 = $\frac{1}{10}$ x $2,256 = $225.60
        difference = [$225.60 + 18($135.36)] - $2,256 = $2,662.08 - $2,256 = $406.08
        Shop **A** has a better deal

22.(a) Usual price - discount = selling price
        Let x be the usual price.
        x - 15% of x = 276.25
        $x - \frac{15}{100}x = 276.25$
        $\frac{85}{100}x = 276.25$
        $x = 325$
        The usual price was **$325**.

(b)   Let y be the monthly installment.
        10% of $325 + 10$y$ = $325
        (0.10 x $325) + 10$y$ = $325
        $32.5 + 10$y$ = $325
        10y = $292.5
        y = $29.25
        The monthly installments are **$29.25**.

Exercise 8.3 (pp. 224-226)

1. Tax = 0.05($4,500 - $750)
    = 0.05($3,750)
    = **$187.50**

2. Taxable income = $5,000 - $700
    = $4,300
    Amount taxed at 8%
    = $4,300 - $875
    = $3,425
    Tax = 6% of $875 + 8% of $3,425
    $$= (\frac{6}{100} \times \$875) + (\frac{8}{100} \times \$3,425)$$
    = $52.50 + $274
    = **$326.50**

3. total cost = $1,680 + $920 + $80
    = $2,680
    tax = 3% of $2,680
    $$= \frac{3}{100} \times \$2,680$$
    = $80.40
    total = $2,680 + $80.40
    = **$2,760.40**

4. To make a profit of 45.5% he must sell at 145.5% of cost.
    sale price = 145.5% of $1,800
    $$= \frac{145.5}{100} \times \$1,800$$
    = $2,619
    If the tax is 3%, the final price will be 103% of sale price.
    final price = 103% of $2,619
    $$= \frac{103}{100} \times \$2,619$$
    = **$2,697.57**

5. amount taxed at 12% = $22,888 - $20,000 = $2,888
    tax = 12% of $2,888 + $1,375
    $$= \frac{12}{100} \times \$2,888 + \$1,375$$
    = $346.56 + $1,375
    = $1,721.56
    Amount left = income - tax = $22,888 - $1,721.56 = **$21,166.44**

6. (a) chargeable income = $16,800 + $288 - $2,168 = **$14,920**

   (b) tax = 5.25% of $10,000 + 8% of ($14,920 - $10,000)
        $$= \frac{5.25}{100}(\$10,000) + \frac{8}{100}(\$4,920)$$
        = $525 + $393.6
        = **$918.60**

7. (a) $$\$1 = \frac{100\,p}{\$2.15} \times \$1$$
        = **47** p

   (b) $$45\,p = \frac{\$2.15}{100\,p} \times 45\,p$$
        = **$0.97**

   (c) $$72\,p = \frac{215¢}{100\,p} \times 72\,p$$
        = **155**¢

   (d) $$265¢ = \frac{£1}{215¢} \times 265¢$$
        = **£1.23**

(e) $£2.96 = \dfrac{215\ ¢}{£1} \times £2.96$

$\qquad = \mathbf{636}¢$

(f) $\$5.35 = \dfrac{100\ p}{\$2.15} \times \$5.35$

$\qquad = \mathbf{249}\ p$

(g) $\$12.60 = \dfrac{£1}{\$2.15} \times \$12.60$

$\qquad = \$\mathbf{5.86}$

(h) $£17.25 = \dfrac{\$2.15}{£1} \times £17.25$

$\qquad = \$\mathbf{37.09}$

(i) $£25 \text{ and } 45\ p = \dfrac{\$2.15}{£1} \times £25.45$

$\qquad = \$54.72$

$\qquad = \$\mathbf{54} \text{ and } \mathbf{72}¢$

(j) $\$38 \text{ and } 72¢ = \dfrac{£1}{\$2.15} \times \$38.72$

$\qquad = £18.01$

$\qquad = £\mathbf{18} \text{ and } \mathbf{1}\ p$

8. (a) US$1 = S$1.40
US$2 = S$1.40 × 2
$\qquad$ = S$**2.80**

(b) £1 = S$2.15
£9 = S$2.15 × 9
$\qquad$ = S$**19.35**

(c) A$1 = S$1.10
A$7 = S$1.10 × 7
$\qquad$ = S$**7.70**

(d) US$1 $\quad$ = S$1.40
US$9.40 = S$1.40 × 9.40
$\qquad$ = S$**13.16**

(e) £1.00 $\quad$ = S$2.15
£12.30 = S$2.15 × 12.30
$\qquad$ = S$**26.45**

(f) S$1.40 = US$1

$\quad$ S$1.00 = US$$\dfrac{1}{1.40}$

$\qquad$ = US$**0.71**

(g) S$2.15 = £1.00

$\quad$ S$1.00 = £$\dfrac{1.00}{2.15}$

$\qquad$ = £**0.47**

(h) S$1.10 = A$1

$\quad$ S$1.00 = A$$\dfrac{1}{1.10}$

$\qquad$ = A$**0.91**

(i) S$1.40 = US$1

$\quad$ S$1.00 = US$$\dfrac{1}{1.40}$

$\quad$ S$2.50 = US$$\dfrac{1}{1.40}$ × 2.50

$\qquad$ = US$**1.79**

(j) S$2.15 = £1.00

$\quad$ S$1.00 = £$\dfrac{1}{2.15}$

$\quad$ S$6.30 = £$\dfrac{1}{2.15}$ × 6.30

$\qquad$ = £**2.93**

(k) S$1.10 $\quad$ = A$1

$\quad$ S$1.00 $\quad$ = A$$\dfrac{1}{1.10}$

$\quad$ S$15.40 = A$$\dfrac{1}{1.10}$ × 15.40

$\qquad$ = A$**14**

(l) 100 Francs = S$27
$\quad$ 1 Franc $\;$ = S$0.27
450 Francs = S$0.27 × 450
$\qquad$ = S$**121.50**

(m) S$27 = 100 Francs

$\quad$ S$1 $\quad$ = $\dfrac{100}{27}$ Francs

$\quad$ S$95 = $\dfrac{100}{27}$ × 95 Francs

$\qquad$ = **351.85** Francs

(n) HK$100 = S$18
HK$1 $\quad$ = S$0.18
HK$745 = S$0.18 × 745
$\qquad$ = S$**134.10**

(o)   S\$18   = HK\$100

S\$1   = HK\$$\dfrac{100}{18}$

S\$108 = HK\$$\dfrac{100}{18}$ x 108

= HK\$**600**

9.   100 baht = S\$5.50
1 baht = S\$0.0550
5,000 baht = S\$0.0550 x 5,000
= S\$**275**

10.   HK\$1.60   = 1 franc

HK\$1   = $\dfrac{1}{160}$ franc

HK\$200,000 = $\dfrac{1}{160}$ x 200,000 francs

= **125,000 francs**

11.   from bank:
S\$2.20 = £1

S\$1   = £$\dfrac{1}{2.20}$

S\$2,500 = £$\dfrac{1}{2.20}$ x 2,500

= **£\$1,136.36**
from the money changer:
S\$2.10 = £1

S\$1   = £$\dfrac{1}{2.10}$

S\$2,500 = £$\dfrac{1}{2.10}$ x 2,500

= £\$1,190.48
£1,190.48 - £1,136.36 = £54.12
He would get **£54.12** more.

12.   75% of 100,000 = 0.75 x 100,000
= 75,000
He is buying dollars with rupiahs.
1,000 rupiahs = \$0.20

1 rupiah   = \$$\dfrac{0.20}{1,000}$

75,000 rupiahs = \$$\dfrac{0.20}{1,000}$ x 75,000

= **\$15**

13.(a) HK\$100 = \$18.35
HK\$1   = \$0.1835
\$23.65 = 100 kroner

\$1   = $\dfrac{100}{23.65}$ kroner

\$0.1835 = $\dfrac{100}{23.65}$ x 0.1835 kroner

= 0.78 kroner
So HK\$1 = **0.78 kroner**

(b)   100 francs = \$28.10
10 francs = \$2.810
\$57.60 = 100 ringgit

\$1   = $\dfrac{100}{57.60}$ ringgit

\$2.810 = $\dfrac{100}{57.60}$ x 2.810 ringgit

= 4.88
So 10 francs = **4.88 ringgit**

(c)   100 Deutschemarks = $95.90
       10 Deutschemarks = $9.59
      $1.45 = 100 yen

$1 $\quad = \dfrac{100}{1.45}$ yen

$9.59 \quad = \dfrac{100}{1.45}$ x 9.59 yen

$\quad\quad\quad = 661.38$ yen

So 10 Deutschemarks = **661.38 yen**.

(d)   100 rupees = $4.60
        1 rupee = $0.046
      270 rupees = $0.046 x 270
                 = **$12.42**

14. $\quad \dfrac{C\$1}{S\$1.06}$ x S$1,000 = C$943.40

$\dfrac{US\$1}{s\$1.47}$ x S$1,500 = US$1,020.41

He has C$943.40 and US$1,020.41 which he must change back.
(943.40 C$ x 1.02 S$/C$) + (1,020.41 US$ x 1.42 S$/US$) = S$2,411.25
He started with $2,500 and ended with $2,411.25.
He lost $2,500 - $2,411.25 = **$88.75**.

Chapter 9

Exercise 9.1

1. Acute angles are less than 90º.
    Obtuse angles are between 90º and 180º.
    Reflex angles are between 180º and 360º.

    (a)   60º is acute.

    (b)   115º is obtuse.

    (c)   21º is acute.

    (d)   150º is obtuse.

    (e)   195º is reflex.

    (f)   5º is acute.

    (g)   56º is acute.

    (h)   160° is obtuse.

    (i)   254º is reflex.

2. To find the supplement of an angle, subtract it from 180º.

    (a)   180º - 10º = **170º**

    (b)   180º - 117º = **63º**

    (c)   180º - 82º = **98º**

    (d)   180º - 90º = **90º**

    (e)   180º - 165º = **15º**

    (f)   180º - 22º = **158º**

    (g)   180º - 68º = **112º**

    (h)   180º - 131º = **49º**

    (i) $180º - 92\frac{1}{2}º = \mathbf{87\frac{1}{2}}$ **º**

3. To find the complement of an angle, subtract it from 90º.

    (a)   90º - 37º = **53º**

    (b)   90º - 48º = **42º**

    (c)   90º - 45º = **45º**

    (d)   90º - 9º = **81º**

    (e)   90º - 90º = **0º**

    (f)   90º - 22º = **68º**

    (g)   90º - 39º = **51º**

    (h)   90º - 87º = **3º**

    (i) $90º - 22\frac{1}{2}º = \mathbf{67\frac{1}{2}}$ **º**

4. $\angle PQX = 81º$, $\angle QXT = 88º$, $\angle CRQ = 99º$, $\angle UYD = 88º$

    (a) $\angle QXT = \angle UYD$

    (b) $\angle PQX$ is supplementary to $\angle CRQ$

5.   A compass can be used to construct a bisector by first
        placing the point of the compass on the vertex, marking the
        arcs of equal radii along the arms, then placing the point of
        the compass on each of the points where the arcs intersect
        the arms and drawing two arcs of equal radii from those
        points at a spot between the arms. The bisector is the line
        from the vertex to the intersection of those arcs

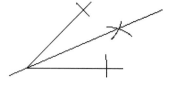

6.

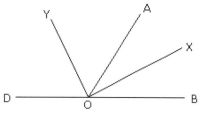

$\angle AOB = 60º$
$\angle XOB = 30º$
$\angle AOX = 30º$
$\angle DOA = 120º$
$\angle DOX = 150º$
$\angle DOY = 60º$
$\angle YOA = 60º$
$\angle YOX = 90º$
$\angle YOB = 120º$

    (e)   Complementary angles: $\angle AOB$ and $\angle XOB$, $\angle AOB$ and $\angle AOX$, $\angle XOB$ and $\angle DOY$, $\angle XOB$
          and $\angle YOA$, $\angle AOX$ and $\angle DOY$, $\angle AOX$ and $\angle YOA$

    (f)   Supplementary angles: $\angle DOA$ and $\angle AOB$, $\angle DOX$ and $\angle XOB$, $\angle DOY$ and $\angle YOB$

Exercise 9.2 (pp. 240-242)

The point O is the point where all the lines intersect.

1. (a) $x = 95^o$ vert. opp. $\angle$s
           $180^o = 20^o + y + x + 45^o$ adj. $\angle$s on a straight line
           $180^o = 20^o + y + 95^o + 45^o$
           $180^o = 160^o + y$
           $y = 20^o$

   (b) $180^o = \angle AOC + 90^o + 35^o$ adj. $\angle$s on a straight line
           $180^o = x + 90^o + 35^o$ vert. opp. $\angle$s
           $x = 55^o$
           $180^o = 90^o + y + x$ adj. $\angle$s on a straight line
           $180^o = 90^o + y + 55^o$
           $y = 35^o$

   (c) $90^o = x + 30^o$ complementary $\angle$s
           $x = 60^o$
           $90^o = \angle COA + y$ complementary $\angle$s
           $90^o = x + y$ vert. opp. $\angle$s
           $90^o = 60^o + y$
           $y = 30^o$

   (d) $90^o = x + 30^o$ complementary $\angle$s
           $x = 60^o$
           $180^o = 75^o + 90^o + y$ adj. $\angle$s on a straight line
           $y = 15^o$

2. (a) $180^o = 2x + 90^o + x$ adj. $\angle$s on a straight line
           $90^o = 3x$
           $x = 30^o$

   (b) $180^o = 105^o + 2x$ adj. $\angle$s on a straight line
           $75^o = 2x$
           $x = 37.5^o$

   (c) $180^o = 4x + 90^o + x$ adj. $\angle$s on a straight line
           $90^o = 5x$
           $x = 18^o$

   (d) $180^o = 3x + 2x + x + 60^o$ adj. $\angle$s on a straight line
           $120^o = 6x$
           $x = 20^o$

   (e) $75^o = 3x + 15^o$ vert. opp. $\angle$s
           $3x = 60^o$
           $x = 20^o$

   (f) $3x + 2x = 90^o + 20^o$ vert. opp. $\angle$s
           $5x = 110^o$
           $x = 22^o$

   (g) $180^o = 90^o + x + 30^o + 2x$ adj. $\angle$s on a straight line
           $60^o = 3x$
           $x = 20^o$

(h) $360° = 5x + 36° + x + 90°$ ∠s at a point
        $324° = 6x$
            $x = \textbf{39°}$

(i) $360° = 2x + 90° + 3x + 220°$ ∠s at a point
        $50° = 5x$
            $x = \textbf{10°}$

(j) $5x + 4x° = 27° + 90°$ vert. opp. ∠s
                $9x = 117°$
                $x = \textbf{13°}$

(k) $167° = 3x + 4x + 90°$ vert. opp. ∠s
        $77° = 7x$
            $x = \textbf{11°}$

(l) $180° = 3x° + 63° + x° + (90° - x°)$ adj. ∠s on a straight line
        $27° = 3x$
            $x = \textbf{9°}$

Exercise 9.3 (pp. 244-245)

1 - 2.   Another way to draw a perpendicular
           bisector using only a compass is to draw the
           arcs of two overlapping circles of equal radii
           and centers at the two points. A line drawn
           through the intersection of these arcs is the
           perpendicular bisector.

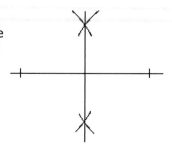

The following figures are drawn with an approximate scale of ⊢⊣ = 1 cm. Angles are not exact.

3.

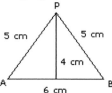

$\textbf{AP = BP = 5 cm}$

4.

5.

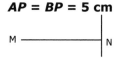

6.

7. (a)

AC = 5 cm

(b)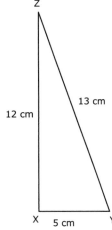

YZ = 13 cm

8. (a)

(b)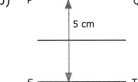

(c)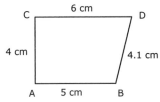

Yes, *CD* is parallel to *AB*.

9.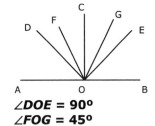

∠*DOE* = 90°
∠*FOG* = 45°

Exercise 9.4 (pp. 248-252)

1. (a)   ∠*BQC* (corr. ∠s)
∠*NQT* (alt. ∠s)
∠*SBQ* (vert. opp. ∠s)

(b)   ∠*CQT* (vert. opp. ∠s)
∠*QBR* (alt. ∠s)
∠*HBS* (corr. ∠s)

Figures are not drawn to scale.

2.
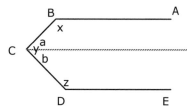

$b = 180 - z$ corr. ∠s
$y = a + b$ alt. ∠s
  $= (180 - x) + (180 - z)$
  $= 360 - x - z$
$x + y + z = x + (360 - x - z) + z$
       $= \mathbf{360^o}$

A line through *C* parallel to *BA* splits
angle *y* into two angles, called here a
and b.
$a = 180 - x$

3.
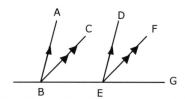

∠ABE = ∠DEG   corr. ∠s
∠CBE = ∠FEG   corr. ∠s
∴ ∠ABE - ∠CBE = ∠DEG - ∠FEG
∠ABC = ∠DEF

4.   ∠QAC = ∠ACS   alt. ∠s

$\angle BAC = \frac{1}{2}\angle QAC$

$\angle ACD = \frac{1}{2}\angle ACS$

∴∠BAC = ∠ACD   *AB* and *CD* are cut by the transversal *MN* such that alternate
∴AB // CD   angles *BAC* and *ACD* are equal.

5. (a)   ∠ABC = ∠DCE   corr. ∠s
   (b)   ∠ADC = ∠DCE   alt. ∠s
   (c)   ∠ABC = ∠ADC   both are equal to ∠DCE
   (c)   ∠BAD = ∠BCD   by similar reasoning

6.
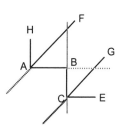

∠HAF = ∠BCG   corr. ∠s
∠FAB = ∠GCE   corr. ∠s

7.   FG // BC   corr. ∠s *a* and *b*
      FB // CD   alt. ∠s *b* and *c*
      BC // DE   alt. ∠s *c* and *d*
      FG // DE   corr. ∠s *a* and *d*

8. (a)

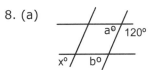

$a = 180 - 120 = 60$ adj. ∠s on a straight line
$b = a = 60$ corr. ∠s
$x = b = \mathbf{60}$ corr. ∠s

(b)

$a = 25$ alt. ∠s
$b = 20$ alt. ∠s
$x = a + b$
$x = 25 + 20$
$x = \mathbf{45}$

(c)

$a = 180 - 105 = 75$ int. ∠s
$b = 180 - 115 = 65$ int. ∠s
$x = 75 + 65$
$x = \mathbf{140}$

(d)

$a = 35$ corr. ∠s
$b = 65$ corr. ∠s
$x = a + b$
$x = 35 + 65$
$x = \mathbf{100}$

(e)

$a = 180 - 130 = 50$ int. ∠s
$b = 60$ alt. ∠s
$x = a + b$
$x = 50 + 60$
$x = \mathbf{110}$

(f)

$a = 25$ corr. ∠s
$b = x$ alt. ∠s
$a + b = 40$
$25 + x = 40$
$x = \mathbf{15}$

(g)

$a = x$ alt. ∠s
$b = 40$ alt. ∠s
$a + b = 40$
$x + 40 = 106$
$x = \mathbf{66}$

(h)

$a = 180 - x$ int. ∠s
$b = 180 - 106 = 74$ int. ∠s
$a + b = 150$ vert. opp. ∠s
$180 - x + 74 = 150$
$x = 180 + 74 - 150$
$x = \mathbf{104}$

(i)

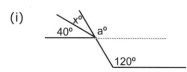

$a = 120$ corr. ∠s
$x + 40 + 120 = 180$ adj. ∠s on a st. line
$x = \mathbf{20}$

(j)

$a = 80$ corr. ∠s
$b = a = 80$ alt. ∠s
$x = b$ corr. ∠s
$x = \mathbf{80}$

9. (a)

$a = 180 - 2x$ adj. ∠s on a st. line
$a = 3x$ alt. ∠s
$3x = 180 - 2x$
$5x = 180$
$x = \mathbf{36}$

(b)

$a = x$ corr. ∠s
$a = 180 - 4x$ int. ∠s
$x = 180 - 4x$
$5x = 180$
$x = \mathbf{36}$

(c)

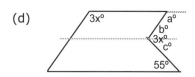

∠s marked a are equal   vert. opp. ∠s
$b = 150$ corr. ∠s
$a + 2x = b$ alt. ∠s
$a + 2x = 150$
$a = 150 - 2x$
$a = 90 - x$ complementary ∠s
$90 - x = 150 - 2x$
$x = \mathbf{60}$

(d)

$a = 3x$ corr. ∠s
$b = 180 - 3x$ int. ∠s
$c = 55$ alt. ∠s
$3x = b + c$
$3x = 180 - 3x + 55$
$6x = 235$
$x = \mathbf{39\dfrac{1}{6}}$

10.(a)

$z = 360 - 260 = 100$ ∠s at a point
$w = z = 100$ corr. ∠s
$x = 360 - 240 = 120$ ∠s at a point
$y = x = 120$ corr. ∠s
$a = y - w$ vert. opp. ∠s
$a = 120 - 100$
$a = \mathbf{20°}$

(b)

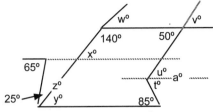

line forming ∠s *x*, *u*, and *t* are parallel to bottom line.

z = 65	alt. ∠s
y = 65 - 25 = 40	
x = 40	corr. ∠s
w = 180 - 140 = 40	adj. ∠s on a st. line
∴ the top line is // to	Two lines are // if corr. ∠s
the other horizontal	of a transverse are =
lines	vert. opp. ∠s
v = 50	corr. ∠s
u = 50	alt. ∠s
t = 85	
a = *u* + *t*	
a = 50 + 85	
a = **135°**	

(c)

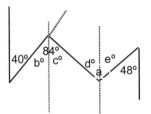

b = 40	alt. ∠s
c = 84 - 40 = 44	
d = 44	alt. ∠s
e = 48	alt. ∠s
a = d + e	
a = 44 + 48	
a = **92°**	

(d)

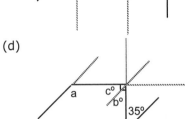

b = 35	alt. ∠s
c = 90 - 25 = 55	
a = 180 - 55	int. ∠s
a = **125°**	

11.(a) *DX // YQ*   alt. ∠s are equal: 20 + 5 = 15 + 10
        BX // YR   alt. ∠s are equal: 20 + 5 + 10 + 10 = 15 + 10 + 20

   (b) *CD // EF*   alt. ∠s are equal: 180 - 91 = 89
        AB // GH   corr. ∠s are equal: 180 - 91 = 89
        JK // PQ   Since *AB // GH* the upper left angle formed at the intersection of *PQ*
                      and *GH* is 91°, (corr. ∆s with the intersection of *AB* and *PQ*); this is
                      equal to the corr. ∆formed by the line GH transversing *JK* and *PQ*.

Chapter 10

Exercise 10.1 (pp. 261-262)

⊢⊣
1 cm
Angles may not be exact; figures are for illustration purposes only.

1.   Place the compass point on *B* in the text, and set the compass radium to the same
      length as *BC*. Draw and arc with the same radius on another paper. Label and
      draw line *BC* from the center to the arc. Measure the length of *BA* in the text using
      the compass, then draw an arc of the same radius with *B* as center. Do the same
      for *CA*. Draw lines from *B* and *C* to the point where the arcs intersect.

2.   It is an isosceles triangle, and the two angles are 45º.

3.   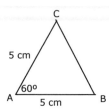   ∠C = 60º
                              ∠B = 60º
                              CB = 5 cm
                              Δ *ABC* is an equilateral triangle - all angles and sides are equal.

4. (a)   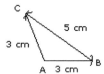   ∠A = 112º   (b)   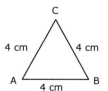   AC = 2.8 cm
                                 ∠B = 34º   BC = 2.8 cm
                                 ∠C = 34º   ∠C = 90º
                                 isosceles   isosceles
                                 obtuse   right

   (c)   ∠A = 46º   (d)   ∠A = 60º
                                 ∠B = 105º   ∠B = 60º
                                 ∠C = 29º   ∠C = 60º
                                 scalene   equilateral
                                 obtuse   acute

   (e)   ∠C = 60º   (f)   ∠A = 54º
                                 AC = 5.7 cm   ∠B = 90º
                                 BC = 3.7 cm   ∠C = 36º
                                 scalene   scalene
                                 acute   right

(g)   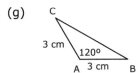 BC = 5.2 cm
                                  $\angle B$ = 30º
                                  $\angle C$ = 30º
                                  isosceles
                                  obtuse

5.-8.   The sum of the angles will be 180º.

9.   The other two angles of a right triangle are complementary.

10.   A generalized drawing is given here. In all
        cases, $\angle ACX = \angle A + \angle B$
   (a) $\angle ACX$ = 70º
   (b) $\angle A$ = 75º, $\angle B$ = 75º, $\angle ACX$ = 150º
   (c) $\angle A$ = 87º, $\angle ACX$ = 157º
   (d) $\angle ACX$ = 120º

Exercise 10.2 (pp. 263-266)

1. (a) $\angle c$ and $\angle a$ are interior opposite angles of $\angle y$.
         $\angle a$ and $\angle b$ are interior opposite angles of $\angle z$.

   (b) $\angle e$ and $\angle d$ are interior opposite angles of $\angle q$.
         $\angle f$ and $\angle d$ are interior opposite angles of $\angle r$.

2. (a)   **True**. The other two angles = 180º - 90º = 90º.

   (b)   **False**. Two right angles = 180º; there could be no third angle.

   (c)   **True**. The exterior angle = 180 minus an angle less than 90º (adj. $\angle$s on a st. line)
         would have to be greater than 90º.

3. (a) $124 = x + 62$ ext. $\angle$of a Δ (b) $180 = x + 35 + 105$ $\angle$sum of a Δ
              $x = \mathbf{62}$ $x = \mathbf{40}$

   (c) $x = 30 + 36$ ext. $\angle$of a Δ (d) $x + 58 = 32 + 90$ ext. $\angle$of a Δ
         $x = \mathbf{66}$ $x = \mathbf{64}$

   (e) $135 = x + 90$ ext. $\angle$of a Δ (f) $x = 60 + 60$ ext. $\angle$of a Δ
             $x = \mathbf{45}$ $x = \mathbf{120}$

   (g)   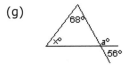 $a = 180 - 56$ adj. $\angle$s on a st. line
                                        $= 124$
                                 $124 = x + 68$ ext. $\angle$of a Δ
                                      $x = \mathbf{56}$

(h)

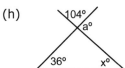

$a = 180 - 104$ adj. ∠s on a st. line
    $= 76$
$76 = x + 36$ ext. ∠of a Δ
     $x = \mathbf{40}$

(i)

$a = 180 - 92$ adj. ∠s on a st. line
    $= 88$
$125 = x + a$ ext. ∠of a Δ
$125 = x + 88$
     $x = \mathbf{37}$

(j)

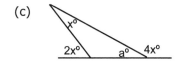

$a = 180 - 60 - 90$ adj. ∠s on a st. line
    $= 30$
$60 = x + a$ ext. ∠of a Δ
$60 = x + 30$
     $x = \mathbf{30}$

4. (a) $x + 2x = 180 - 3x$ ext. ∠of a Δ   (b) $3x = 58 + x$ ext. ∠of a Δ
        $6x = 180$ $2x = 58$
         $x = \mathbf{30}$ $x = \mathbf{29}$

(c)

$a = 180 - 4x$ adj. ∠s on a st. line
$2x = a + x$ ext. ∠of a Δ
$2x = 180 - 4x + x$
$5x = 180$
    $x = \mathbf{36}$

(d)

$a = 180 - (78 + x)$ int. ∠s
    $= 102 - x$ ext. ∠of a Δ
$a = x + 2x$
$x + 2x = 102 - x$
     $4x = 102$

        $x = \mathbf{25\frac{1}{2}}$

(e)

$a = x$ alt. ∠s
$180 = 2x + x + a$ ∠sum of Δ
$180 = 2x + x + x$
$180 = 4x$
    $x = \mathbf{45}$

(f)

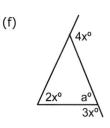

$a = 180 - 3x$ adj. ∠s on a st. line
$4x = 2x + a$ ext. ∠of a Δ
$4x = 2x + (180 - 3x)$
$5x = 180$
    $x = \mathbf{36}$

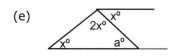

(g)

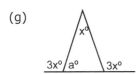

$a = 180 - 3x$ adj. ∠s on a st. line
$3x = a + x$ ext. ∠of a Δ
$3x = 180 - 3x + x$
$5x = 180$
$x = \mathbf{36}$

(h)

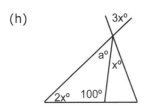

$3x = a + x$ vert. opp. ∠s
$a = 2x$
$180 = 100 + 2x + a$ ∠sum of Δ
$180 = 100 + 2x + 2x$
$80 = 4x$
$x = \mathbf{20}$

(i)

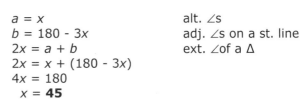

$a = x$ alt. ∠s
$b = 180 - 3x$ adj. ∠s on a st. line
$2x = a + b$ ext. ∠of a Δ
$2x = x + (180 - 3x)$
$4x = 180$
$x = \mathbf{45}$

(j)

$a = x$ alt. ∠s
$180 = x + a + 42$ ∠sum of Δ
$180 = x + x + 42$
$138 = 2x$
$x = \mathbf{69}$

(k)

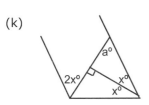

$a = 2x$ alt. ∠s
$90 = a + x$ ext. ∠of a Δ
$90 = 2x + x$
$90 = 3x$
$x = \mathbf{30}$

(l)

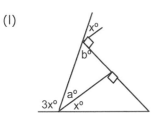

$a = 180 - 3x - x$ adj. ∠s on a st. line
$\;\;\; = 180 - 4x$
$b = 180 - 90 - x$ adj. ∠s on a st. line
$\;\;\; = 90 - x$
$90 = a + b$
$90 = 180 - 4x + 90 - x$
$5x = 180$
$x = \mathbf{36}$

(m)

$180 = (20 + a) + (x + b) + 85$ ∠sum of Δ (large)
$\;\;\; = a + b + 105 + x$
$180 = a + b + 4x$ ∠sum of Δ (small)
$a + b + 4x = 105 + a + b + x$ subtract $a + b$ from both
$4x = 105 + x$ sides
$3x = 105$
$x = \mathbf{35}$

(n)

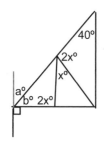

$a = 40$ alt. $\angle$s
$180 = 90 + a + b$ adj. $\angle$s on a st. line
$90 = a + b$
$b = 90 - a$
$b = 90 - 40$
$= 50$
$2x + x = b + 2x$ ext. $\angle$of a Δ
$2x + x = 50 + 2x$
$x = \mathbf{50}$

(o)

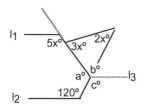

$a = 2x + 3x$ ext. $\angle$of a Δ
$= 5x$
$b = 5x$ alt. $\angle$s ($l_1 \parallel l_3$)
$c = 120$ alt. $\angle$s ($l_3 \parallel l_2$)
$360 = a + b + c$ $\angle$s at a point
$360 = 5x + 5x + 120$
$240 = 10x$
$x = \mathbf{24}$

(p)

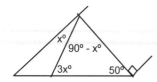

$180 = 3x + (90 - x) + 50$ $\angle$ sum of Δ
$40 = 2x$
$x = \mathbf{20}$

Exercise 10.3 (pp. 268-270)

1. (a) $x = \mathbf{62}$ iso. Δ (b) $2x = 90$ rt. iso. Δ
                                                           $x = \mathbf{45}$

   (c) $x = 60 + 60$ ext. $\angle$of a equi. Δ (d) $2x = 180 - 68$ $\angle$ sum of iso. Δ
          $x = \mathbf{120}$ $x = \mathbf{56}$

   (e) $x = 180 - 2(58)$ $\angle$sum of iso. Δ (f) $2x + 120 = 180$ $\angle$ sum of Δ, 3rd $\angle$ is
          $x = \mathbf{64}$ $x = \mathbf{30}$ ext. $\angle$of a equi. Δ

2. (a)

$3x = x + a$ ext. $\angle$ of a Δ
$a = 2x$
$180 = 2a + x$ $\angle$ sum of Δ
$180 = 2(2x) + x$
$180 = 5x$
$x = \mathbf{36}$

  (b)

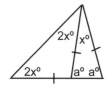

$a = 2x + 2x$ ext. $\angle$ of a Δ
$= 4x$
$180 = 2a + x$ $\angle$ sum of Δ
$180 = 2(4x) + x$
$180 = 9x$
$x = \mathbf{20}$

(c)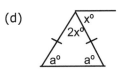

$a = x$	alt. ∠s
$180 = 3x + a$	adj. ∠s on a st. line
$180 = 3x + x$	
$180 = 4x$	
$x = \mathbf{45}$	

(d)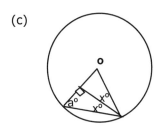

$a = x$	alt. ∠ s
$180 = 2a + 2x$	∠ sum of Δ
$180 = 2x + 2x$	
$180 = 4x$	
$x = \mathbf{45}$	

3. (a) $180 = x + 2(2x)$ ∠ sum of iso. Δ   (b) $180 = 42 + 2x$ ∠ sum of iso. Δ
$180 = 5x$ $138 = 2x$
     $x = \mathbf{36}$ $x = \mathbf{69}$

(c)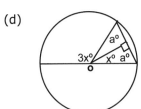

$a = 2x$	iso. Δ
$90 = a + x$	compl. ∠s of a rt. Δ
$90 = 2x + x$	
$90 = 3x$	
$x = \mathbf{30}$	

(d)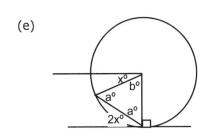

$a = 90 - x$	compl. ∠s of a rt. Δ
$3x = 2a$	ext. ∠of a Δ
$3x = 2(90 - x)$	
$3x = 180 - 2x$	
$5x = 180$	
$x = \mathbf{36}$	

(e)

$b + x = 90$	alt. ∠s
$b = 90 - x$	
$a + 2x = 90$	adj. ∠s on a st. line
$a = 90 - 2x$	
$180 = 2a + b$	∠ sum of Δ
$180 = 2(90 - 2x) + 90 - x$	
$180 = 180 - 4x + 90 - x$	
$5x = 90$	
$x = \mathbf{18}$	

(f)

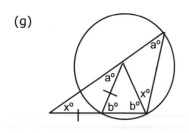

$a = 180 - 3x$ adj. ∠s on a st. line
$b = 180 - 130 = 50$ adj. ∠s on a st. line
$c = 180 - (a + b)$ ∠ sum of Δ
  $= 180 - (180 - 3x + 50)$
  $= 3x - 50$
$d = c$ corr. ∠s
  $= 3x - 50$
$180 = x + 2d$ ∠ sum of Δ
$180 = x + 2(3x - 50)$
$180 = x + 6x - 100$
$280 = 7x$
  $x = \mathbf{40}$

(g)

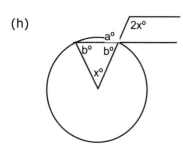

$a = x$ iso. Δ
$b = a + x$ ext. ∠ of a Δ
  $= 2x$
$180 = x + a + (x + b)$ ∠ sum of Δ (large Δ)
$180 = 2x + a + b$
$180 = 2x + x + 2x$
$180 = 5x$
  $x = \mathbf{36}$

(h)

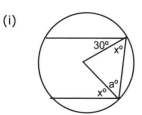

$a = 2x$ alt. ∠s
$b = 180 - a$ adj. ∠s on a st. line
  $= 180 - 2x$
$a = b + x$ ext. ∠ of a Δ
$2x = 180 - 2x + x$
$3x = 180$
  $x = \mathbf{60}$

(i)

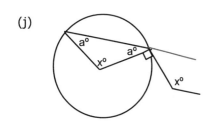

$a = x$ iso. Δ
$180 = (x + a) + (30 + x)$ int. ∠s
$180 = (x + x) + (30 + x)$
$180 = 3x + 30$
$150 = 3x$
  $x = \mathbf{50}$

(j)

$a + 90 = x$ alt. ∠s
$a = x - 90$
$180 = x + 2a$ ∠ sum of Δ
$180 = x + 2(x - 90)$
$180 = x + 2x - 180$
$360 = 3x$
  $x = \mathbf{120}$

(k)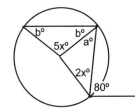

$a = 2x$ iso. Δ

$b + a = 80$ alt. $\angle$s

$b = 80 - a$

$\quad = 80 - 2x$

$180 = 5x + 2b$ $\angle$ sum of Δ

$180 = 5x + 2(80 - 2x)$

$180 = 5x + 160 - 4x$

$\quad x = \mathbf{20}$

(l)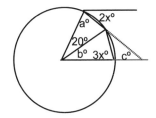

$180 = 2a + 20$ $\angle$ sum of Δ

$\quad 2a = 160$

$\quad\quad a = 80$

$b = 180 - 2(3x)$ $\angle$ sum of iso. Δ

$\quad = 180 - 6x$

$c = 2x$ alt. $\angle$s

$180 = a + (20 + b) + c$ $\angle$ sum of Δ

$160 = a + b + c$

$160 = 80 + 180 - 6x + 2x$

$\quad 4x = 100$

$\quad\quad x = \mathbf{25}$

Exercise 10.4 (pp. 274-276)

1. (a) $(20 - 2) \times 180^\circ$
        $= \mathbf{3,240^\circ}$

      (b) $(30 - 2) \times 180^\circ$
            $= \mathbf{5,040^\circ}$

      (c) $(50 - 2) \times 180^\circ$
            $= \mathbf{8,640^\circ}$

2. $2n - 4 = 20$

        $2n = 24$

         $n = 12$

     There are **12 sides**

3. (a) $\dfrac{360^\circ}{20} = \mathbf{18^\circ}$
               $\dfrac{360^\circ}{30} = \mathbf{12^\circ}$
               $\dfrac{\mathbf{360^\circ}}{\mathbf{n}}$

4. $\dfrac{(8 - 2) \times 180^\circ}{8} = \mathbf{135^\circ}$

5. (a) $\dfrac{180^\circ(n - 2)}{n} = 144^\circ$

      $180n - 360 = 144n$

         $36n = 360$

           $n = 10$

     There are **10** sides.

      (b) $\dfrac{180^\circ(n - 2)}{n} = 135^\circ$

          $180n - 360 = 135n$

             $45n = 360$

              $n = 8$

      There are **8** sides.

6.   Let a be the measure of the remaining angle. There are 4 angles.

      $85 + 95 + 110 + a = (4 - 2) \times 180$

              $290 + a = 360$

                  $a = 70$

     The remaining angle is **70°.**

7.   Let *a* be the measure of the three equal angles.
        $3a + 60 = 360$
            $3a = 300$
              $a = 100$
        Angle *P* is **100°**.

8.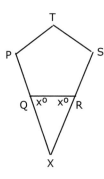

$x = \dfrac{360°}{5} = 72°$

$\angle QXR + 2x = 180°$
$\angle QXR + 2(72°) = 180°$
$\angle QXR + 144° = 180°$
$\angle QXR = 180° - 144°$
$\angle QXR = \mathbf{36°}$

Let *x* be one of the 5 equal exterior angles.

∠ sum of Δ

9.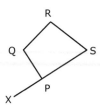

$\angle Q + \angle S + \angle R + \angle QPS = 360°$
$\angle Q + \angle S = 180°$
$180° + \angle R + \angle QPS = 360°$
$\angle R = 180° - \angle QPS$
$\angle QPX + \angle QPS = 180°$
$\angle QPX = 180° - \angle QPS$
$\therefore \angle QPX = \angle R$

∠ sum of quad.
given

adj. ∠ s on st. line

10.(a) $360 = 63 + 2x + 3x + x$
        $360 = 63 + 6x$
        $297 = 6x$
          $x = \mathbf{49.5}$

    (b) $360 = 90 + 2x + 5x + 3x$
         $360 = 90 + 10x$
         $270 = 10x$
           $x = \mathbf{27}$

   (c) $360 = 2x + x + 38 + 44 + 3x + 56$
        $360 = 6x + 138$
        $222 = 6x$
          $x = \mathbf{37}$

    (d) $360 = 60 + x + (180 - 108)$
                $+ (180 - 100) + (180 - 2x)$
         $360 = 60 + x + 72 + 80 + 180 - 2x$
           $x = \mathbf{32}$

11.   The reflex angle opposite *p* is 360 - *p*. Since the interior angles of a quadrilateral add up
        to 360, it is also 360 - the other 3 angles, or 360 - 170.
        $360 - p = 360 - 170$
              $p = \mathbf{170°}$

12.(a) Marked angles are interior angles of a pentagon.
        sum of angles = $180°(5 - 2) = \mathbf{540°}$

    (b)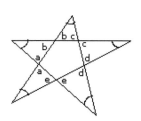

∠s marked with same letter are equal (vert. opp. ∠s).
$360 = a + b + c + d + e$
sum of lettered ∠s = $2 \times 360 = 720$
sum of ∠s of one triangle = 180
sum of ∠s of the 5 triangles = $5 \times 180 = 900$.
sum of marked ∠s = sum of ∠s of the 5 triangles - sum of
lettered ∠s = 900 - 720 = **180°**

(c)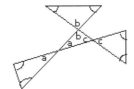

$a + b + c = 180$ (∠sum of Δ, vert. opp. ∠s)
Sum of ∠s of 3 triangles = 3 x 180 = 540
Sum of marked angles = 540 - 180 = **360°**

(d)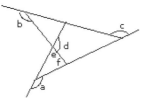

$b + c + f = 360$ (ext. ∠of a polygon)
$d + e = 180$ (adj. ∠s on a st. line)
$a = e + f$ (ext. ∠of a Δ)
$a + b + c + d = (e + f) + b + c + d$
$= (b + c + f) + (d + e)$
$= 360 + 180$
$= $ **540°**

13.   Sum of angles of a quadrilateral = 360°

Smallest angle = $\dfrac{2}{12}$ x 360° = **60°**

14.   Sum of angles of a pentagon = 540°

largest angle = $\dfrac{4}{12}$ x 540° = **180°**

Exercise 10.5 (pp. 278-279)

1.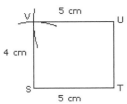

The figure is a rectangle.

2.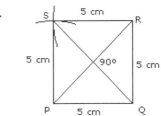

The angle where the diagonals meet is 90°.

3.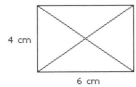

Length of diagonals is **7.2 cm**.

4.   Draw *AB* first, then find intersection of diagonal *AC* and side *BC* using arcs of circle. Then find intersection of *CD* and *AD*.

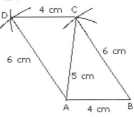

AB // DC, *AD // BC*. The figure is a parallelogram.

5. Draw *AB* first, then find intersection of diagonal *AC* and side *BC* using arcs of circle. Then find intersection of *CD* and *AD*.

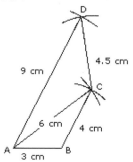

DA // BC. The figure is a trapezoid.

6. Draw *AB* first, then find intersection of diagonal *DB* and side *DA* using arcs of circle. Then find intersection of *BC* and *CD*.

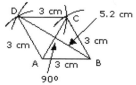

It is a rhombus. The angle where the diagonals meet is 90°.

7.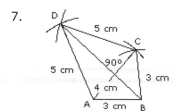

The figure is a kite. The angle where the diagonals meet is 90°.

8. To make copies, measure and draw *AB* (*PQ*). Then measure *BC* (*QR*) and draw an arc of the same radius with center at *B* (*Q*). Measure diagonal *AC* (*PR*) and draw arc of the same radius with center at *A* (*P*). Draw line *BC* (*QR*) to the intersection of these arcs. Measure length of *CD* (*RS*) and *AD* (*PS*) and draw corresponding arcs. Draw lines *AD* (*PS*) and *CD* (*RS*) to the intersection of the arcs.

Exercise 10.6 (pp. 281-284)

1. (a) **True**, it is a parallelogram.
   (b) **True**, it is a rhombus.
   (c) **True**, it can be a rhombus.
   (d) **False**, it could be a parallelogram.
   (e) **False**, the fourth angle has to be a right angle.
   (f) **False**, a rectangle does not have to be a square.
   (g) **True**.
   (h) **True**, a rectangle has four right angles.
   (i) **True**.
   (j) **True**.
   (k) **False**. It could be a kite.
   (l) **True**.

2.

Properties	Trap-ezoid	Kite	Parallel-ogram	Rect-angle	Rhom-bus	Square
(a) There is a pair of parallel sides.	T	F	T	T	T	T
(b) There are two pairs of adjacent sides.	F	T	F	F	T	T
(c) The diagonals are perpendicular to each other.	F	T	F	F	T	T
(d) There is a pair of equal opposite angles.	F	T	T	T	T	T
(e) There is a diagonal which bisects a pair of opp. angles.	F	T	F	F	T	T
(f) The opposite sides are parallel.	F	F	T	T	T	T
(g) The opposite sides are equal.	F	F	T	T	T	T
(h) The opp. angles are equal.	F	F	T	T	T	T
(i) The diagonals bisect each other.	F	F	T	T	T	T
(j) There are four right angles.	F	F	F	T	F	T
(k) The diagonals are equal.	F	F	F	T	F	T
(l) The sides are all equal.	F	F	F	F	T	T
(m) The diagonals are bisectors of opposite angles.	F	F	F	F	T	T

3. (a) $x = 180 - 130$ int. $\angle$s, $DC // AB$
   $x = 50$
   $\angle ABC = 360 - x - 45 - 130$ $\angle$ sum of a quadrilateral
   $= 360 - 50 - 45 - 130$
   $= 135$
   $\angle ABD = \angle ABC - 110$
   $= 25$
   $\angle ADB = 180 - 130 - 25$ $\angle$ sum of Δ
   $= 25$
   $\therefore \Delta ABD$ is isosceles   If $\angle ADB = \angle ABD$ then $AD = AB$
   $y = 5$
   $x = 50$; $y = 5$

   (b) $\angle ADC = 100$ opp. $\angle$s of a parallelogram are equal
   $70 + x = 100$
   $x = 30$
   $\angle DCB = 180 - 100$ int. $\angle$s, $DC // AB$
   $= 80$
   $\angle DCA = \angle DCB - 30$
   $= 80 - 30$
   $= 50$
   $y = 180 - \angle DCA - x$ $\angle$ sum of Δ
   $= 180 - 50 - 30$
   $= 100$
   $x = 30$; $y = 100$

(c) $y = 180 - 2(75)$ iso. Δ, $DC = BC$
      $y = 30$ $\angle$ sum of iso. Δ, $DC = BC$
      $\angle DAB = y = 30$ opp. $\angle$s of a rhombus are equal
                                          line from A bisects BD, so is a diagonal,
      $x = \dfrac{1}{2}\angle DAB = 15$ diagonals of rhombuses bisect the $\angle$.
      $x = 15; y = 30$

(d) $\angle BCD - x = 90 - 35$ complementary $\angle$s of rt. Δ
                  $= 55$
      $90 - x = 55$
           $x = 35$
      $\angle ADB = 90 - 35$
             $= 55$
      $y = \angle ADB = 55$ iso. Δ
      $x = 35; y = 55$

(e) $\angle ABC = 110$ prop. of kite, there is a pair of = opp $\angle$s
      $\angle ABC - 45 = 90 - x$ complementary $\angle$s of rt. Δ
        $110 - 45 = 90 - x$
              $x = 25$
      $\angle CAB = 90 - 45$ complementary $\angle$s of rt. Δ
             $= 45$
      $y = \angle CAB = 45$ prop. of kite, the diagonal bisects opp. $\angle$s
      $x = 25, y = 45$

(f) $\angle DCB = 180 - 80 - 43$ $\angle$sum of Δ CDE
              $= 57$
      $x + 43 = 180 - 2(57)$ iso. Δ CBD
          $x = 23$
      $\angle BED = 180 - 80 = 100$ adj. $\angle$s on a st. line
      $\angle BED = \angle BAD$
      $\therefore ABED$ is a parallelogram   opp. $\angle$s are equal
      $y = 18$ cm   opp. sides of a parallelogram are equal
      $x = 23; y = 18$

(g) $DG = CG = BG$ diagonals are = and bisect each other
      $\angle BCG = x$ iso. Δ
      $2x = 105$ ext. $\angle$of a Δ
      $x = 52.5$
      $y = 90 - 52.5$
        $= 37.5$
      $x = 52.5; y = 37.5$

(h) $AB = BC$ prop. of a rhombus
$\angle ACD = x$ diagonal bisects angle
$\angle ADC = y$ opp. $\angle$s are equal
Mark 0 as midpoint of AC, DO is a   diagonals bisect
diagonal.

$\angle ODC = \frac{1}{2}y$ diagonal bisects angle
                                                   opp. $\angle$s are equal
$3x = \frac{1}{2}y + x$ $\angle$sum of Δ
                                                   ext. $\angle$of ΔCOD
$4x = y$
$AB = BC$ prop. of a rhombus
$\angle BAC = x$ diagonal bisects angle
$180 = 2x + y$ $\angle$sum of Δ
$180 = 2x + 4x$ $4x = y$
$180 = 6x$
$x = 30$
$y = 4x$
$y = 120$
$x = 30; y = 120$

(i) $\angle BAC = 45$ diagonals bisect 90º angle
$180 = 45 + 2x$ adj. $\angle$s on a st. line
$x = 67.5$
$90 = x + y$ complementary $\angle$s of rt. Δ, diagonals of a
$90 = 67.5 + y$ square are perpendicular so $\angle$s at center are
$y = 22.5$ 90º
$x = 67.5; y = 22.5$

(j) $\angle GBH = 45$ diagonals bisect 90º angle
$45 = 180 - 2y$ $\angle$sum of iso. Δ
$y = 67.5$
$90 = x + y$ $\angle$s at center are 90º
$90 = x + 67.5$
$x = 22.5$
$x = 22.5; y = 67.5$

Chapter 11

Exercise 11.1 (pp. 291-293)

1. (i)   No lines of symmetry

   (ii) 2 lines of symmetry, one horizontal and one vertical

   (iii) No lines of symmetry

   (iv) 8 lines of symmetry from opposite vertices and opposite midpoints

   (v)   3 lines of symmetry from a vertex through the midpoint of the opposite side.

   (vi) No lines of symmetry

   (vii) No lines of symmetry

   (viii) 1 line of symmetry, horizontally through points

   (ix) 1 line of symmetry, vertically through center

   (x)   4 lines of symmetry, through vertices and midpoint of opposite side

2. (a)

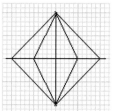

   (b)

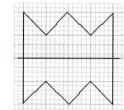

   (c)

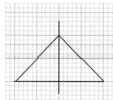

   (d)

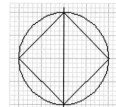

   (e)

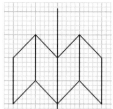

   (f)

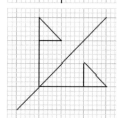

   (g)

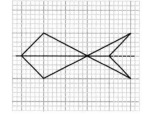

   (h)

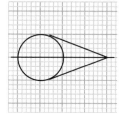

3. A method for making a symmetrical figure using a compass is shown below, and can be applied to these figures.

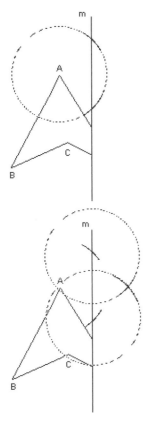

Use the compass to draw two arcs on the line of symmetry with a center at a point on the figure, in this case A.

Using the same radius and centers at the intersection of the arcs and the line of symmetry, draw two more arcs which intersect on the other side of the line of symmetry. This point of intersection will be the mirror image of the original point A.

Other points can be similarly drawn and connected to get the symmetrical figure.

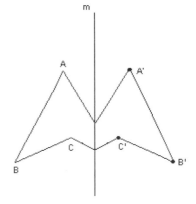

4. Several answers are possible. See answers in text.

(a)

(b)

(c)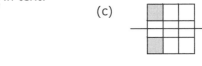

(d)

(e)

Exercise 11.2 (pp. 295-298)

1. (i)   1 vertical line of symmetry

(ii)   rotational symmetry of order 2

(iii) 4 lines of symmetry, 1 horizontal, 1 vertical, and 2 diagonal; rotational symmetry of order 4

(iv)   3 lines of symmetry through each line; rotational symmetry of order 3

(v)   rotational symmetry of order 2

(vi)   no symmetry

(vii) 1 vertical line of symmetry

(viii) 1 vertical line of symmetry

(ix)   no symmetry

(x)   1 horizontal line of symmetry

(xi)   rotational symmetry of order 2

(xii) rotational symmetry of order 2

2. (i)   An isosceles triangle has 1 line of symmetry.

(ii)   A rectangle has 2 lines of symmetry and rotational symmetry of order 2. See problem 4(vi).

(iii) A circle has an infinite number of lines of and orders of rotational symmetry.

(iv)   A regular hexagon has 8 lines of symmetry and rotational symmetry of order 8. See problem 3.

(v)   A trapezium does not have symmetry if the non-parallel sides are not equal.

(vi)   A rhombus has rotational symmetry and at least one line of symmetry.

(vii) An equilateral triangle has 3 lines of symmetry and rotational symmetry of order 3.

(viii) A regular pentagon has 5 lines of symmetry and rotational symmetry of order 5. See problem 3.

(ix)   A kite has one line of symmetry. See problem 4(v).

(x)   A right-angled triangle does not have symmetry unless it is isosceles.

(xi)   A square has 4 lines of symmetry and rotational symmetry of order 4. See problem 3.

(xii) A parallelogram has rotational symmetry of order 2. See problem 4(i).

3.   A regular polygon with an odd number of sides has a line of symmetry through each vertex and midpoint of the opposite side. One with an even number of vertices has lines of symmetry from vertex to opposite vertex, and from midpoint of a side to midpoint of the opposite side.

		Number of lines of symmetry	Order of rotational symmetry
(a)	Equilateral triangle	3	3
(b)	Square	4	4
(c)	Regular pentagon	5	5
(d)	Regular hexagon	6	6
(e)	Regular heptagon	7	7
(f)	Regular octagon	8	8
(g)	Regular nonagon	9	9
(h)	Regular decagon	10	10

4. (i)

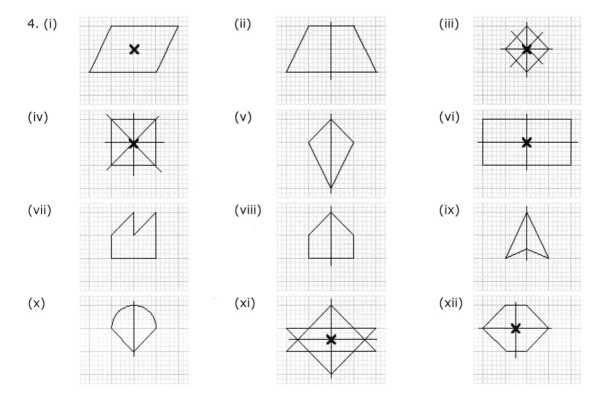

5.   See answers in text.

6.   See answers in text.

7. (a)   **True**.   (b)   **True**.

   (c)   **True**.   (d)   **False**. See 4(i) above. A parallelogram
                                                                has rotational symmetry of order 2 but
                                                                no line of symmetry.

   (e)   **False**. See fig. 11.3 in text   (f)   **False**. See fig. (ii) on p. 294. It has a
          (p. 294) - It has a rotational symmetry   rotational symmetry of order 4, but no
          of order 3 but no line of symmetry.   line of symmetry.

Exercise 11.3 (pp. 300-301)

See answers in text.

Exercise 11.4 (pp. 307-309)

1. (i)   No symmetry   (ii)   Both a plane and axis of symmetry

   (iii)   Both a plane and axis of symmetry   (iv)   Both a plane and axis of symmetry

   (v)   Both a plane and axis of symmetry   (vi)   Both a plane and axis of symmetry

   (vii)   Both a plane and axis of symmetry   (viii)   A plane of symmetry (parallel to the
                                                          page)

   (ix)   No symmetry   (x)   No symmetry

3.		Number of planes of symmetry	Number of axes of rotational symmetry
(a)	Rectangular prism	3	3
(b)	Right circular cylinder	Infinitely many. Two possibilities given.	Infinitely many. Two possibilities given.
(c)	Regular tetrahedron	6	7
(d)	Right square pyramid	4	1

(e)	Hemisphere	Infinitely many, one example only is given. 	1
(f)	Right circular cone	Infinitely many, one example only is given. 	1
(g)	Sphere	Infinitely many.	Infinitely many.
(h)	Right triangular prism	4 	4
(i)	Right pentagonal prism	6 	6

(j) Cube	9	13
	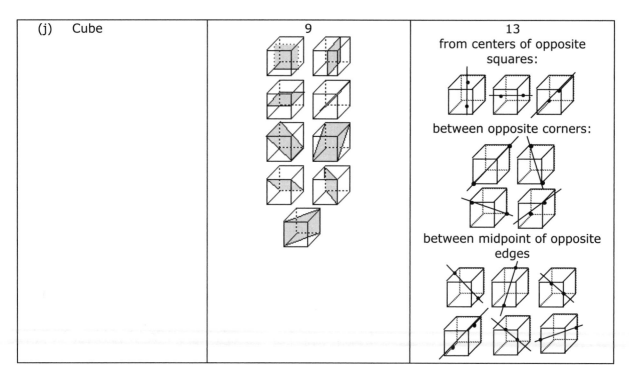	from centers of opposite squares: between opposite corners: between midpoint of opposite edges

Exercise 11.5 (pp. 311-314)

1. (a)
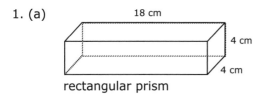

rectangular prism

(b)

8 cm

8 cm

regular tetrahedron
(or triangular pyramid)

(c)
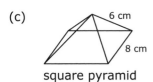

6 cm

8 cm

square pyramid

(d)
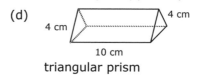

4 cm   4 cm

10 cm

triangular prism

(e)
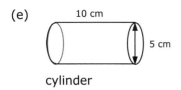

10 cm

5 cm

cylinder

(f)
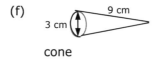

9 cm

3 cm

cone

2.   Answers will vary.

3. (a)

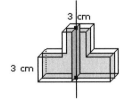

(b)   2 planes of symmetry

(c)   Rotational symmetry with order 2

4.

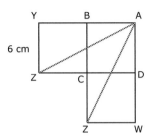

Draw a net of the 3 sides with each edge 6 cm.   The shortest distance from A to Z is a straight line, which would pass through either the midpoint of edge CD or the midpoint of edge BC. The length of these lines is 13.4 cm.

5.

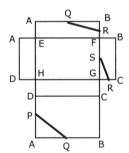

A can be made from B and C.

6. (a)

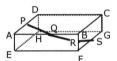

Label vertices and points where line intersects edges.

(i)

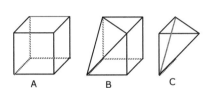

(ii)

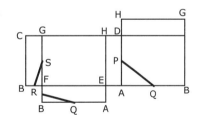

This is a possible net.

This net won't work, puts R between G and C and between B and F.

(iii)

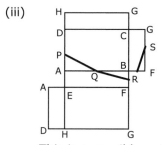

This is a possible net.

(iv)

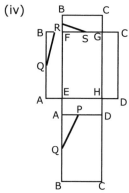

This is a possible net.

(b)   See answers in text.

7.   See #1

8. (a)

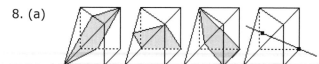

3 planes of symmetry, 1 axis of rotational symmetry with order 3.

(b)

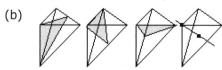

3 planes of symmetry, 1 axis of rotational symmetry with order 3.

Revision Exercise 3

Revision 3A (pp. 318-319)

⊢⊣
1 cm

1.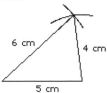

2. Let n be the number of sides. The number of angles is also n.
$$140 + 100(n - 1) = 180(n - 2)$$
$$140 + 100n - 100 = 180n - 360$$
$$400 = 80n$$
$$5 = n$$
There are **5** sides.

3. $100 + x = 135$ alt. ∠s
       $x = 35$
$y = x + 50$ ext. ∠of a Δ
$y = 35 + 50$
$y = 85$

4. (a)   S\$ 1.75 = US\$1
S\$ 1 $= US\$\dfrac{1}{1.75}$
S\$437.50 $= US\$\dfrac{1}{1.75}(437.50)$
      = **US\$250**

(b)   £ 1 = S\$ 3.70
£45 = S\$ 3.70 x 45
    = **S\$166.50**

5. (a) $180 = 4x + 6x$ (adj. ∠s on a st. line)
$180 = 10x$
 18 $= x$

(b) $71 + 3x = 4x + 15 + x$ (vert. opp. ∠s)
$56 = 2x$
$x = $ **28**

6. The polygon has 5 angles, so its interior angles = $180(5 - 2) = 540$
Totql number of parts in the ratio = 15.
second largest angle = $\dfrac{4}{15}(540°) = $ **144°**

7. (a) 140° a° 100° b° x°
$a = 180 - 140$ int. ∠s
   $= 40$
$b = a = 40$ vert. opp. ∠s
$100 = x + b$ ext. ∠of a Δ
$100 = x + 40$
    $x = $ **60**

(b) 120° a° x° b° 115°
$a = 180 - 120$ int. ∠s
   $= 60$
$b = 180 - 115$ int. ∠s
   $= 65$
$x = a + b$
   $= 60 + 65$
   = **125**

8. $I = \dfrac{PRT}{100} = \dfrac{(\$500)(8)(3)}{100} = \mathbf{\$120}$

9. (a)

$a = 2x$	iso. Δ
$2x = 180 - (x + a)$	int. $\angle$s
$2x = 180 - (x + 2x)$	
$2x = 180 - 3x$	
$5x = 180$	
$x = \mathbf{36}$	

(b)

$a = x$	iso. Δ
$180 = a + x + 120$	$\angle$sum of Δ
$180 = x + x + 120$	
$60 = 2x$	
$x = \mathbf{30}$	

10.

Cost of cards = $\dfrac{510}{3}$ x $4 = $680

Number sold at 2 for $3 = $\dfrac{2}{3}$ x 510 = 340

Amount received = $\dfrac{340}{2}$ x $3 = $510

Number sold at 5 for $6.50 = 510 - 340 = 170

Amount received = $\dfrac{170}{5}$ x $6.50 = $221

Profit = $510 + $221 - $680 = **$51**

11.(a) figure is an equilateral triangle, all angles   (b) figure is an isosceles triangle, so the
        are 60°   third angle = $x°$.
        $x = 2(60)$ (ext. $\angle$of a Δ) $180 = 2x + 40$ ($\angle$sum of Δ)
        $x = \mathbf{120}$ $140 = 2x$
                                                                 $x = \mathbf{70}$

Revision 3B (pp. 319-320)

1.

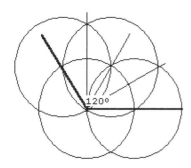

2.   Sum of the angles = $180°(8 - 2)$
                          $= 1,080°$
      Let x be the measure of the equal
      angles. There are 7 of them.
      $1,080° = 86° + 7x$
        $994° = 7x$
          $x = \mathbf{142°}$

3. (a) $180 = 3x + x + 2x$ (b) $40 + 90 = 3x + 5x$
          $180 = 6x$ $130 = 8x$
            $x = \mathbf{30}$ $x = \mathbf{16.25}$

4. $a = 180 - 5x$ adj. ∠s on a st. line
                               $a = x + 2x$ ext. ∠of a Δ
                               $180 - 5x = x + 2x$
                                     $180 = 8x$
                                         $x = $ **22.5**

5. (a) 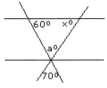 $a = 70$ vert. opp. ∠s
                               $180 = 60 + a + x$ ∠sum of Δ
                               $180 = 60 + 70 + x$
                                     $x = $ **50**

  (b) 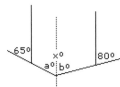 $a = 65$ corr. ∠s
                               $b = 80$ corr. ∠s
                               $x = a + b$
                               $x = 65 + 80$
                               $x = $ **145**

6. (a)   The figure has rotational symmetry of   (b)   e.g. a regular pentagon.
         order **4**.

7. (a)   25% of $40 = 0.25 × 40 = **$10**   (b) $10 - $8 = **$2**
         $\dfrac{1}{5}$ of $40 = **$8**

8. (a)   (b)

9. (a)   amt. credit terms = $30 + 12($24)   (b)   amt. saved with cash = $318 - $265
                            = **$318**   = **$53**

10.(a) 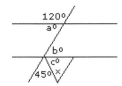 $a = 180 - 120 = 60$ adj. ∠s on a st. line
                               $b = 60$ alt. ∠s
                               $c = 180 - 45 - b$ adj. ∠s on a st. line
                                 $= 180 - 45 - 60$
                                 $= 75$
                               $x = 180° - 2c$ ∠sum of iso. Δ
                                 $= 180° - 2(75°)$
                                 $= $ **30°**

(b)

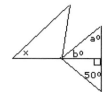

$a = 50$ iso. Δ
$b = 90 - a$ compl. $\angle$s of rt. Δ
  $= 90 - 50$
  $= 40$
$x = b$ corr. $\angle$s
  $= \mathbf{40°}$

11.(a) 9.5% discount is 90.5% of cost   (b) 5.5 % discount is 94.5% of cost
        He pays 90.5% of $1,600   Total cost = 94.5% of $1,600

$$= \frac{90.5}{100} \times \$1,600$$ $$= \frac{94.5}{100} \times \$1,600$$

        $= 90.5 \times \$16$ $= 94.5 \times \$16$
        $= \mathbf{\$1,488}$ $= \$1,512$

                                             Monthly payments $= \dfrac{\$1,512}{12}$

                                                      $= \mathbf{\$126}$

Revision 3C (pp. 320-322)

1.

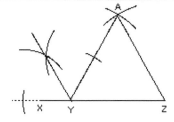

$YZ = 3XY = 3 \times 2$ cm $= 6$ cm
Construct equilateral triangle by using arcs
of circles of radii 6 with centers at Y and Z.
Their intersection is A.
The angle can be bisected using
measurements on a protractor, or to
construct bisector with a compass, use Y as
the center of a circle and mark arcs along
YX and YA, then use those intersections as
center of circles of the same radius and
mark intersecting arcs. The line from Y to
that intersection is the bisector of AYX.

2.   Let x be the size of the remaining 4 angles.

$90° + 4x = 180°(5 - 2)$
$90° + 4x = 540°$
$\quad 450° = 4x$

$$x = \mathbf{112\frac{1}{2}°}$$

3. (a)

$a = x$ alt. $\angle$s
$85 = a + 20$ ext. $\angle$of a Δ
$85 = x + 20$
$\quad x = \mathbf{65°}$

(b)
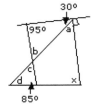

$a = 90 - 30$
  $= 60$
$b = 180 - 95 - 30$ ∠sum of Δ
  $= 55$
$c = b = 55$ vert. opp. ∠s
$d = 180 - c - 85$ ∠sum of Δ
$d = 180 - 55 - 85$
  $= 40$
$x = 180 - d - a$ ∠sum of Δ
  $= 180 - 40 - 60$
  $= \mathbf{80°}$

4. $4x = x + 60$ ext. ∠of a Δ
      $3x = 60$
      $x = \mathbf{20}$

5. (a) $90 = 2x + 2x$ (b) $160 = 2x + 90 - x$ (opp. ∠s of
       $90 = 4x$ $160 = x + 90$ parallelogram are
       $x = \mathbf{22\dfrac{1}{2}}$ $x = \mathbf{70}$ equal)

6. (a)
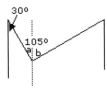

$a = 30$ alt. ∠s
$b = 105 - a$
  $= 105 - 30$
  $= 75$
$x = b$ alt. ∠s
  $= \mathbf{75}$

(b)

$a = 40$ alt. ∠s
$b = 45$
$x = a + b$
  $= 40 + 45$
  $= \mathbf{85}$

7. (a)
   bonus = $1\dfrac{1}{2}$ x $850 = $1,275

   annual salary = 12($850) + $1,275 = **$11,475**

(b) Wording is unclear in this problem. To get answer in book assume he saves all of his
     bonus, not 10% of (remaining salary + bonus)
     6 months earnings = 6 x $850 = $5,100
     savings = 15% of $5,100 + $10 of $5,100 + $1,275
           = (0.15)($5,100) + (0.10)($5,100) + $1,275
           = $765 + $510 + $1,275
           = **$2,550**

8.   Let p be the principal.

$$\$650 = \frac{12.5}{100}(p)(2)$$

$$\$650 = \frac{1}{8}(p)(2)$$

$\$2,600 = p$
He needs **$2,600** in the bank.

9. (a)   **5** axes of symmetry

(b)   **2** lines of symmetry

10.   For a profit of 12%, the article was sold at 112% of cost.
        112% of cost = $2,450

$$1\% \text{ of cost} = \frac{\$2,450}{112}$$

$$\text{total of cost} = \frac{\$2,450}{112} \times 100$$

$$= \mathbf{\$2,187.50}$$

11.   total money = 6% of $5.50(3,000) + 8% of $5.50(6,500 - 3,000)

$$= (\frac{6}{100})(\$5.50)(3,000) + (\frac{8}{100})(\$5.50)((3,500)$$

$$= \$990 + \$1,540$$

$$= \mathbf{\$2,530}$$

Revision 3D (pp. 322-323)

1.   (angles not exact)

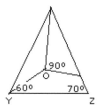

2. (a)   Larger Δ is equilateral - 2 sides are equal   (b)   The third angle in the smallest rt. Δ,
        and the apex angle is 60º.   containing x, is a base ∠ of an isosceles
        $x = 90 - 60$ Δ with apex 50º.
        $x = \mathbf{30}$

$$x = 90 - \frac{1}{2}(180 - 50)$$

$$= 90 - 65$$

$$= \mathbf{25}$$

3. (a)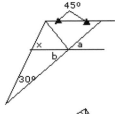

$a = 45$ alt. $\angle$s
$b = a = 45$ vert. opp. $\angle$s
$x = 30 + b$ ext. $\angle$of a Δ
$\quad = 30 + 45$
$\quad = \mathbf{75}$

(b)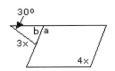

$a = 90$ $\perp$ lines
$b = 90$ $\perp$ lines
$x + a = 30 + b$ ext. $\angle$of a Δ
$x + 90 = 30 + 90$
$x = \mathbf{30}$

4. (a)

$180 = 5x + 115$ adj. $\angle$s on a st. line
$65 = 5x$
$x = \mathbf{13}$

(b)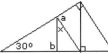

$a = 4x$ opp. $\angle$s of a parallelogram
$b = 180 - 4x$ adj. $\angle$s on a st. line
$3x = 30 + b$ ext. $\angle$of a Δ
$3x = 30 + 180 - 4x$
$7x = 210$
$x = \mathbf{30}$

5. (a)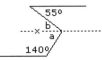

$a = 180 - 140$ int. $\angle$s
$\quad = 40$
$b = 55$ alt. $\angle$s
$x = a + b$
$x = 40 + 55$
$\quad = \mathbf{95}$

(b)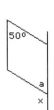

$a = 50$ opp. $\angle$s of a parallelogram
$x = 180 - a$
$x = 180 - 50$
$\quad = \mathbf{130}$

6. (a)

$a = \dfrac{1}{2}(180 - x)$ iso. Δ

$3x = x + a$ ext. $\angle$of a Δ

$3x = x + \dfrac{1}{2}(180 - x)$

$3x = x + 90 - \dfrac{1}{2}x$

$2\dfrac{1}{2}x = 90$

$x = \mathbf{36}$

(b)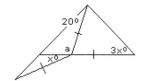

$a = 2(3x)$ ext. ∠of an iso. Δ
$x + a = 180 - 2(20)$ ∠sum of iso. Δ
$x + 6x = 180 - 40$
$7x = 140$
$x = \mathbf{20}$

7. (a) Vertical line of symmetry.

(b) Center of rotational symmetry at the center of the image.

(c) Center of rotational symmetry at the center of the image.

(d) Vertical line of symmetry.

8. Discount of 40% is 60% of cost. Let C be the list price.
60% of C = \$72

$C = \dfrac{\$72}{60} \times 100 = \mathbf{\$120}$

9. (a) A profit of 12% is 112% of cost.
112% of C = \$84

$C = \dfrac{\$84}{112} \times 100 = \mathbf{\$75}$

(b) 5% discount is 95% of price.

95% of \$84 $= \dfrac{95}{100} \times \$84$

$= \$79.80$

10. $\angle ADB = 105$ alt. ∠s
$y = \angle ADB + 20$ ext. ∠ of a Δ
$= 105 + 20$
$= 125$
$\angle BDC = 180 - 105 - 50$ ∠ sum of Δ
$= 25$
$\angle ABD = 25$ alt. ∠s
$x = 180 - y - \angle ABD$ ∠ sum of Δ
$= 180 - 125 - 25$
$= 30$
$\mathbf{x = 30;\ y = 25}$

11. $\angle CDA = 180 - 75$ adj. ∠s on a st. line
$= 105$
$x = \angle CDA$ opp. ∠s of a parallelogram
$= 105$
$42 + \angle ACD = 180 - \angle CDA$ int. ∠s
$\angle ACD = 180 - 105 - 42$
$= 33$
$\angle CAD = 180 - \angle ACD - \angle CDA$ ∠ sum of Δ
$= 180 - 33 - 105$
$= 42$
$y + \angle CAD = 180 - 2(\angle ACD)$ ∠ sum of iso. Δ
$y + 42 = 180 - 2(33)$
$y = 180 - 66 - 42$
$= 72$
$\mathbf{x = 105;\ y = 72}$

Revision 3E (pp. 324-325)

1.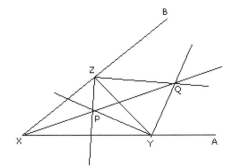

PQ does pass through the vertex at X, and does bisect the angle at X.

2. If the sum of the interior angles is equal to a multiple of the sum of the exterior angles, the problem can be written as follows, where n is the number of sides and *m* is the multiple.

$180(n - 2) = 360m$
$n - 2 = 2m$

(a) $m = 1$
$n - 2 = 2$
$n = 4$
4 sides

(b) $m = 2$
$n - 2 = 2(2)$
$n - 2 = 4$
$n = 6$
6 sides

$m = 5$
$n - 2 = 2(5)$
$n - 2 = 10$
$n = 12$
12 sides

3. (a) The marked ∠s are adj. ∠s on a st. line
$180 = 4x + 2x + 2x + 56$
$180 = 8x + 56$
$124 = 8x$
$x = \mathbf{15\frac{1}{2}}$

(b) The marked angles are vert. opp. ∠s.
$80 = 17 + 3x$
$63 = 3x$
$\mathbf{x = 21}$

(c)

$a = 2x$ alt. ∠s
$a = 180 - 6x$ int. ∠s
$2x = 180 - 6x$
$8x = 180$
$x = \mathbf{22\frac{1}{2}}$

4. (a)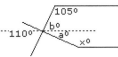

$a = 180 - x$ int. ∠s
$b = 180 - 105$ int. ∠s
$\ = 75$
$110 = a + b$ vert. opp. ∠s
$110 = 180 - x + 75$
$x = \mathbf{145}$

(b)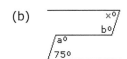

$a = 180 - 75$ int. ∠s
$\ = 105$
$b = 105$ alt. ∠s
$x = 180 - 105$ int. ∠s
$\ = \mathbf{75}$

5. (a)   US$1 = S$1.40
          US$2,500 = S$1.40 x 2,500
                   = **S$3,500**

   (b)   S$ 1.40 = US$1

          S$ 1 = US$$\dfrac{1}{1.40}$

          S$2,310 = US$$\dfrac{1}{1.40}$ x 2,310
                  = **$1,650**

6.   A 15% discount is a sale price 85% of cost.

          cost = $$\dfrac{510}{85}$ x 100 = $600

          Discount = 15% of $600 = $\dfrac{15}{100}$ x 600 = **$90**

7. (a)   **(iii) and (iv)** both have line symmetry about a vertical line through the middle.

   (b)   **(i) and (ii)** have rotational symmetry.

8.   Amount repaid = Interest + $1,750

                       = $\dfrac{6}{100}$ x $1,750 x 2 + $1,750

                       = $210 + $1,750
                       = **$1,960**

9. (a)   Order of rotation of **2**

   (b)   Order of rotation of **4**

10.(a)   120% of cost = $420

          100% of cost = $\dfrac{420}{120}$ x 100

                       = **$350**

   (b)   80% of cost = $420

          100% of cost = $$\dfrac{420}{80}$ x 100

                       = **$525**

11.(a)   Sale price = 80% of $2,500

                     = $\dfrac{80}{100}$ x $2,500

                     = **$2,000**

   (b)   Total = 10% x $2,500 + ($105 x 24)
                = $250 + $2,520
                = **$2,770**

Miscellaneous Exercise 3 (pp. 326-327)

1. (a)   2, 7, 12, 17, 22, **27**   each term increases by 5.

   (b)   tenth term is 6th term + (4 x 5) = 27 + 20 = **47**

   (c)   0th term is -3, 1st is 5 - 3, 2nd is 10 - 3, 3rd is 15 - 3. So formula is *5n - 3*

2. (a) $7\frac{1}{2}$% of $1,280 = $\frac{7.5}{100}$ x $1,280 = $96
   List price - discount = $1,280 - $96 = $1,184
   He paid **$1,184**.

   (b)   Hire purchase cost = $\frac{1,280}{5}$ + 10($106.4)

   $$= \$256 + \$1,064$$
   $$= \mathbf{\$1,320}$$

   (c) $\frac{1,320 - 1,184}{1,184}$ x 100% = 11.5%
   Mr. Hwang paid **11.5%** more.

3. $\angle AOD$ = 180º - $\angle BOC$ = 180º - 20º = 160º
   $\angle COD$ = $\angle AOD$ - $\angle AOB$ - $\angle BOC$ = 160º - 20º - 20º = **120º**

4.
   Let x be *BE*. Then *EF* is $3x$, *FC* is $2(3x) = 6x$, $AB = \frac{1}{2}(x + 3x + 6x) = 5x$,

   $AD = \frac{1}{2}(5x)$ and $DF = \frac{1}{2}(5x) + x + 3x = \frac{1}{2}(5x) + 4x$

   $\vdash\!+\!+\!+\!|\!+\!|\!+\!+\!+\!|\!+\!+\!+\!|\!+\!+\!+\!+\!+\!|$
   A   D   B E   F   C

   If *AB* = 20 cm
      $5x$ = 20 cm
       x = 4 cm
   $DF = \frac{1}{2}(5)(4) + (4)(4) = 10 + 16 = \mathbf{26\ cm}$.

5.   The difference between the complementary $\angle$s A and B is 20º
   The supplementary angle of $\angle A$ = 180º - $\angle A$
   The supplementary angle of $\angle B$ = 180º - $\angle B$
   Their difference = 180º - $\angle A$ - (180º - $\angle B$) = -$\angle A$ + $\angle B$ = $\angle B$ - $\angle A$
   By the first statement above $\angle B$ - $\angle A$ = 20º
   ∴ the difference between their supplementary angles is also **20º**

6. $\angle A$ - $\angle B$ = 24º
   $\angle A$ = 180º - $\angle B$ since they are supplementary
   ∴180º - $\angle B$ - $\angle B$ = 24º
             156º = 2($\angle B$)
              78º = $\angle B$
   The complementary angle of $\angle B$ = 90º - 78º = **12º**

7.   For every quarter hour, the hour hand will move $\frac{1}{4}$ of $\frac{1}{12}$, or $\frac{1}{48}$ of the distance around
the clock face. Let this distance be q. So the circle can be divided up into 48 equal
angles. At 1:15 the hour hand is $5q$ from 12, and the minute hand is $12q$ from 12. The
difference between them is $12q - 5q = 7q$. The angle between them $= 7 \times \frac{360^0}{48} =$
52.5⁰

8.   If the arms are parallel, there are two possibilities, one
in which the two angles are supplementary and one in
which the two angles are equal.
Equal angles:
$\angle A = \angle B = 3(\angle B) - 20^0$
$\quad\quad 20^0 = 2(\angle B)$
$\quad\quad \angle B = 10^0$
Supplementary angles:
$\angle A = 3(\angle B) - 20^0 = 180^0 - \angle B$
$\quad\quad 4(\angle B) = 200^0$
$\quad\quad\quad \angle B = 50^0$
$\angle A = 180^0 - \angle B = 180^0 - 50^0 = 130^0$
$\angle A = 130^0$, $\angle B = 50^0$ or $\angle A = \angle B = 10^0$

9.   For him to return to his starting point, he would have to turn a total of some multiple of
360⁰. Since he turns 36⁰ each time, he would have to turn 10 times. He walks 2 m for
each turn, so he walks $2 \times 10 =$ **20 m**.

10.(a) The sum of the exterior angles of the central pentagon is 360⁰. The base angles of the
five triangular "arms" are two sets of exterior angles for the polygon. (See solution to
Ex. 10.4 #12(b).)
The sum of the base angles $= 360^0 \times 2 = 720^0$
The sum of all the angles of the 5 triangles $= 180^0 \times 5 = 900^0$
The sum of the "points" = sum of all the angles - sum of the base angles
$\quad\quad\quad\quad\quad\quad = 900^0 - 720^0$
$\quad\quad\quad\quad\quad\quad$ **$= 180^0$**

(b) $2(\angle A) = \angle B = \angle C = \angle D = \angle E$
$180^0 = \angle A + \angle B + \angle C + \angle D + \angle E$
$180^0 = \angle A + 2(\angle A) + 2(\angle A) + 2(\angle A) + 2(\angle A)$
$180^0 = 9(\angle A)$
$\angle A =$ **20⁰**

11.(a) $180^o = 2p + 2q + 80^o$
         $100^o = 2(p + q)$
            $\mathbf{50^o} = p + q$

   (b)   The sum of the angles of the two triangles $= 2 \times 180^o = 360^o$
         $360^o = (96^o + 2p + q) + (84^o + 2q + p)$
            $= 180^o + 3(p + q)$
         $180^o = 3(p + q)$
            $60^o = p + q$
         $\angle A = 180^o - 2(p + q) = 180^o - 120^o = \mathbf{60^o}$

12.(a)   Problem provides insufficient information. Assume ΔABC is an isosceles triangle.
         $\angle \mathbf{LCB} = \dfrac{1}{2}(180^o - 130^o) = \dfrac{1}{2}(50^o) = \mathbf{25^o}$

   (b)   Let $a = \angle A$, $b = \angle ABL = \angle LBC$ and $c = \angle ACL = \angle LCB$
         $b + c = 180^o - 130^o$
         $b + c = 50^o$
         $a = 180^o - 2b - 2c$
           $= 180^o - 2(b + c)$
           $= 180^o - 2(50^o)$
           $= 80^o$
         $\angle A = \mathbf{80^o}$

13.   Let $a = \angle A$
         $\angle ACB = a$
         $\angle CBD = 2a$ ext. $\angle$ of iso. Δ
         $\angle BDC = 2a$ iso. Δ BCD
         $\angle BCD = 180^o - 4a$ $\angle$ sum of iso. Δ
         $\angle DCE = 180^o - (180^o - 4a) - a$ adj. $\angle$ on a st. line
           $= 3a$
         $\angle CED = 3a$ iso. Δ CDE
         $\angle CDE = 180^o - 6a$ $\angle$ sum of iso. Δ
         $\angle EDF = 180^o - (180^o - 6a) - 2a$ adj. $\angle$ on a st. line
           $= 4a$
         $\angle DFE = 4a$ iso. Δ DEF
         $\angle CEF = 180^o - 8a$ $\angle$ sum of iso. Δ
         $\angle GEF = 180^o - (180^o - 8a) - 3a$ adj. $\angle$ on a st. line
           $= 5a$
         $\angle EFG = 180^o - 10a$ $\angle$ sum of iso. Δ
         $90^o = 180^o - (180^o - 10a) - 4a$ adj. $\angle$ on a st. line
         $90^o = 6a$
         $a = 15^o$
         $\angle A = \mathbf{15^o}$

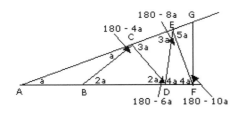

14.

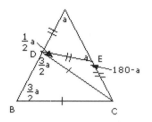

Let $a = \angle A$	
$\angle AED = a$	iso. $\triangle ADE$
$\angle DEC = 180 - a$	adj. $\angle$ on a st. line
$\angle CDE = \frac{1}{2}[180 - (180 - a)]$	$\angle$ sum of iso. $\triangle$
$\quad\quad = \frac{1}{2}a$	
$\angle BDE = 2a$	ext. $\angle$ of iso. $\triangle$
$\angle BDC = 2a - \frac{1}{2}a$	
$\quad\quad = \frac{3}{2}a$	
$\angle DBC = \frac{3}{2}a$	iso. $\triangle BCD$
$a + 2(\frac{3}{2}a) = 180$	$\angle$ sum of iso. $\triangle$
$\quad\quad 4a = 180$	
$\quad\quad\quad a = 45$	
$\angle A = \mathbf{45^o}$	

15.

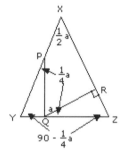

$\angle YXZ = \frac{1}{2}a$	$a = 2b,\ b = \frac{1}{2}a$
$\angle YPQ = \frac{1}{4}a$	$a = 4c,\ c = \frac{1}{4}a$
$\angle XYZ = \frac{1}{2}(180 - \frac{1}{2}a)$	$\angle$ sum of iso. $\triangle$
$\quad\quad = 90 - \frac{1}{4}a$	
$\angle XZY = 90 - \frac{1}{4}a$	iso. $\triangle XYZ$
$\angle PQY = 180 - (90 - \frac{1}{4}a) - \frac{1}{4}a$	$\angle$ sum of $\triangle$
$\quad\quad = 90$	
$\angle RQZ = 90 - (90 - \frac{1}{4}a)$	$\angle$ sum of $\triangle$
$\quad\quad = \frac{1}{4}a$	
$a + \frac{1}{4}a = 90$	compl. $\angle$s
$\quad\quad 5a = 360$	
$\quad\quad\quad a = 72$	
$\angle a = \mathbf{72^o}$	

Chapter 12

Exercise 12.1 (pp. 336-339)

1.   Area fig. a = $\frac{1}{2}(h)(a + b)$ = $\frac{1}{2}(12)(38 + 52)$ cm^2 = 540 cm^2

   Area fig. b = b x h = (15 x 45) cm^2 = 675 cm^2
   675 – 540 = 135
   fig **b.** is larger by **135 cm^2**

2.   Area of rectangle = (35 x 12) cm^2 = 420 cm^2

   Area of triangle = $\frac{1}{2}$ (22 x 32) cm^2 = 352 cm^2

   Difference = (420 - 352) cm^2 = **68 cm^2**

3. (a) $A = \frac{1}{2}bh$

   $A = \frac{1}{2}(10 \times 6)$ cm^2 = **30 cm^2**

   (b) $A = \frac{1}{2}bh$

   $A = \frac{1}{2}(6 \times 4)$ cm^2 = **12 cm^2**

4. BF = 11 - 5 = 6 cm
   $A = bh$ = (6 x 6) cm^2 = **36 cm^2**

5. ED = 15 - 6 = 9 cm
   BF = 15 - 3 = 12 cm
   $A = \frac{1}{2}(h)(a + b)$ = $\frac{1}{2}(7)(9 + 12)$ cm^2 = **73.5 cm^2**

6. (a) P = (6.5 + 4 + 2.5 + 10) cm
      = **23 cm**

   $A = \frac{1}{2}(h)(a + b)$

      = $\frac{1}{2}(2.5)(10 + 4)$ cm^2

      = **17.5 cm^2**

   (b) P = (15 + 6 + 13 + 20) cm
      = **54 cm**

   $A = \frac{1}{2}(h)(a + b)$

      = $\frac{1}{2}(12)(6 + 20)$

      = **156 cm^2**

7. $A = \frac{1}{2}b_1h_1 + \frac{1}{2}(h_2)(a_2 + b_2) + b_3h_3$

      = $\frac{1}{2}(132)(220) + \frac{1}{2}(176)(429+341) + (385)(132)$ m^2

      = 14,520 + 67,760 + 50,820 m^2
      = 133,100
   gain = (134,000 - 133,100) m^2 = **900 m^2**

8.   Let h be the height.

   $35 = \frac{1}{2}(7)h$

   $70 = 7h$
   $10 = h$
   Height is **10 cm**.

9.   Let b be the base.

   $46 = \frac{1}{2}(b)(10)$

   $92 = 10b$
   $9.2 = b$
   Base is **9.2 units**.

10.   Let h be the width.
       $40 = 8h$
       $5 = h$
       Perimeter = 2(5 + 8) = **26 cm**

11.   Let b be the length.
       $35 = 5b$
       $7 = b$
       Perimeter = 2(7 + 5) = **24 cm**

12.   Let h be the height.
       $25 = 4h$
       $6\frac{1}{4} = h$

       The height is **$6\frac{1}{4}$** units.

13.   Let h be the height for base 8.
       $72 = 8h$
       $9 = h$
       One of the heights is **9 cm**.
       Let b be the base for height 6.
       $72 = 6b$
       $12 = b$
       Perimeter = 2(12 + 8) = **40 cm**

14.   Calculate area using PQ as base:
       $A = \frac{1}{2}(12)(4) = 24$ cm^2

       Area will be the same as with PR as
       base. Let QB be h.
       $24 = \frac{1}{2}(6)(h)$
       $24 = 3h$
       $8 = h$
       QB = **8 cm**

15.   Area = $\frac{1}{2}(9)(4)$ cm^2
            = 18 cm^2
       Let h be BE.
       $18 = \frac{1}{2}(6)h$
       $18 = 3h$
       $6 = h$
       BE = **6 cm**

16.(a) Let b be BC.
        $6 = \frac{1}{2}b(3)$
        $12 = 3b$
        $4 = b$
        Perimeter = 4 + 3 + 5 = **12 cm**

16.(b) Let b be KL.
        $84 = \frac{1}{2}b(7)$
        $168 = 7b$
        $24 = b$
        Perimeter = 24 + 25 + 7 = **56 cm**

17.(a)   1 cm = 0.01 m
           1 cm^2 = (0.01)^2 m^2
                = 0.0001 m^2
        6.5 cm^2 = 6.5 x 0.0001 m^2
                = **0.00065 m^2**

   (b)   1 mm = 0.1 cm
           1 mm^2 = (0.1)^2 cm^2
                = 0.01 cm^2
        1.5 mm^2 = 1.5 x 0.01 cm^2
                = **0.015 cm^2**

   (c)   1 m = 100 cm
           1 m^2 = (100)^2 cm^2
                = 10,000 cm^2
        5.2 m^2 = 5.2 x 10,000 cm^2
                = **52,000 cm^2**

   (d)   1 cm = 10 mm
           1 cm^2 = (10)^2 mm^2
                = 100 mm^2
        44.2 cm^2 = 44.2 x 100 mm^2
                = **4,420 mm^2**

   (e)   1 km = 1,000 m
             1 km^2 = (1,000)^2 m^2
                  = 1,000,000 m^2
             1 km^2 = 10,000 x 100 m^2
                  = 10,000 a
        33.3 km^2 = 33.3 x 10,000 a
                = **333,000 a**

   (f)   1 a = 100 m^2
          3.1 a = 3.1 x 100 m^2
                = **310 m^2**

(g) $1 \text{ m} = 0.001 \text{ km}$
         $1 \text{ m}^2 = (0.001)^2 \text{ km}^2$
               $= 0.000001 \text{ km}^2$
         $62.7 \text{ m}^2 = 62.7 \times 0.000001 \text{ km}^2$
               $= 0.\mathbf{0000627} \text{ km}^2$

(h) $1 \text{ a} = 100 \text{ m}^2$
         $1.1 \text{ a} = 1.1 \times 100 \text{ m}^2$
               $= 110 \text{ m}^2$
         $1 \text{ m}^2 = 10,000 \text{ cm}^2$ (see 17.c)
         $110 \text{ m}^2 = 110 \times 10,000 \text{ cm}^2$
               $= \mathbf{1,100,000} \text{ cm}^2$

(i) $1 \text{ km}^2 = 10,000 \text{ a}$ (see 17.e)
         $3,246.7 \text{ km}^2 = 3,246.7 \times 10,000 \text{ a}$
               $= \mathbf{32,467,000} \text{ a}$

(j) $1 \text{ cm} = 0.00001 \text{ km}$
         $1 \text{ cm}^2 = (0.00001)^2 \text{ km}^2$
         $1 \text{ cm}^2 = 0.0000000001 \text{ km}^2$
         $73,150 \text{ cm}^2 = \mathbf{0.000007315} \text{ km}^2$

(k) $10,000 \text{ a} = 1 \text{ km}^2$ (see 17.e)
         $100 \text{ a} = 0.01 \text{ km}^2$
         $1 \text{ ha} = 0.01 \text{ km}^2$ ($100 \text{ a} = 1 \text{ ha}$)
         $3.4 \text{ ha} = 3.4 \times 0.01 \text{ km}^2$
               $= \mathbf{0.034} \text{ km}^2$

(l) $1 \text{ a} = 0.01 \text{ ha}$
         $46.2 \text{ a} = 46.2 \times 0.01 \text{ ha}$
               $= \mathbf{0.462} \text{ ha}$

18.(a) $s = \sqrt{100\text{mm}^2} = \mathbf{10 \text{ mm}}$

(b) $s = \sqrt{81\text{cm}^2} = \mathbf{9 \text{ cm}}$

(c) $s = \sqrt{225\text{cm}^2} = \mathbf{15 \text{ cm}}$

(d) $s = \sqrt{169\text{m}^2} = \mathbf{13 \text{ m}}$

(e) $s = \sqrt{441\text{km}^2} = \mathbf{21 \text{ km}}$

(f) $s = \sqrt{1,296\text{m}^2} = \mathbf{36 \text{ m}}$

Exercise 12.2 (pp. 341-342)

1. (a) $C = 2 \times \dfrac{22}{7} \times 7 \text{ cm}$
        $= \mathbf{44 \text{ cm}}$
        $A = \dfrac{22}{7} \times 7^2 \text{ cm}^2$
        $= \mathbf{154 \text{ cm}^2}$

(b) $C = 2 \times \dfrac{22}{7} \times 14 \text{ cm}$
        $= \mathbf{88 \text{ cm}}$
        $A = \dfrac{22}{7} \times 14^2 \text{ cm}^2$
        $= \mathbf{616 \text{ cm}^2}$

(c) $C = 2 \times \dfrac{22}{7} \times 16.8 \text{ cm}$
        $= \mathbf{105.6 \text{ cm}}$
        $A = \dfrac{22}{7} \times 16.8^2 \text{ cm}^2$
        $= \mathbf{887.04 \text{ cm}^2}$

(d) $C = 2 \times \dfrac{22}{7} \times 25.2 \text{ cm}$
        $= \mathbf{158.4 \text{ cm}}$
        $A = \dfrac{22}{7} \times 25.2^2 \text{ cm}^2$
        $= \mathbf{1,995.84 \text{ cm}^2}$

(e) $C = 2 \times \dfrac{22}{7} \times 28 \text{ cm}$
        $= \mathbf{176 \text{ cm}}$
        $A = \dfrac{22}{7} \times 28^2 \text{ cm}^2$
        $= \mathbf{2,464 \text{ cm}^2}$

(f) $C = 2 \times \dfrac{22}{7} \times 63 \text{ cm}$
        $= \mathbf{396 \text{ cm}}$
        $A = \dfrac{22}{7} \times 63^2 \text{ cm}^2$
        $= \mathbf{12,474 \text{ cm}^2}$

2. (a) $P = (\dfrac{22}{7} \times \dfrac{1}{2} \times 35) + 35 \text{ cm}$
        $= \mathbf{90 \text{ cm}}$
        $A = \dfrac{1}{2} \times \dfrac{22}{7} \times (\dfrac{1}{2} \times 35)^2 \text{ cm}^2$
        $= \mathbf{481.25 \text{ cm}^2}$

(b) $P = (\dfrac{22}{7} \times \dfrac{1}{2} \times 21) + 21 \text{ cm}$
        $= \mathbf{54 \text{ cm}}$
        $A = \dfrac{1}{2} \times \dfrac{22}{7} \times (\dfrac{1}{2} \times 21)^2 \text{ cm}^2$
        $= \mathbf{173.25 \text{ cm}^2}$

(c)
$$P = (\frac{22}{7} \times \frac{1}{2} \times 14) + 14 \text{ cm}$$
$$= \textbf{36 cm}$$
$$A = \frac{1}{2} \times \frac{22}{7} \times (\frac{1}{2} \times 14)^2 \text{ cm}^2$$
$$= \textbf{77 cm}^2$$

(d)
$$P = (\frac{22}{7} \times \frac{1}{2} \times 8.4) + 8.4 \text{ cm}$$
$$= \textbf{21.6 cm}$$
$$A = \frac{1}{2} \times \frac{22}{7} \times (\frac{1}{2} \times 8.4)^2 \text{ cm}^2$$
$$= \textbf{27.72 cm}^2$$

3. (a)
$$11 \text{ cm} = 2 \times \frac{22}{7} \times r$$
$$77 \text{ cm} = 44r$$
$$\textbf{1}\frac{\textbf{3}}{\textbf{4}} \textbf{ cm} = r$$

(b)
$$21 \text{ cm} = 2 \times \frac{22}{7} \times r$$
$$147 \text{ cm} = 44r$$
$$\textbf{3}\frac{\textbf{15}}{\textbf{44}} \textbf{ cm} = r$$

(c)
$$30 \text{ cm} = 2 \times \frac{22}{7} \times r$$
$$210 \text{ cm} = 44r$$
$$\textbf{4}\frac{\textbf{17}}{\textbf{22}} \textbf{ cm} = r$$

(d)
$$1 \text{ m} = 2 \times \frac{22}{7} \times r$$
$$7 \text{ m} = 44r$$
$$\frac{7}{44} \text{ m} = r$$
$$\frac{7}{44} \text{ m} = \frac{700}{44} \text{ cm} = \textbf{15}\frac{\textbf{10}}{\textbf{11}} \textbf{ cm}$$

4.
$$C = 2\pi r \quad r = \frac{C}{2\pi}$$
$$A = \pi r^2 = \pi\left(\frac{C}{2\pi}\right)^2 = \frac{C^2}{4\pi} = \frac{C^2}{4\left(\frac{22}{7}\right)} = \frac{7}{88}C^2$$

(a)
$$A = \frac{7}{88}\left(29\frac{1}{3}\right)^2$$
$$= \frac{7}{88}\left(\frac{88}{3}\right)^2$$
$$= \frac{7 \times 88}{9}$$
$$= \textbf{68}\frac{\textbf{4}}{\textbf{9}} \textbf{ cm}^2$$

(b)
$$A = \frac{7}{88} \times 44^2$$
$$= 7 \times 22$$
$$= \textbf{154 cm}^2$$

(c)
$$A = \frac{7}{88} \times 132^2$$
$$= 7 \times 3 \times 66$$
$$= \textbf{1,386 cm}^2$$

5.
$$A = \pi r^2 \quad r = \sqrt{\frac{A}{\pi}} = \sqrt{\frac{A}{\frac{22}{7}}} = \sqrt{\frac{7A}{22}}$$

(a)
$$r = \sqrt{\frac{(7)(2,464)}{22}}$$
$$= \textbf{7 cm}$$

(b)
$$r = \sqrt{\frac{(7)(616)}{22}}$$
$$= \textbf{14 cm}$$

(c)
$$r = \sqrt{\frac{(7)(1,386)}{(22)}}$$
$$= \textbf{21 cm}$$

6. $C = 2\pi r = 2\pi\sqrt{\dfrac{A}{\pi}} = 2\left(\dfrac{22}{7}\right)\sqrt{\dfrac{7A}{22}} = \dfrac{44}{7}x\sqrt{\dfrac{7A}{22}}$

(a) $C = \dfrac{44}{7}x\sqrt{\dfrac{(7)(2,464)}{22}}$

$= \dfrac{44}{7} \times 28$

$= \textbf{176 cm}$

(b) $C = \dfrac{44}{7} \times \sqrt{\dfrac{(7)(3,850)}{22}}$

$= \dfrac{44}{7} \times 35$

$= \textbf{220 cm}$

(c) $C = \dfrac{44}{7} \times \sqrt{\dfrac{(7)(5,544)}{22}}$

$= \dfrac{44}{7} \times 42$

$= \textbf{264 cm}$

7. $C = 2\pi r = 2(3.142)(5)$ cm $= 32.42$ cm

45 min is $\dfrac{3}{4}$ of C

$\dfrac{3}{4} \times 32.42 = 23.6$ cm

The tip of the hand will move a distance of **23.6 cm**.

8. C_m for minute hand $= 18\pi$ cm

Hour hand is $\dfrac{2}{3} \times 9$ cm $= 6$ cm long.

C_h for hour hand $= 12\pi$ cm (or: C_h is $\dfrac{2}{3} \times 18\pi = 12\pi$)

Hour hand moves $\dfrac{1}{12}$ of $C_m = \dfrac{1}{12} \times 12\pi = \pi$

Difference $= 18\pi - \pi = 17\pi = 17(3.142) = 53.4$

Minute hand moves **53.4 cm** farther than the hour hand in an hour.

9. $C = 60(3.142) = 188.52$ cm

distance $= 140 \times 188.52$ cm $= 26,392.8$ cm $\approx$ **264 m**

10. $C = 2(20)(3.142)$ cm $= 125.68$ cm

1.1 km $= 110,000$ cm

Number of revolutions $= \dfrac{110,000}{125.68} \approx$ **875**

11.(a) distance $= 100C$

$= 100(20,000 \text{ km})(3.142)$

$= \textbf{6,284,000 km}$

(b) distance $= 100C$

$= 100(20,000 \text{ km})(3.1416)$

$= \textbf{6,283,200 km}$

difference $= 6,284,000 - 6,283,200 = \textbf{800 km}$

Exercise 12.3 (pp. 344-347)

1. (a)   Area of shaded part = area of larger rectangle - area of smaller rectangle.
A = (12 x 9) - (6 x 5) cm^2
   = 108 - 30 cm^2
   = **78 cm^2**

   (b)   Area of shaded part = area of large rectangle - area of each of the small rectangles.
A = (15 x 10) - [(3 x 5) + (4 x 2)]
   = 150 - (15 + 8) cm^2
   = 150 - 23 cm^2
   = **127 cm^2**

2.   Area of floor = area of room - area of carpet
A = (12 x 12) - (10 x 8) = 144 - 80 = **64 m^2**

3.   Area including path is 2 m more in both length and width on both sides, or 4 m total, so is 30 + 4 = 34 m long and 16 + 4 = 20 m wide.
Area of path = area of garden and path - area of path.
A = (34 x 20) - (30 x 16) = 680 - 480 = **200 m^2**

4.   8 m by 12 m = 800 cm by 1,200 cm.
Number of tiles along width = 800 ÷ 20 = 40
Number of tiles along length = 1,200 ÷ 20 = 60
Total number of tiles = 40 x 60 = 2,400 tiles
For every 20 cm-square tile he needs 4 10 cm-square tiles.
Total number of 10 cm tiles = 2,400 x 4 = **9,600 tiles**

5. (a)   Area of path = total area - garden area
   = (18 + 2) x (10 + 2) - (18 x 10)
   = (20 x 12) - 180
   = **60 m^2**

   (b)   Shaded area = garden area - shed area - (4 x bush areas)
   = (18 x 10) - (5 x 3) - 4(1.5)(1.5)
   = 180 - 15 - 9
   = **156 m^2**

   (c)   Fraction not covered = $\dfrac{\text{total} - \text{covered}}{\text{covered}} = \dfrac{180 - 156}{180} = \dfrac{24}{180} = \dfrac{\mathbf{2}}{\mathbf{15}}$

6.   Surface area to be covered = area walls + area ceiling - area windows and door
A = 2(6 x 3) + 2(5 x 3) + (6 x 5) - 2(2 x 1.5) - (2 x 1)
   = 36 + 30 + 30 - 6 - 2
   = 88 m^2
He needs $\dfrac{88}{11}$ = **8 cans**.

7. (a)   The two semicircles = one whole circle
P = 2(124) + 63π = 248 + 63 x $\dfrac{22}{7}$ = 248 + 198 = **446 m**

   (b)   Area = area rectangle + area two semicircles - area pond
   = (124 x 63) + [$\dfrac{22}{7}$ x $\left(\dfrac{63}{2}\right)^2$] - [$\dfrac{22}{7}$ x $\left(\dfrac{21}{2}\right)^2$]
   = 7,812 + 3,118.5 - 346.5
   = **10,584 m^2**

8.   The four semicircles and 4 quarter-circles = 3 whole circles
     P = perimeter of square - 16 radii + circumference of 3 circles

$$= (4 \times 5) - (16 \times 1) + 3(2 \times 1 \times \frac{22}{7})$$

$$= 20 - 16 + 18\frac{6}{7}$$

$$= \mathbf{22\frac{6}{7}}\ \textbf{cm}$$

9.   Area of shaded region = area larger circle - area smaller circle

$$A = \frac{22}{7}(6^2 - 4^2) = \frac{22}{7} \times 20 = \frac{440}{7} = 62\frac{6}{7}\ \text{cm}$$

In finding area for shaded region, 20 is multiplied by π, and in finding area of small circle,

16 is multiplied by π. So the shaded region is $\frac{20}{16} = \mathbf{1\frac{1}{4}}$ **larger** in area than the small

circle.

10. Length of carpet = 20 - 2(1.5) = 17 m
     Width of carpet = 18 - 2(1.5) = 15 m
     Area of carpet = 17 x 15 = 255 m^2
     Cost of carpet = 255 m^2 x \$15 /m^2 = **\$3,825**

11. Each plank is 0.2 m wide. 5 planks are needed for each m.
     Number of planks needed along length of land = 45 x 5 = 225
     Number of planks needed along width of land = 35 x 5 = 175
     Total number of planks = 2(225 + 175) = 800
     Total length = 1.5 m x 800 = **1,200 m**

12. Let w be the width.
     The length is $6w$.
     $154 = 2(w + 6w)$
     $154 = 14w$
     $\quad w = 11$
     width = **11 cm**

13. Let w be the width.
     The length is $4 + w$.
     $100 = 2(w + 4 + w)$
     $100 = 4w + 8$
     $\quad 96 = 4w$
     $\quad\quad w = 23$
     width = **23 cm**

14. Let w be the width.
     The length is $w + 10$.
     $140 = 2(w + w + 10)$
     $140 = 4w + 20$
     $120 = 4w$
     $\quad w = 30$
     width = **30 cm**

15. Let w be the width.
     The length is $w + 3$.
     $34 = 2(w + w + 3)$
     $34 = 4w + 6$
     $28 = 4w$
     $w = 7$ cm
     width = 7 cm
     length = 7 + 3 cm
     $\quad\quad\quad = \textbf{10 cm}$

16.   Let s be the sum of the two parallel sides.

$$A = \frac{1}{2}hs$$

$$264 = \frac{1}{2}(11s)$$

$$528 = 11s$$

$$s = 48$$

Let b be the shorter side. Longer side is $2b$.

$$48 = 2b + b$$
$$\;\;\; = 3b$$
$$b = 16$$

Longer side is $2(16) =$ **32 cm**

17.   Area of one of the unshaded portions = area of square - area of one quadrant

$$A = 7^2 - (\frac{1}{4} \times \frac{22}{7} \times 7^2) = 49 - 38.5 = 10.5$$

Area of shaded region = area of quadrant - area of one unshaded portion
$$A = 38.5 - 10. = 28$$
Area of shaded region = **28 cm²**

18.   Area of all 4 quadrants = area of one circle with radius 7 cm
Area of shaded region = area of square - area of circle

$$A = 14^2 - (\frac{22}{7} \times 7^2) = 196 - 154 = 42$$

Area of shaded region = **42 cm²**

19.   If the lengths are in the ratio of 1 : 2 : 3, then so are the radii. Take the radii to be 1, 2, and 3 units.

Area region $X = (\frac{1}{2}\pi \times 3^2) - (\frac{1}{2}\pi \times 2^2) - (\frac{1}{2}\pi \times 1^2) = \frac{1}{2}\pi(3^2 - 2^2 - 1^2) = \frac{1}{2}\pi \times 4 = 2\pi$

Area region $Y = (\frac{1}{2}\pi \times 3^2) - (\frac{1}{2}\pi \times 2^2) + (\frac{1}{2}\pi \times 1^2) = \frac{1}{2}\pi(3^2 - 2^2 + 1^2) = \frac{1}{2}\pi \times 6 = 3\pi$

Or, area of region Y is one small circle larger. Area of one small circle is π, so area of region Y is $2\pi + \pi = 3\pi$
Area region X : area region Y = **2 : 3**
(Answer in the text is incorrect.)

20.   Consider the shape to be a square of side 7 cm where a quadrant is cut out of the square and moved to the other side. The area would therefore be the area of the original square.
$$A = 7^2 = 49$$
Area of the shaded region = **49 cm²**

21.(a) Draw bisector DB. $BC = AD$ (b)   Let $s = AB = DC$
        Area parallelogram = 2(area $\triangle BCD$) $10s = 180$
        Area $= 2(\frac{1}{2} \times 15 \times 12) =$ **180 cm²** $s = 18$
                                                    perimeter $= 2(18 + 15) =$ **66 cm**

22.   The area of the two quadrants is equal to the area of the rectangle since the area of the overlap (*CDF*) is equivalent to the rest of the area (*ABC*). Two quadrants is a semicircles. Let s be the length *GE*.

$7s = \dfrac{1}{2} \times \dfrac{22}{7} \times 7^2$

$7s = 77$

$s = 11$

$GE = \textbf{11 cm}$

23.   If *OA* is perpendicular to *BA* then Δ *OAB* is a right triangle. If *OA* = *BA* it is an isosceles Δ and ∠ *BOA* is 45º. The area *OCA* is therefore a eighth of a circle. The area *BAC* is the area of the triangle - the area of the eighth-circle with radius OA.

area $BAC = \dfrac{1}{2}(14)(14) - (\dfrac{1}{8} \times \dfrac{22}{7} \times 14^2) = 98 - 77 = 21$

Area of shaded region = area of semicircle (with radius 7) - area BAC

$A = (\dfrac{1}{2} \times \dfrac{22}{7} \times 7^2) - 21 = 77 - 21 = 56$

Area of shaded region = **56 cm²**

24.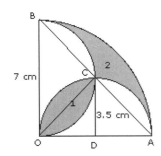

The triangles *ODC* and *ADC* drawn as shown are triangles with base and height 3.5 cm and same area.

Area 1 = area semicircle - 2(area Δ *ODC*)

$= (\dfrac{1}{2} \times \dfrac{22}{7} \times 3.5^2) - 2(\dfrac{1}{2} \times 3.5^2)$

$= 19.25 - 12.25$

$= 7$ cm²

Area 2 = area quadrant - area of Δ *AOB* - area 1

$= (\dfrac{1}{4} \times \dfrac{22}{7} \times 7^2) - (\dfrac{1}{2} \times 7^2) - 7$

$= 38.5 - 24.5 - 7$

$= 7$ cm²

Area shaded region = area 1 + area 2

$= 7 + 7$

$= \textbf{14 cm}^2$

Chapter 13

Exercise 13.1 (pp. 357-359)

1. (a) V = area rectangle x h
     = 2 cm x 3 cm x 5 cm
     = **30 cm³**

    (b) V = area rectangle x h
     = 3 cm x 5 cm x $\frac{1}{2}$ cm

     = **$7\frac{1}{2}$ cm³**

2. Let w be the width. $V = lwh$
  30 cm³ = 5 cm x w x 2 cm
  30 cm³ = 10 cm² x w
   3 cm = w
  The width is **3 cm**.

3. (a) V = area base x h
     = 3 x 4 x 6 cm³
     = **72 cm³**
    S = 2(area base + area opp. sides)
    2[(3 x 4) + (6 x 4) + (6 x 3) cm²
     = 2(12 + 24 + 18) cm²
     = **108 cm²**

    (b) V = area base x h
     = 4³ cm³
     = **64 cm³**
    S = 6 x area square side
     = 6(4 x 4) cm²
     = **96 cm²**

4. (a) Divide into two cuboids.
    V = (2 x 6 x 1) + (2 x 2 x 1) cm³
     = 12 + 4 cm³
     = **16 cm³**

    (b) Volume can be determined by subtracting the small cuboid from the larger.
    V = (3 x 5 x 1) - (1 x 1 x 1) cm³
     = **14 cm³**

5. (a) V = area triangle x h

     = $\frac{1}{2}$(3 x 4) x 6 cm³

     = 6 x 6 cm³
     = **36 cm³**

    (b) V = area triangle x h

     = $\frac{1}{2}$(3 x 10) x 11 cm³

     = 15 x 11 cm³
     = **165 cm³**

  (c) V = area trapezoid x h

     = $\frac{1}{2}$(2) x (5 + 3) x 10 cm³

     = 1 x 8 x 10 cm³
     = **80 cm³**

    (d) V = area trapezoid x h

     = $\frac{1}{2}$(3) x (6 + 5) x 12 cm³

     = 3 x 11 x 6 cm³
     = **198 cm³**

6. Let s be the length of the side.
  27 cm³ = s^3
     s = 3 cm
           S = 6(s^2) cm²
           = 6(3²) cm²
           = 54 cm²

  The surface area is **54 cm³**.

7. S = 2(area base + area each opposite side)
    = 2[(3 x 2) + (3 x 4) + (2 x 4)] sq. units
    = 2(6 + 12 + 8)
    = **52 sq. units**

8. (a)   1 cm = 0.01 m
                $1 \text{ cm}^3 = (0.01)^3 \text{ m}^3$
                       $= 0.000001 \text{ m}^3$
       $11,034 \text{ cm}^3 = 11,034 \times 0.000001 \text{ m}^3$
                       $= \mathbf{0.011034 \text{ m}^3}$

(b)   1 m = 100 cm
             $1 \text{ m}^3 = (100)^3 \text{ cm}^3$
                    $= 1,000,000 \text{ cm}^3$
       $11.5 \text{ m}^3 = 11.5 \times 10^6 \text{ cm}^3$
                    $= \mathbf{11,500,000 \text{ cm}^3}$

(c)   1 mm = 0.1 cm
        $1 \text{ mm}^3 = (0.1)^3 \text{ cm}^3$
                 $= 0.001 \text{ cm}^3$
       $34,567 \text{ mm}^3 = 34,567 \times 0.001 \text{ cm}^3$
                    $= \mathbf{34.567 \text{ cm}^3}$

(d) $1 \text{ cm}^3 = 0.000001 \text{ m}^3$ (see (a))
       $5,699 \text{ cm}^3 = 5,699 \times 0.000001 \text{ m}^3$
                    $= \mathbf{0.005699 \text{ m}^3}$

(e)   1 mm = 0.001 m
        $1 \text{ mm}^3 = (0.001)^3 \text{ m}^3$
                 $= 0.000000001 \text{ m}^3$
       $691,250 \text{ mm}^3 = \mathbf{0.00069125 \text{ m}^3}$

9. (a) $V = \pi r^2 h$
                $= \frac{22}{7}(2)^2 \times 3$ cu. units
                $= \frac{264}{7}$ cu. units
                $= \mathbf{37\frac{5}{7}}$ **cu. units**

(b)   Curved area $= 2\pi r h$
                $= 2 \times \frac{22}{7} \times 2 \times 3$
                $= \mathbf{37\frac{5}{7}}$ **sq. units**

(c)   area base $= \pi r^2$
                $= \frac{22}{7}(2)^2$ sq. units
                $= \mathbf{12\frac{4}{7}}$ **sq. units**

Total area $= 37\frac{5}{7} + (2 \times 12\frac{4}{7})$
                $= 37\frac{5}{7} + 25\frac{1}{7}$
                $= \mathbf{62\frac{6}{7}}$ **sq. units**

10(a)   The radius is 4 cm.
        $V = \pi r^2 h$
                $= \frac{22}{7} \times 4^2 \times 14 \text{ cm}^3$
                $= \mathbf{704 \text{ cm}^3}$

(b) $S = 2\pi r(h + r)$
                $= (2 \times \frac{22}{7} \times 4)(14 + 4)$
                $= \frac{3168}{7}$
                $= \mathbf{452\frac{4}{7} \text{ cm}^2}$

11. $V = 8 \ell = 8,000 \text{ cm}^3$. The radius is 10 cm. Let h be the height.
                $V = \pi r^2 h$
        $8,000 = \frac{22}{7} \times (10)^2 \times h$
        $8,000 = \frac{2,200}{7} h$
                $h \approx \mathbf{25 \text{ cm}}$

12.   All units must be the same. Length of the trough = 6 m = 600 cm
       V = area triangle x length

       $= (\frac{1}{2}$ x 30 x 20) x 600

       = 180,000 cm^3
       It can hold **180,000 cm^3**.

13.(a) Curved area = circumference x h   (b) base area $= \frac{C^2}{4\pi}$ (see ex. 12.2, #4)
                  = 44 x 8 cm^2
                  = **352 cm^2**   base area $= \frac{44^2}{\frac{88}{7}}$ = 154 cm^2

                                                           total area = 2(154) + 352
                                                                      = **660 cm^2**

14.   Curved area = 2πrh

              880 = 2 x $\frac{22}{7}$ x r x 10

              r = 14 cm
       Circumference = 2πr Base area = πr^2

              $= 2 \times \frac{22}{7} \times 14$ $= \frac{22}{7} \times 14^2$

              = **88 cm**   = **616 cm^2**

Exercise 13.2 (pp. 360-361)

1.   Density $= \frac{\text{Mass}}{\text{Volume}}$

   (a) $\frac{1,200 \text{ g}}{150 \text{ cm}^3}$ = **8 g/cm^3**   (b) $\frac{51 \text{ g}}{85 \text{ cm}^3}$ = **0.6 g/cm^3**   (c) $\frac{198 \text{ kg}}{0.22 \text{ m}^3}$ = **900 kg/m^3**

2.   Mass = Density x Volume
   (a) 2.2 g/cm^3 x 350 cm^3 = **770 g**   (b)   0.9 g/cm^3 x 560 cm^2 = **504 g**
   (c) 0.7 g/cm^3 x 400 cm^3 = **280 g**

3.   Volume $= \frac{\text{Mass}}{\text{Density}}$

   (a) $\frac{265.2 \text{ g}}{10.4 \text{ g / cm}^3}$ = **25.5 cm^3** (b) $\frac{28.8 \text{ g}}{0.8 \text{ g / cm}^3}$ = **36 cm^3** (c) $\frac{42.6 \text{ g}}{1.1 \text{ g / cm}^3}$ = **38.$\overline{72}$ cm^3**

4. (a) $V = \pi r^2 h$ (b) Density $= \frac{\text{Mass}}{\text{Volume}}$
        = 3.14 x 1.5^2 x 10 cm^3
        = **70.65 cm^3** $= \frac{423.9 \text{ g}}{70.65 \text{ cm}^3}$

                                                         = **6 g/cm^3**

5. (a) $V = lwh$
   $= 20 \times 35 \times 5 \text{ cm}^3$
   $= \textbf{3,500 cm}^3$

   (b) Mass = Density x Volume
   $= 2.2 \text{ g/cm}^3 \times 3,500 \text{ cm}^3$
   $= \textbf{7,700 g}$

6. Volume $= \dfrac{\text{Mass}}{\text{Density}} = \dfrac{500 \text{ g}}{3.2 \text{ g} / \text{cm}^3} = \textbf{156.25 cm}^3$

7. (a) V = volume top part + volume "leg"
   $= (10 \times 4 \times 1) + (10 \times 5 \times 1)$
   $= 40 + 50 \text{ cm}^3$
   $= \textbf{90 cm}^3$

   (b) Mass = Density x Volume
   $= 7.6 \text{ g/cm}^3 \times 90 \text{ cm}^3$
   $= \textbf{684 cm}^3$

8. Use mass and density to determine volume first. 9.42 kg = 9,420 g.
   Radius is 2 cm.

   Volume $= \dfrac{\text{Mass}}{\text{Density}} = \dfrac{9,420 \text{ g}}{6 \text{ g} / \text{cm}^3} = 1,570 \text{ cm}^3$

   $V = \pi r^2 h$
   $1,570 = 3.14 \times 2^2 \times h$
   $h = 125 \text{ cm}$
   The length of the rod is **125 cm**.

9. Use mass and density to determine volume first.

   Volume $= \dfrac{\text{Mass}}{\text{Density}} = \dfrac{520 \text{ g}}{6.5 \text{ g} / \text{cm}^3} = 80 \text{ cm}^2$

   $80 = 2 \times 5 \times h$
   $80 = 10 \times h$
   $h = 8$
   The length of the metal is **8 cm**.

Exercise 13.3 (pp. 363-366)

1. (a) diam. of hollow = outer diam. - both walls = 10 cm - 2(2 cm) = **6 cm**

   (b) inner curved surface area = $2\pi rh = 2 \times \dfrac{22}{7} \times 3 \times 70 = \textbf{1,320 cm}^2$

   (c) outer curved surface area = $2\pi rh = 2 \times \dfrac{22}{7} \times 5 \times 70 = \textbf{2,200 cm}^2$

2. Volume = volume top layer + volume bottom layer. Radii are 10 and 15 cm.
   $= (3.14 \times 10^2 \times 3) + (3.14 \times 15^2 \times 3) \text{ cm}^3$
   $= 942 + 2,119.5 \text{ cm}^3$
   $= \textbf{3,061.5 cm}^3$

3. Volume = 2 x volume of wheels + volume of rod. Radius of rod is 1 cm.
   $= 2(3.14 \times 5^2 \times 3) + (3.14 \times 1^2 \times 4) \text{ cm}^3$
   $= 2(235.5) + (12.56) \text{ cm}^3$
   $= \textbf{483.56 cm}^3$

4. (a) Volume $= \dfrac{3}{4}$ x volume whole cheese $= \dfrac{3}{4} \times 3.14 \times 6^2 \times 4 \text{ cm}^3 = \textbf{339.12 cm}^2$

(b)   Surface area = curved surface area + 2(top area) + 2(cut side)

Curved surface area = $\frac{3}{4}$ of total surface area = $\frac{3}{4}$ x 3.14 x 12 x 4 = 113.04 cm^2

Area of top (or bottom) = $\frac{3}{4}$ of whole circle = $\frac{3}{4}$ x 3.14 x 6^2 = 84.78 cm^2

Area of one cut side = 6 x 4 = 24 cm^2

Surface area = 113.04 + (2 x 84.78) + (2 x 24) = **330.6 cm^2**

5.   Each side of a single cube has an area of 1 cm^2. There are 9 exposed sides facing left, 9 facing right, 10 facing forward, 10 facing backwards, 9 facing up, and 9 facing down. So there are 10 + 10 + 9 + 9 + 9 + 9 = 56 exposed sides.

Total surface area = **56 cm^2**

6.   The length of the trough is 10 m = 1,000 cm

Think of this as a rectangular prism on top of a triangular.

The dimensions of the rectangular prism are 40 cm by 1,000 cm by 5 cm.

The height of the triangle at the base of the triangular prism is 25 cm - 5 cm = 20 cm.

Volume = (5 x 40 x 1,000) + ($\frac{1}{2}$ x 40 x 20 x 1,000)

= 200,000 + 400,000

= 600,000

It can hold **600,000 cm^3**.

7.   The bricks would displace a volume equivalent to the volume of the tank not filled with

water. The height remaining above the water is $\frac{1}{4}$ m = 25 cm. Lengths can be changed

to cm so tank is 300 cm by 200 cm by 100 cm and bricks are 20 cm by 12.5 cm by 10 cm.

Volume left for bricks = 300 x 200 x 25 = 1,500,000 cm^3

Volume of one brick = 20 x 12.5 x 10 = 2,500 cm^3

Number of bricks that can displace remaining volume = $\frac{1,500,000}{2,500}$ = **600**

8.   16 - 4 = 12; 28 - 4 = 24; 40 - 4 = 36

Internal measurements are 12 cm by 24 cm by 36 cm.

Volume metal used = external volume - internal volume

= (16 x 28 x 40) - (12 x 24 x 36) cm^3

= 17,920 - 10,368 cm^3

= **7,552 cm^3**

9.   Volume of stone is volume of water displaced.

Volume = 25 x 50 x 1 = **1,250 cm^3**

10.   Volume = volume cylinder - volume rectangular hole

= (3.14 x 10^2 x 12) - (3 x 4 x 12) cm^3

= 3,768 - 144 cm^3

= **3,624 cm^3**

11.   Shape of pool can be divided into a
        rectangular prism and a triangular prism
        with height 5.5 - 1.5 = 4 m.
        Volume = (1.5 x 50 x 25) +

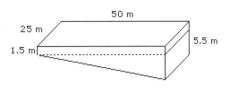
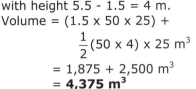

$$\frac{1}{2}(50 \times 4) \times 25 \text{ m}^3$$

$$= 1{,}875 + 2{,}500 \text{ m}^3$$

$$= \mathbf{4{,}375 \text{ m}^3}$$

12.(a) Pentagonal prism can be divided into two trapezoidal prisms. For the bases, the height of
        one trapezoid is 12 cm and the two parallel sides are 11 and 16 cm, the height of the
        other is 16 cm and the two parallel sides are 14 and 26 cm.
        Base area = volume of each trapezoidal prism

$$= \frac{1}{2} \times 12 \times (11 + 16) + \frac{1}{2} \times 16 \times (14 + 26)$$

$$= 162 + 320$$

$$= 482 \text{ cm}^2$$

        Volume = 482 x 12 cm^3 = **5,784 cm³**

   (b) All the rectangles around the sides have the same height.
        Total surface area = surface area of bases + area of 5 rectangles around side.

$$= (2 \times 482) + [12 \times (13 + 26 + 20 + 14 + 12 + 11)]$$

$$= 964 + (12 \times 96)$$

$$= \mathbf{2{,}116 \text{ cm}^2}$$

13.   Distance water flows in 1 min = 70 cm/s x 60 s = 4,200 cm
        Distance water flows in 5 min = 4,200 cm x 5 = 21,000 cm
        Radius of pipe is 1.5 cm.

$$V = \pi r^2 h = \frac{22}{7} \times 1.5^2 \times 21{,}000 = 148{,}500 \text{ cm}^3 = \mathbf{148.5\ \ell}$$

14.   Distance water flows in 1 min = 3.5 m/s x 60 s = 210 m = 21,000 cm.
        The volume it occupies during that minute is the internal volume of the pipe, taking
        21,000 cm to be the length. The internal radius of the pipe is one half of 3 cm, or 1.5
        cm.

$$V = \pi r^2 h = \pi \times 1.5^2 \times 21{,}000 \text{ cm}^3$$

        The volume of the water level in the tank will be the same. Let h be the height of the
        water. The internal radius is half of 30 cm, or 15 cm.

$$V = \pi \times 15^2 \times h$$

$$h = \frac{V}{\pi \times 15^2} = \frac{\pi \times 1.5^2 \times 21{,}000}{\pi \times 15^2} = \frac{15^2 \times 21{,}000}{(10 \times 1.5)^2} = \frac{15^2 \times 21{,}000}{100 \times 15^2} = \mathbf{210 \text{ cm}}$$

15.   The volume of the tank is 2 x 2 x 1 = 4 m^3
      Distance water flows in 1 min = 2 m/s x 60 s = 120 m
      The volume the water occupies in the pipe needs to be the same as the volume of the
      tank. Radius of the pipe is half of 7 cm = 3.5 cm = 0.035 m.
      Let h be the length of pipe.

$$h = \frac{4}{\pi \times 0.035^2} = \frac{4}{\frac{22}{7} \times 0.035^2} = \frac{4 \times 7}{22 \times 0.035^2} = 1{,}038.96 \text{ m}$$

      The length of the pipe the water travels to occupy a volume equivalent to the tank is
      1,038.96 m. The water flows 120 m in 1 minute.

$$\frac{1038.96}{120} = 8{,}658$$

      It flows the required distance in about **9 minutes**.

16.   Let h be the length of the original pipe. The radius is 3 cm.
      Volume of original pipe = $\pi \times 3^2 \times h = 9\pi h$
      The new pipe is 80% longer, so its height is 1.8h.
      Let t be the thickness of the new pipe. External radius is 3 cm. Radius of hole in the
      center is (3 - t) cm.
      Volume of new pipe = volume of entire pipe - volume of hole
$$= (\pi \times 3^2 \times 1.8h) - \pi \times [(3 - t)^2 \times 1.8h]$$
$$= 1.8\pi h[(3^2 - (3 - t)^2]$$
$$= 1.8\pi h[9 - (3 - t)^2]$$
      Volume of old pipe = volume of new pipe
$$9\pi h = 1.8\pi h[(9 - (3 - t)^2]$$
$$5 = 9 - (3 - t)^2 \qquad\qquad \text{divide both sides by } 1.8\pi h$$
$$(3 - t)^2 = 4$$
      3 - t = 2 or 3 - t = -2
      t = 1 or t = 5
      5 is not a possible answer if the external radius is 3 cm.
      The thickness of the pipe is **1 cm**.

17.   The metal displaces a volume of water equal to its own volume. The radius of the
      container is 14 cm. The mass of the metal is 91 kg = 91,000 g.

$$\text{Volume of metal} = \frac{\text{mass}}{\text{density}} = \frac{91{,}000 \text{ g}}{6.3 \text{ g/cm}^3}$$

      Let h be the height the water rises.
      Volume of water displaced = 3.14 x 14^2 x h
      Volume of water displaced = Volume of metal

$$3.14 \times 14^2 \times h = \frac{91{,}000}{6.3}$$
$$h = \frac{91{,}000}{6.3 \times 3.14 \times 14^2}$$
$$h = 23.47$$

      The water rises to a height of about **23 cm**.

18.   The volume of the space is 1,717 ml = 1,717 cm^3.
       Radius of cylinder = 10 cm
       1,717 cm^3 = volume of box - volume of cylinder
         1,717 = (20 x 20 x 20) - π x 10^2 x 20
         1,717 = 8,000 - 2,000π
       2,000π = 6,238
            π = 3.1415

   (a) π = **3.142**

   (b) π = **3.14**

19.   The cross-section of this part could be considered a rectangle of length 30 cm and height 16 cm from which was cut two rectangles with total length 30 - 20 = 10 cm and height 10 cm and a semicircle of radius 9 cm.

       Area = (30 x 16) - (10 x 10) - ($\frac{1}{2}$ x $\frac{22}{7}$ x 9^2) = 480 - 100 - 127.29 = 252.71 cm^2

       Volume = 252.71 x 8 = 2,021.68
       Volume of the part is about **2,022 cm^3**

20.   The cross-section of this part could be considered a rectangle of base 10 cm and height 2 cm, from which was cut two triangles of total base 10 - 6 cm = 4 cm and height 2 cm, to which was added a semicircle of radius 3 cm, and from which was cut a circle of radius 1 cm. The depth is 4 mm = 0.4 cm.
       Area = area of rectangle - area of triangles + area of semicircle - area of circle

       Area = (10 x 2) - ($\frac{1}{2}$ x 4 x 2) + ($\frac{1}{2}$ x 3.14 x 3^2) - (3.14 x 1^2)

              = 20 - 4 + 14.13 - 3.14
              = 26.99 cm^2
       Volume = 26.99 x 0.4 = 10.796 cm^3
       Mass = Density x volume = 7.2 g/cm^3 x 10.796 cm^3 = 77.7312 g
       Mass of 2,000 pieces = 2,000 x 77.7312 g = 155,462.4 g = **155.5 kg**

Chapter 14

Exercise 14.1 (pp. 377-381)

1. (a)   yes   (b)   yes   (c)   No. second one should start at Q.

     (d)   No. Points should be listed in order.   (e)   yes   (f)   yes

2.(a)(i) XY (ii) YZ (iii) ZX

    (iv) $\angle X$ (v) $\angle Y$ (vi) $\angle Z$

  (b)(i) US (ii) ST (iii) TU

    (iv) $\angle U$ (v) $\angle S$ (vi) $\angle T$

  (c)(i) GH (ii) HE (iii) EF

    (iv) FG (v) $\angle G$ (vi) $\angle H$

   (vii) $\angle E$ (viii) $\angle F$

3. (a) $\dfrac{8}{4} = \dfrac{2}{1} = \dfrac{4}{x} = \dfrac{y}{5}$

       $2x = 4$

       $\boldsymbol{x = 2}$

       $\boldsymbol{y = 10}$

    (b) $\dfrac{6}{10} = \dfrac{3}{5} = \dfrac{8}{x} = \dfrac{3}{y} = \dfrac{w}{8\frac{1}{3}}$

        $3x = 40$

          $\boldsymbol{x = \dfrac{40}{3} = 13\dfrac{1}{3}}$

        $3y = 15$

        $\boldsymbol{y = 5}$

        $5w = 25$

        $\boldsymbol{w = 5}$

   (c)   One of the shapes needs to be "flipped" to correspond to the other.

       $\dfrac{3}{1} = \dfrac{x}{5}$

       $\boldsymbol{x = 15}$

    (d)   One of the shapes needs to be "flipped" to correspond to the other.

        $\dfrac{6}{4} = \dfrac{3}{2} = \dfrac{x}{3} = \dfrac{7\frac{1}{2}}{y}$

        $2x = 9$

          $\boldsymbol{x = \dfrac{9}{2} = 4\dfrac{1}{2}}$

        $3y = 15$

        $\boldsymbol{y = 5}$

4. (a) $\angle A = \angle P$
       $\angle B = \angle Q$
       $\angle C = \angle R$
       $\angle D = \angle S$
       $x = \angle P = \angle A = \boldsymbol{60^o}$
       $y = \angle R = \angle C = \boldsymbol{120^o}$

   (b) $\angle W = \angle E$
       $\angle X = \angle F$
       $\angle Y = \angle G$
       $\angle Z = \angle H$
       $a = \angle W = \angle E = \boldsymbol{130^o}$
       $b = \angle Y = \angle G = \boldsymbol{50^o}$

   (c) $\angle A = \angle X$
       $\angle B = \angle Y$
       $\angle C = \angle Z$
       $q = \angle Z = \angle C = \boldsymbol{70^o}$
       $p = \angle Y = \angle B = \boldsymbol{45^o}$

5.-6.   In 5.(a) one figure is "flipped" relative to the others. In all the others, one figure is rotated relative to the other.

5. (a) $x = 8$
      $y = 6$

(b) $x = 5$
      $y = 4$
      $z = 2$

(c) $w = 11$
      $x = 5$
      $y = 9$
      $z = 4$

(d) $a = 3$
      $b = 5$
      $c = 4$
      $d = 1$
      $e = 2$

6. (a) $a = 113°$
      $b = 85°$
      $c = 87°$
      $d = 75°$

(b) $a = 30°$
      $b = 110°$
      $c = 90°$
      $d = 90°$
      $e = 130°$

(c) $a = 24°$
      $b = 65°$
      $c = 92°$

(d) $a = 240°$
      $b = 75°$
      $c = 120°$
      $d = 115°$
      $e = 100°$
      $f = 70°$

7.   All the right triangles are similar.
       $\triangle ABC$, $\triangle AFE$, $\triangle DGC$, $\triangle EBD$

8.   There are 5 sets. $\triangle AFG$, $\triangle BDH$, $\triangle CEI$
       $\triangle ABH$, $\triangle BCI$, $\triangle CAG$ $\triangle ABD$, $\triangle BCE$, $\triangle CAF$
       $\triangle AEH$, $\triangle BFI$, $\triangle CDG$ $\triangle AEB$, $\triangle BFC$, $\triangle CDA$

Exercise 14.2 (pp. 384-386)

1.   All can tessellate except for (h). See answers in text for drawings.

2.   Let a be the interior angle of the regular polygon. If the regular polygon can tessellate, then a must be a factor of $360°$, or $\dfrac{360}{a}$ must be a whole number. The interior angle of a regular polygon is $\dfrac{180(n-2)}{n}$.

So $\dfrac{360}{\dfrac{180(n-2)}{n}} = \dfrac{2n}{n-2}$ must be a whole number.

(a) $n = 8$; $\dfrac{2n}{n-2} = \dfrac{16}{6}$
A regular octagon will not tessellate.

(b) $n = 5$; $\dfrac{2n}{n-2} = \dfrac{10}{3}$
A regular pentagon will not tessellate.

(c) $n = 6$; $\dfrac{2n}{n-2} = \dfrac{12}{4} = 3$
A regular hexagon will tessellate.

(d) $n = 4$; $\dfrac{2n}{n-2} = \dfrac{8}{2} = 4$
A regular square will tessellate.

(e) $n = 9$; $\dfrac{2n}{n-2} = \dfrac{18}{7}$
A regular nonagon will not tessellate.

(f) $n = 10$; $\dfrac{2n}{n-2} = \dfrac{20}{8}$
A regular decagon will not tessellate.

3. (a) This figure can tessellate. Derived from a square with cut and paste.

(b) This figure will not tessellate. Was not derived from a tessellating figure.

(b) This figure can tessellate. Derived from a regular triangle with cut and paste.

4. - 6.   Answers will vary. See answers in text for examples.

Exercise 14.3 (pp. 390-392)

1.   1 cm : 20,000 cm = 1 cm : 0.2 km
        5.2 cm : 5.2 x 0.2 km
        5.2 cm : 1.04 km
        The railway is **1.04 km** long.

2.   1 cm : 2 m
        1 cm : 200 cm
          1 : 200
        1 cm : 2 m = 0.5 cm : 1 m
        2.5 m : 2.5 x 0.5 cm
        2.5 m : 1.25 cm
        1.5 m : 1.5 x 0.5 cm
        1.5 m : 0.75 cm
        length = 1.25 cm, width = 0.75 cm

3.   Let d be the distance between the roads.

$$\frac{5 \text{ cm}}{1 \text{ km}} = \frac{4 \text{ cm}}{d \text{ km}}$$

        $5d = 4$
          $d = 0.8$ km
          1 km : 3 cm on the other map.
        0.8 km : 0.8 x 3 cm
              : 2.4 cm
        The distance would be **2.4 cm** on the other map.

4.   1 km : 2.5 cm
        20 km : 20 x 2.5 cm
               : 50 cm
        Their distance would be 50 cm on the first map.
        Let d be the distance on the second map.

$$\frac{1 \text{ cm}}{15,000 \text{ km}} = \frac{1 \text{ cm}}{0.15 \text{ km}} = \frac{d \text{ cm}}{20 \text{ km}}$$

        $0.15d = 20$

$$d = 133\frac{1}{3}$$

        The distance on the second map would be **$133\frac{1}{3}$ cm**.

5.   Let d be the distance on the map.

$$\frac{1 \text{ mm}}{200,000 \text{ mm}} = \frac{1 \text{ mm}}{0.2 \text{ km}} = \frac{d \text{ mm}}{120 \text{ km}}$$

        $0.2d = 120$
           $d = 600$
        The distance on the map is **600 mm**.

6.   1 cm : 500,000 cm
        1 cm : 5 km
        14 cm : 14 x 5 km
        14 cm : 70 km
        The actual distance is **70 km**.

7.   Let d be the distance on the map.

$$\frac{1 \text{ cm}}{100,000 \text{ cm}} = \frac{1 \text{ cm}}{1,000 \text{ m}} = \frac{d \text{ cm}}{45,520 \text{ m}}$$

        $1,000d = 45,520$
            $d = 45.52$
        The distance on the map between the two points is 45.52 cm.
        1 cm : 100,000 cm
        1 cm : 1 km
        4.3 cm : 4.3 km
        The length of the stream is **4.3 km**.

8.   Muar to Batu Bahat is about 2 cm.
        Scale is about 4.8 cm : 100 km
        Let d be the actual distance between Muar and Batu Bahat.

$$\frac{4.8 \text{ cm}}{100 \text{ km}} = \frac{2.2 \text{ cm}}{d \text{ km}}$$

        $4.8d = 220$
           $d \approx 46$
        Distance between the two cities is about **46 km**.

Revision 4

Revision 4A (pp. 398-399)

1. $A = \pi r^2$

$$\frac{77}{2} = \frac{22}{7}r^2$$

$$\frac{77}{2} \times \frac{7}{22} = r^2$$

$$\frac{49}{4} = r^2$$

$$\frac{7}{2} = r$$

diameter $= 2r =$ **7 cm**

2. (a) $V =$ base area x height
   $= 3 \times 5 \times 6$ cm^3
   $=$ **90 cm^3**

   (b) $V =$ base area x height
   $= 3 \times 4 \times 6$ cm^3
   $=$ **72 cm^3**

3. (a) 2 x area base x area curved surface
   $= 2\pi r^2 \times 2\pi rh$
   $= \mathbf{2\pi r(r + h)}$

   (b) $112\pi = 2\pi r(r + h)$
   $56 = r^2 + rh$

$$h = \frac{56 - r^2}{r}$$

$$r = 1, h = \frac{56 - 1}{1} = 55$$

$$r = 2, h = \frac{56 - 4}{2} = 26$$

$$r = 4, h = \frac{56 - 16}{4} = 10$$

$$r = 7, h = \frac{56 - 49}{7} = 1$$

4. (a) The corner blocks would have 3 green faces. There are **8** of them.

   (b) The blocks along the edges, except for the corner blocks, would have 2 green faces. There are **12** of them.

   (c) The blocks in the middle, not along an edge, would have 1 green face. There are **4** of them.

5. $C = 2\pi r$

$$88 = 2 \times \frac{22}{7}r$$

$$\frac{7 \times 88}{2 \times 22} = r$$

$$14 = r$$

radius $=$ **14 cm**

6. (a) $A = \frac{1}{2}(6 \times 2) \text{ cm}^2$

   $\qquad = \textbf{6 cm}^2$

   (b) $A = \frac{1}{2}(3 \times 5) + \frac{1}{2}(4 \times 3) \text{ cm}^2$

   $\qquad = 7\frac{1}{2} + 6 \text{ cm}^2$

   $\qquad = \textbf{13}\frac{1}{2} \textbf{ cm}^2$

7. $\quad V = (4 \text{ cm} \times 6 \text{ cm} \times 8 \text{ cm}) - (4 \text{ cm}^2 \times 8 \text{ cm}) = 192 \text{ cm}^3 - 32 \text{ cm}^3 = \textbf{160 cm}^3$

8. $\quad$ Surface area that needs to be painted is 5 x [one base x curved surface].
   Radius is 5 cm = 0.05 m.
   $S = 5(\pi r^2 + 2\pi rh) \text{ cm}^3 = 5\pi r(r + 2h)$
   $\quad = (5)(3.142)(0.05)[(0.05 + (2)(8)] = (0.7855)(16.05) \approx 12.61 \text{ m}^2$
   Cost of paint = 12.61 m² x \$4.50/m² $\approx$ **\$57**

9. $\quad$ Yes, one way of making a tessellating pentagon is to cut and paste from a regular tessellating polygon, such as a square. Example:

10.(a) Since $\triangle APQ$ is similar to $\triangle AXY$, $\angle AXY = \angle AXY$. Since these are corresponding angles with the transversal being PA, $XY \parallel PQ$.

   (b) If the triangles are similar, their heights are proportional. Let h be AR
   $$\frac{4}{6} = \frac{5}{h}$$
   $4h = 30$
   $h = \textbf{7.5}$

   (c) $XYQP$ is a trapezium. Its height is $AR - AZ = 7.5 - 5 = 2.5$ cm.
   $A = \frac{1}{2}(2.5)(6 + 4) \text{ cm}^2$
   $\quad = (2.5)(5) \text{ cm}^2$
   $\quad = \textbf{12.5 cm}^2$

Revision 4B (pp. 399-400)

1. $\quad$ Volume = 30 cm x 15 cm x 1.35 cm = 607.5 cm³
   Mass = Density x volume = 2.5 g/cm³ x 607.5 cm³ $\approx$ **1,518 g**

2. (a) $A = 2[\frac{1}{2}(6)(2)] \text{ cm}^2$

   $\qquad = \textbf{12 cm}^2$

   (b) $A = \frac{1}{2}(5)(6) \text{ cm}^2$

   $\qquad = \textbf{15 cm}^2$

3. $\quad$ 1 m³ = (100)³ cm³ = 1,000,000 cm³ = 1,000 ℓ
   135,000 ℓ = 135 m³
   135 = (24.5)(13.5)h
   $\quad h \approx 0.408$ m = 40.8 cm
   The tank is **40.8** cm deep.

4. (a) $A = s^2$
   400 cm² = s^2
   $\quad$ 20 cm = s
   Its side is **20 cm** long.

   (b) A decrease of 20% is 80% of the side.
   80% of 20 cm = 16 cm
   $A = 16^2 \text{ cm}^2$
   $\quad = \textbf{256 cm}^2$

5.   Surface area S_W of each inside wall is area of
the rectangle.
$S_W = 2$ m x 8 m $= 16$ m^2
Surface area S_A of internal face of arch is half
the internal curved surface of a cylinder.

$S_A = \dfrac{1}{2}(2\pi rh)$

$= \pi rh$
$= (3.14)(1.75)(8)$ m^2
$= 43.96$ m^2
Total surface area S:
$S = 2(S_W) + S_A$
$= 2(16) + 43.96$ m^2
$= $ **75.96 m^2**

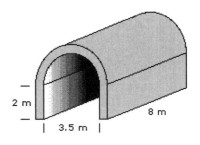

2 m

| 3.5 m |

8 m

6. (a)   1 cm : 20 cm
30 cm : 30 x 20 cm
30 cm : 600 cm
30 cm : 6 m
The boat is **6 m** long.

Let h be the length of the mast of the
model in meters.

$\dfrac{1\,m}{20\,m} = \dfrac{h\,m}{7\,m}$

$20h = 7$
$h = 0.35$
The length of the model's mast is 0.35 m
$= $ **35 cm**.

7.   The "steps" can be moved to form a rectangle. So the
perimeter is the same as that of the rectangle.
Perimeter $= 2(10$ cm $+ 6$ cm$)$
$= $ **32 cm**

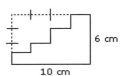

6 cm

10 cm

8.   Area of 4 walls $= 4(470$ cm$)(210$ cm$) = 394{,}800$ cm^2
1 m$^3 = 10{,}000$ cm^3
2.7 m$^2 = 2.7$ x $10{,}000$ cm$^2 = 27{,}000$ cm^2
Area that needs to be painted $= 394{,}800$ cm$^2 - 27{,}000$ cm$^2 = 367{,}800$ cm^2
Let c be the cost in dollars

$\dfrac{c}{0.50} = \dfrac{367{,}800}{500}$

$500c = 183{,}900$
$c = 367.80$
The cost of painting the walls is **$367.80**

9.   A tessellating octagon can be derived from a square.
Example:

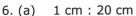

10. $\dfrac{FE}{ED} = \dfrac{3}{2}$ given

$\dfrac{ED}{CB} = \dfrac{AE}{AC}$ $\triangle ABC$ and $\triangle ADE$ are similar.

$\dfrac{ED}{CB} = \dfrac{FE}{AC}$ $AE = FE$ since $\triangle FGE$ and $\triangle ADE$ are congruent.

$(ED)(AC) = (FE)(CB)$

$\dfrac{AC}{CB} = \dfrac{FE}{ED}$ multiply both sides by $(ED)(CB)$

$\dfrac{AC}{5} = \dfrac{3}{2}$ $CB = 5$ cm

$AC = \dfrac{3}{2}(5)$

$AC = \mathbf{7.5}$ **cm**

Revision 4C (pp. 400-401)

1. (a)   Area of parallelogram = bh = 6 cm x 3 cm = 18 cm^2

Area of triangle = $\dfrac{1}{2}bh = \dfrac{1}{2}$ (6 x 3) = 9 cm^2

Area of trapezium = $\dfrac{1}{2}h(a + b) = \dfrac{1}{2}$ (1)(6 + 3) = 4.5 cm^2

Total area = 18 + 9 + 4.5 = **31.5 cm^2**
(answer in text is incorrect)

   (b)   Area of rectangle = bh = 8 cm x 18 cm = 144 cm^2

Area of trapezium = $\dfrac{1}{2}h(a + b) = \dfrac{1}{2}(18 - 9)[(18 - 8) + 7] = \dfrac{1}{2}(9)(17) = 76.5$ cm^2

Total area = 144 cm^2 + 76.5 cm^2 = **220.5 cm^2**

2.   Volume of liquid = 250 cm x 100 cm x 70 cm = 1,750,000 cm^3
Let h be the height of the liquid in the new tank.
1,750,000 cm^3 = (300 cm)(150 cm)h
          $h \approx 38.9$ cm
The depth of the water is about **38.9 cm**.

3.   Radius of hole = 10 cm - 3 cm = 7 cm. Length is 1.5 m = 150 cm
Volume of pipe = external volume - volume of hole
          = $\pi r_e^2 h - \pi r_h^2 h$
          = $\pi h(r_e^2 - r_h^2)$
          = (3.14)(150)(10^2 - 7^2) cm^3
          = 24,021 cm^3
He needs **24,021 cm^3** of cement.

4.   Radius of cake A is 12 cm and radius of cake B is 16 cm. Let h be the thickness.
     Volume cake A $= \pi 12^2 h = 144\pi h$ cm^3
     Volume cake B $= \pi 16^2 h = 256\pi h$ cm^3

     Cost per πh cm^3 of cake A $= \dfrac{5.5}{144} = 0.038$

     Cost per πh cm^3 of cake B $= \dfrac{9}{256} = 0.035$

     Cake B is a better buy.

5.   Area of tile = 21 cm x 20 cm = 420 cm^2
     Area of floor = 480 cm x 420 cm

     Number of tiles needed $= \dfrac{(480)(420)}{420} = 480$

     480 tiles are needed.

6. (a) $A = \dfrac{1}{2}(2)(4.6) + \dfrac{1}{2}(3)(4)$ cm^2
        $\quad = 4.6 + 6$ cm^2
        $\quad = \mathbf{10.6}$ **cm^2**

   (b) A = central rect. + 2(side trapeziums)
        $\quad = (18)(14) + 2(\dfrac{1}{2})(5)(12 + 18)$ cm^2
        $\quad = 252 + 150$ cm^2
        $\quad = \mathbf{402}$ **cm^2**

7.   volume water = 2,500 cm x 1,500 cm x 60 cm = 225,000,000 cm^3
     1,000 cm^3 = 1 ℓ
     225,000,000 cm^3 = 225,000 ℓ
     225,000 ℓ is needed.

8.   7,850 ℓ = 7,850,000 cm^3
     1 m^3 = 100^3 cm^3 = 1,000,000 cm^3
     7,850,000 cm^3 = 7.850 m^3
     Discharge of water in 1 min = 7.850 m^3
     Discharge of water in 1 h = 60 x 7.850 m^3 = 471 m^3
     Capacity of tank = 30 m x 20 m x 5 m = 3,000 m^3
       471 m^3 in 1 h

     3,000 m^3 in $\dfrac{1}{471}(3,000)$ h = 6.4 h

     It will take about **6 h** to fill the tank.

9.   This problem requires the Pythagorean theorem to solve, and therefore is inappropriate
     here.
     Height of rhombus is one leg of equilateral triangle. Let h be this height.
     $h^2 + h^2 = 20^2$ (Pythagorean theorem)
     $\quad 2h^2 = 400$
     $\quad\quad h^2 = 200$
     $h = \sqrt{200}\ = 14.14$ cm
     Area of rhombus = 20 cm x 14.14 cm = 282.8 cm^3
     Area of floor = 1,200 cm x 800 cm = 960,000 cm

     Number of tiles needed $= \dfrac{960,000}{282.8} = 3,394.62$

     About **3,395 tiles** are needed.

10.   If pentagons *ABCDE* and *PQRST* are similar, then $\triangle PQT$ and $\triangle ABE$ are similar (their sides are proportional).

Since $\triangle ARS$ is congruent to $\triangle PQT$, then $\triangle ARS$ is similar to $\triangle ABE$.

Therefore $\angle ARS = \angle ABE$ and $RS \parallel BE$ (corr. $\angle$s)

BESR is a trapezium.

S is the midpoint of *AE*, so *AE* is twice the length of *AS*. Since $\triangle ARS$ is similar to $\triangle ABE$, then *BE* is twice the length of *RS*.

Let *s* be the length of *RS*. 2*s* = the length of *BE*.

Let *h* be the height of $\triangle ARS$. The height of $\triangle ABE$ is 2*s* (since it is similar). So the height of trapezium *BESR* is 2*s* - *s* = *s*

Area $\triangle ARS = \dfrac{1}{2}sh$ = area $\triangle PQT$ ($\triangle ARS$ is congruent to $\triangle PQT$)

Area $BESR = \dfrac{1}{2}h(s + 2s) = \dfrac{1}{2}h(3s)$

$$\frac{\text{Area } \triangle PQT}{\text{Area } BESR} = \frac{\dfrac{1}{2}sh}{\dfrac{1}{2}h(3s)} = \frac{s}{3s} = \frac{1}{3}$$

Miscellaneous Exercise 4 (pp. 402-404)

1. (a)   Numerator and denominator increase by 1. Next term is $\dfrac{6}{7}$.

   (b)   28, 14, 7, 3.5, 1.75, **0.875**. Each term is half the preceding term.

2.   6 line segments. If A, B, and C are the
         ones on a straight line:
         AB, BC, AC, AD, BD, CD.

3.   Let a be the angle. The complementary
         angle is $90 - a$ and the supplementary
         angle is $180 - a$.

$$90 - a = \frac{1}{4}(180 - a)$$

$$360 - 4a = 180 - a$$
$$180 = 3a$$
$$60 = a$$

   The angle is **60°**.

4.   Let a be the angle. $180 - a$ is the
         supplementary angle and $90 - a$ is the
         complementary angle.

$$(180 - a) - 20 = 2(90 - a)$$
$$160 - a = 180 - 2a$$
$$a = 20$$

   The angle is **20°**.

5.   Let x be the width. The length is $3x$. Length reduced by 5 is $3x - 5$.
         Width increased by 3 is $x + 3$.

$$3x - 5 = 2(x + 3)$$
$$3x - 5 = 2x + 6$$
$$x = 11$$
$$3x = 33$$

   Width is 11 cm and length is 33 cm.

6. (a)   Area of shaded part = area large square - 4(area each corner)
         $A = (20)(15) - 4(2)(2)$ cm^2 = 300 - 16 cm^2 = 284 cm^2
         Area is **284 cm²**.

   (b)   Length of base of box is 20 cm - 2(2 cm) and width is 15 cm - 2(2 cm).
         $V = $ (base)(height) $= [(20 - 4)(15 - 4)](2) = (16)(11)(2) = 352$
         Volume is **352 cm³**.

7. (a) $x = 8 - 5$ cm = **3 cm**
         $y = 5 - 2$ cm = **3 cm**

   (b)   Area of central triangle = area of square - area of the other three triangles.

$$A = (8 \times 5) - \frac{1}{2}[(5 \times 5) + (3 \times 3) + (8 \times 2)] = 40 - \frac{1}{2}(50) = 15$$

   The area of $\triangle$EBF is **15 cm²**

8. (a) S = circumference x length

$$= \frac{22}{7} \times 14 \times 35$$
$$= 1,540$$

   Outer curved surface area is
   1,540 cm².

   (b)   Inner diameter = 14 - 2 = 12 cm

$$S = \frac{22}{7} \times 12 \times 35$$
$$= 1,320$$

   Inner curved surface area is
   1,320 cm².

9. (a) $A = \frac{1}{2}h(b_1 + b_2)$

 $= \frac{1}{2}(45)(30 + 60)$

 $= 2,025$

Area of cross-section is **2,025 cm²**.

(b) Volume = base x length
 = 2,025 x 960
 = 1,944,000
Capacity is 1,944,000 cm³ = **1,944 ℓ**

10.(a) Radius including path = 5 m
Circumference = $2\pi r$
 $= \mathbf{10\pi\ m}$

(b) $A = \pi 5^2 - \pi 4^2$
 $= 25\pi - 16\pi$
 $= \mathbf{9\pi\ m^3}$

11.(a) Four quarter circles = one whole circle. Circumference of the flower bed would be the circumference of a circle.

Circumference = $2\pi r = 2(\frac{22}{7})r = \frac{\mathbf{44}}{\mathbf{7}}\mathbf{r\ cm}$

(b) Area = area of square of side $2r$ - area of the four quarter circles. Four quarter circles is equivalent to a whole circle.
$A = (2r)^2 - \pi r^2 = 4r^2 - \pi r^2 = \mathbf{(4 - \pi)r^2\ cm^2}$

(c) $A = (4 - \frac{22}{7})(7^2) = 196 - 154 = \mathbf{42\ cm^2}$

12.(a) Area of face $ABCDE$ = area of rectangle $ABDE$ + area quadrant BCD.

$A = (30 \times 20) + [\frac{1}{4} \times 3.142 \times 20^2] = 600 + 314 = \mathbf{914\ cm^2}$

(b) Volume = base area x length = 914 cm² x 70 cm = 63,980 cm³ ≈ **64,000 cm³**

(c) Length of arc = $\frac{1}{4}$ x 2 x 3.142 x 20 = 31.42 cm ≈ **31.4 cm**

(d) Area curved surface = length arc BC x length of container
 = 31.4 x 70 = 2,199.4 cm² ≈ **2,200 cm²**

(e) Total surface area = area curved surface + area $ETRC$ + area $APTE$ + area $APQB$
 + 2(area face $ABCDE$)
 = 2,199.4 + (50)(70) + (20)(70) + (30)(70) + 2(914) cm²
 = 2,199.4 + 3,500 + 1,400 + 2,100 + 1,828 cm²
 = 11,027.4 cm²
 ≈ **11,000 cm²**

13.(a) (i) AB = 30 + 60 + 30 cm
            = 120 cm
        (ii) Solution involves Pythagorean
        theorem, which hasn't been taught yet in
        this course. Let h be the vertical height
        of the trapezium.
        $h^2 + 30^2 = 60^2$
        $h^2 = 60^2 - 30^2$
            = 2,700
        $h \approx 51.962$ cm

        $A = \dfrac{1}{2}$ x 51.96 x (60 + 120)
            = 4,676.4 cm^3
        $\approx$ **4,677 cm²**

(b) A model can be used to show that the
     shaded part is equivalent to two of the table
     tops.
     The ratio is 6 : 2 = 3 : 1

(c) Total area = 8 x area of one trapezium
               = 8 x 4,676.4 cm^2
               = 37,411.2 cm^2
               $\approx$ **37,411 cm²**

14.(a) The two rounded corners together fit in a square of side
        1 m since the radius of the quarter circle is 1 m.
        Total area = area W + area X + area Y - area Z
                   = (3 x 4) + (6 x 3) + (4 x 4) - (1 x 1)
                   = 12 + 18 + 16 - 1
                   = **45 m²**

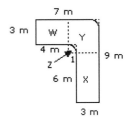

   (b) Volume = area x thickness (15 cm = 0.15 m)
              = 45 x 0.15
              = **6.75 m³**

   (c) Total number of parts = 1 + 2.25 + 3 = 6.25
        Cement = $\dfrac{1}{6.25}$ of total = $\dfrac{1}{6.25}$ x 6.75 m^3 = **1.08 m³**

   (d) Density of cement = 226.6 kg/m^3
        Mass = density x volume = 226.6 kg/m^3 x 1.08 m^3 $\approx$ **245 kg**

15.   A has to be 1 or 2 since A x 4 gives a 1 digit number (E) Since 4 x E
       = A, and multiples of 4 are even, A has to be 2. 4 x E = _2. The
       possibilities for E are 3 and 8 (4 x 3 = 1**2**, 4 x 8 = 3**2**). Since A is
       2, E has to be 8
       Since E is 8, 4 x B has to also give a 1 digit number, so B is 1. 4 x
       D + 3 = _1. D has to be 7 (4 x 7 + 3 = 31).

       4 x C + 3 = _C. C has to be 9 (4 x 9 + 3 = 39).

```
   A B C D E
 x         4
   E D C B A
```

```
       3
   2 B C D 8
 x         4
   8 D C B 2
```

```
     3 3
   2 1 C 7 8
 x         4
   8 7 C 1 2
```

```
   2 1 9 7 8
 x         4
   8 7 9 1 2
```

Assessment 1

Paper I (pp. 407-409)

1. (a) $45\% = \dfrac{45}{100} = \dfrac{\mathbf{9}}{\mathbf{20}}$ (b) $120\% = \dfrac{120}{100} = \dfrac{6}{5} = \mathbf{1\dfrac{1}{5}}$ (b) $\dfrac{1}{4}\% = \dfrac{\mathbf{1}}{\mathbf{400}}$

2. (a)
$$\frac{QR}{MN} = \frac{PQ}{PM}$$
$$\frac{9}{5} = \frac{PQ}{9}$$
$$PQ = \frac{81}{5}$$
$$PQ = 16\frac{1}{5}$$
$$PQ = 16.2$$

   (b)
$$\frac{QR}{MN} = \frac{PR}{PN}$$
$$\frac{9}{5} = \frac{PR}{PR-5}$$
$$9(PR) - 45 = 5(PR)$$
$$4(PR) = 45$$
$$PR = \frac{45}{4}$$
$$PR = 11\frac{1}{4}$$
$$PR = 11.25$$

3.
$$\angle ABC = \frac{1}{2}(180 - x) \qquad \angle \text{ sum of iso. } \Delta$$
$$8x = x + \frac{1}{2}(180 - x) \qquad \text{ext. } \angle \text{ of } \Delta$$
$$8x = x + 90 - \frac{1}{2}x$$
$$7\frac{1}{2}x = 90$$
$$\mathbf{x = 12}$$

4. (a) Cost per magazine $= \$\dfrac{450}{150} = \$3$.

He sold 75 at 20% profit, or 120% of cost.
He sold 50 of them at 10% profit, or 110% cost.
He sold the remaining 25 at 4% loss, or 96% cost.
Total sales $= \$3[(1.20 \times 75) + (1.10 \times 50) + (0.96 \times 25)$
$\qquad\qquad = \$3(90 + 55 + 24)$
$\qquad\qquad = \mathbf{\$507}$

   (b) gain percent $= \dfrac{507 - 450}{450} \times 100\% = \mathbf{13\%}$

5. Total earnings $= (25 \times \$125) + [27 \times (\$125 + \$15)]$
$\qquad\qquad = \$3,125 + \$3,780 = \mathbf{\$6,905}$

6. The product of the LCM and HCF of two numbers is equivalent to the product of those numbers. Let n be one of the numbers.
$136n = (8)(48)$
$\quad n = 24$
The unknown number is **24**.

7. (a) Amt. copper = 55% of 22 kg

$$= \frac{55}{100} \times 22 \text{ kg}$$

= 12.1 kg

Amt. tin = 22 kg - 12.1 kg

= 9.9 kg

(b) Let m be the money.

$4\frac{1}{2}\%$ of m = \$36

$$m = \$\frac{36}{4.5} \times \$100$$

= \$800

$6\frac{1}{4}\%$ of \$800 $= \frac{6.25}{100} \times \$800$

= \$50

8. (a) Let h be the drop in water level.

V = base x h

3,080 cm^3 = 616 cm^2 x h

h = 5 cm

The water level dropped **5 cm**.

(b) Units must be the same.

Thickness is 2 mm = 0.2 cm.

Mass = Density x volume

= 8.9 g/cm^3 x (13 x 4.5 x 0.2) cm^3

= 104.13 g

9. (a) $\angle A = \angle L$

$$\frac{AB}{AC} = \frac{LM}{LN}$$

(b) y = **60°** (equil. Δ)

z = 90° - 60° = **30°**

x = 90° - (90° - y) = **60°**

10. (a)

|----------------|-------|

distance d km

rate   16 km/h

time $\frac{d}{16}$ h $\frac{3}{4}$ h

Total time = $3\frac{1}{2}$ h = $\frac{7}{2}$ h

$$\frac{7}{2} = \frac{d}{16} + \frac{3}{4}$$

$$\frac{56}{16} = \frac{d}{16} + \frac{12}{16}$$

56 = d + 12

44 = d

d is **44 km**.

(b) There are 2 adults paying \$245 and 4 children paying $\frac{1}{2}$ of \$245.

Cost = (2 x \$245) + (4 x $\frac{1}{2}$ x \$245)

= \$490 + \$490

= \$980

11. (a) $w = \frac{xy}{x+y}$

$w = \frac{(5)(3)}{5+3}$

$w = \frac{15}{8}$

$w = 1\frac{7}{8}$

$w = $ **1.875**

(b) Let n be the number.

$$\frac{n}{3} - 5 = 4$$

$$\frac{n}{3} = 9$$

$n = 27$

The number is **27**.

12.(a) $5x - 7 = 13 - x$
         $6x - 7 = 13$
            $6x = 20$
$$x = \frac{20}{6}$$
$$x = 3\frac{1}{3}$$

(b)   New price $= \dfrac{5}{3}$ x \$12
$$= \mathbf{\$20}$$

(c)   Number of men is in inverse proportion to hours. Let x be the hours needed.
$$\frac{x}{\frac{7}{3}} = \frac{6}{7}$$
$$x = \frac{6}{7} \times \frac{7}{3}$$
$$x = 2$$
It takes 7 men **2 h**.

13.   Let h be the water level in the rectangular container. Volume will be the same in both.
$$\frac{22}{7} \times 3.5^2 \times 5 = 7.5 \times 8.5 \times h$$
$$192.5 = 63.75h$$
$$3 \approx h$$
The water level of the rectangular container would be about **3 cm**.

14.(a)   (i) $P = 2[(4x - 2) + (2x - 4)]$ m
          $= 2(6x - 6)$ m
          $= \mathbf{12x - 12}$ **m**

      (ii) $A = (4x)(2x) - (4x - 2)(2x - 4)$
          $= 8x^2 - (8x^2 - 20x + 8)$
          $= \mathbf{20x - 8}$ **m²**

(b)   (i) $A = (4x - 2)(2x - 4)$
          $= [(4)(15) - 2][(2)(15) - 4]$
          $= (58)(26)$
          $= \mathbf{1{,}508}$ **m²**

      (ii) $P = 12x - 12$
          $= (12)(15) - 12$
          $= \mathbf{168}$ **m**

Paper II (pp. 409-411)

1. (a) $3ab - 12bc + 9abc = \mathbf{3b(a - 4c + 3ac)}$

(b)
$$1\frac{1}{5} + \cfrac{1}{\cfrac{1}{2} + \cfrac{1}{1 + \cfrac{1}{3}}} = 1\frac{1}{5} + \cfrac{1}{\cfrac{1}{2} + \cfrac{1}{\frac{4}{3}}} = 1\frac{1}{5} + \cfrac{1}{\cfrac{1}{2} + \cfrac{3}{4}} = 1\frac{1}{5} + \cfrac{1}{\frac{5}{4}} = 1\frac{1}{5} + \frac{4}{5} = \mathbf{2}$$

2.(a)(i) $\mathbf{1\frac{1}{4}}$ Each term increases by $\dfrac{1}{4}$

(ii)
$$\overset{+1}{}\ \overset{+2}{}\ \overset{+3}{}\ \overset{+4}{}$$
$$-1,\ \ 0,\ \ 2,\ \ 5,\ \ \mathbf{9}$$

2.(b)   Add the numbers to be used together. $1 + 2 + 3 + 4 + 5 + 6 + 7 + 8 + 9 = 45$. There are 3 sides which must add to 21. $3 \times 21 = 63$. The difference, $63 - 45 = 18$, is the overlap, and the numbers in the vertices must add to 18. 9 is already in one vertex. So the numbers at the other two vertices must have a sum of 9. By trial and error, only 6 and 3 work. NOTE: The solutions in the text are for a sum of 23 along the sides.

3. (a) $x = 2,560 - (262 + 1,424 + 362)$
          $= 2,560 - 2,048$
          $= \textbf{512}$

(b) adults $= 512 + 262 = 774$
    children $= 1,424 + 362 = 1,786$
    $\dfrac{774}{1,786}$ x 100% = **43.3%**

(c) $\dfrac{3}{5+3} = \dfrac{3}{8}$ of the boys did not wear uniforms.

Number of boys without uniforms $= \dfrac{3}{8}$ x 1,424 = **534**

4. (a) $\angle TPR = \textbf{180 - 2}\textbf{\textit{x}}$ ($\angle$sum of iso. Δ)

(b) $\angle QPR = 180 - 110$ (adj. $\angle$s on st. line)
           $= 70$
    $\angle PQT = 180 - 70 - x$ ($\angle$ sum of Δ)
           $= \textbf{110 - }\textbf{\textit{x}}$

(c) $\angle QPT = 110 - x$ (iso. Δ)
    $\angle QPR = 110 - x + (180 - 2x)$
      $70 = 110 - x + (180 - 2x)$

(d) $70 = 110 - x + (180 - 2x)$
    $70 = 290 - 3x$
    $3x = 220$
      $x = \mathbf{73\dfrac{1}{3}}$

5. (a) (i) 8% of \$1,850 $= \dfrac{8}{100}$ x \$1,850
                    $= \textbf{\$148}$
    His increase is \$148 under A.

(ii) 6% of \$1,850 $= \dfrac{6}{100}$ x \$1,850
                $= \$111$
    Increase under B $= \$111 + \$39$
                  $= \textbf{\$150}$

(b) $\dfrac{150}{1,850}$ x 100% $\approx$ **8%**

His increase under B is about 8% of his present salary.

(c) Let s be his present salary. His increase is the same under both schemes.
$$\dfrac{8}{100}s = \dfrac{6}{100}s + 39$$
$8s = 6s + 3,900$ mult. by 100
$2s = 3,900$ subtract 6s
 $s = 1,950$ divide by 2
His present salary is **\$1,950**.

6. (a) (i) Let s be length of a side.
      $s^3 = 216$ cm^3
       $s = \textbf{6 cm}$

(ii) Let n be the number.
    $n^2 = 23.04$
    $n = \textbf{4.8}$

(b) (i)(a) $V = 6$ cm x 8 cm x 10.5 cm
             $= \textbf{504 cm}^\textbf{3}$
      (b) Since the cylindrical butter is twice the amount of the rectangular butter, and density is the same, then volume is twice. Let h be the height.
      $2(504) = (3.142)(3.9^2)h$
       $1,008 = 47.8h$
        $21.09 = h$
    It is about **21.09 cm** high.

(ii) Volume of new packs is same as rectangular packs. Let r be the radius.
    $504 = (3.142)(r^2)(13.2)$
    $504 = 41.48r^2$
  $12.15 = r^2$
   $3.49 = r$
    The radius is about **3.49 cm**.

7. (a) Since $0 < n < 1$, n can be represented by a fraction. Squaring n would cause the denominator to increase more than the numerator, making a smaller fraction. Taking the inverse would create a larger number since the numerator is now larger than the denominator.

$$n^2 < n < \frac{1}{n}$$

  (b) (i) The sum of the exterior angles is equal to 360º. Let a be an exterior angle.

$5a = 360º$

$a = \textbf{72º}$

(ii)(a) $\angle AXE = 180 - (2 \times 72º)$

$= \textbf{36º}$

(b) $BCDX$ is a **kite**. $AX = EX$ since $\triangle AEX$ is equilateral (the exterior angles of the pentagon are equal) $\therefore BX = DX$

(c) One **line of symmetry** CX

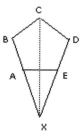

8.(a) The length will be 80 cm plus 3 cm for every 500 g or 0.5 kg weight. So for every kg, it stretches 6 cm.

$L = \textbf{80 + 6}\textbf{\textit{M}}$

  (b) $L = 80 + 6(2)$

$= 80 + 12$

$= \textbf{92 cm}$

  (c) $92 = 80 + 6M$

$12 = 6M$ subtract 80 both sides

$\textbf{2} = M$ divide both sides by 6

  (c) $y \text{ g} = \dfrac{1}{1{,}000}$ kg

From formula derived in (a):

$$L = 80 + \frac{6}{1{,}000}y$$

$$= 80 + \frac{3}{500}y$$

L is 100% + x% of unstretched length.

$$L = 80 + \frac{x}{100}(80)$$

$$= 80 + \frac{4}{5}x$$

$$80 + \frac{3}{500}y = 80 + \frac{4}{5}x$$

$$\frac{3}{500}y = \frac{4}{5}x$$

$$\boldsymbol{y = \frac{400}{3}x}$$

Assessment 2

Paper I (pp. 412-414)

1. (a) $2 \mid \underline{28, 42, 98}$
         $7 \mid \underline{14, 21, 49}$
         $\quad\; 7, \;\; 3, \;\; 7$

   HCF = 2 x 7 = **14**

   (b)   (i) $\dfrac{3.25}{6.5}$ x 100% = **50%**

         (ii) 1 km = 100,000 cm

         $\dfrac{95}{100,000}$ x 100% = **0.095%**

2. (a)   Biggest share = $\dfrac{4}{2+3+4}$ of $2,700

         $= \dfrac{4}{9}$ x $2,700

         = **$1,200**

   (b)   Number of pumps is inversely proportional to time needed. Let t be time needed with 3 pumps.

         $\dfrac{t}{12 \text{ h}} = \dfrac{5 \text{ pumps}}{3 \text{ pumps}}$

         $t = \dfrac{5}{3} \, x \, 12 \;\; h$

         t = 20 h
         Answer in books is for 2 pumps working, but problem states that 2 pumps were not working.

3.   Density $= \dfrac{\text{Mass}}{\text{Volume}} = \dfrac{340 \text{ g}}{120 \text{ cm x 15 cm x 0.3 cm}} = \dfrac{340 \text{ g}}{540 \text{ cm}^3}$ = **0.63 g/cm³**

4.   Let w be the breadth. The length is 1.5w.
     $2(w + 1.5w) = 30$
     $2w + 3w = 30$
     $\quad\;\; 5w = 30$
     $\quad\;\;\; w = 6$ cm
     area = 6 cm x (1.5 x 6) cm = **54 cm²**

5.
     $a = 45^\circ$ iso. rt. Δ
     $b = 90^\circ - 30^\circ$ compl. $\angle$s of rt. Δ
     $\quad = 60^\circ$
     $x = 180^\circ - a - b$ adj. $\angle$s on a st. line
     $\quad = 180^\circ - 45^\circ - 60^\circ$
     $\quad = $ **75°**

6.   Volume = volume of rectangular solid - volume of center hole. (radius is 1.5 cm)

     $= (4 \text{ x } 4 \text{ x } 1.5) - (\dfrac{22}{7} \text{ x } 1.5^2 \text{ x } 1.5) = 24 - 10.6 \approx$ **13 cm³**

7. (a) (i) $AB = DC$ since $ABCD$ is a rectangle.
$AQ : QD = AB : PD$ since $\triangle ABQ$ and $\triangle PBC$ are similar.
$$\therefore \frac{AQ}{QD} = \frac{5}{3}$$

(ii) $PC = PD + DC = 3 + 5 = 8$
$PD : PC = QD : BC$
$$\therefore \frac{QD}{BC} = \frac{3}{8}$$

(b) (i) $\angle ALM = \angle ACB = 70^{\circ}$

(ii) sides of similar $\triangle$s are proportional.
$$\frac{AB}{AM} = \frac{BC}{ML}$$
$$\frac{AB}{13} = \frac{24}{12}$$
$$AB = \frac{24}{12}(13)$$
$$AB = 26$$

8. (a) Let n be one number. The other two numbers are $n + 2$ and $n + 4$.
$n + n + 2 + n + 4 = 162$
$3n + 6 = 162$
$3n = 156$
$n = 52$
The numbers are **52, 54, and 56**.

(b)
$3a + 5 = 32(3 - 2a)$
$3a + 5 = 96 - 64a$
$3a + 64a + 5 = 96 - 64a + 64a$
$67a + 5 - 5 = 96 - 5$
$67a = 91$
$a \approx 1.358$

9. (a) Let p be the price.
$5\frac{1}{2}\%$ of $p = \$22$
$$\frac{11}{200}p = \$22$$
$$p = \$(22)\frac{200}{11}$$
$$p = \$400$$
$3\frac{1}{2}\%$ of $\$400 = \frac{7}{200}(\$400)$
$$= \$14$$

(b) Value of car is 80% of previous year's cost.

(i) 80% of $\$55,000 = \frac{80}{100}(\$55,000)$
$$= \$44,000$$

(ii) 80% of $\$44,000 = \frac{80}{100}(\$44,000)$
$$= \$35,200$$

10. (a) $y = kx^2$
$y = (9)(6^2)$
$y = 324$

(b) (i) length = $(3)(4) - 1 = $ **11 cm**
width = $4 + 3 = $ **7 cm**

(ii) $P = 2(11 + 7) = $ **36 cm**

(iii) $A = 11 \times 7 = $ **77 cm²**

11. (a)
```
2 | 126        126 = 2 x 3 x 3 x 7
3 |  63
3 |  21
      7
```

(b) (i) Surface area of surface facing up is the same as the surface facing down. Surface area of sides is same as that of rectangle 10 by 11. Total surface area is twice the surface area of an end, a side, and a bottom.
$S = 2[3 \times 20) + (8 \times 6) + (11 \times 10) + (20 \times 10)]$ cm²
$= 2(60 + 48 + 110 + 200)$ cm²
$= $ **836 cm²**

(ii) $V = (20 \times 10 \times 3) + (6 \times 8 \times 10)$ cm³
$= 600 + 480$ cm³
$= $ **1,080 cm³**

12. 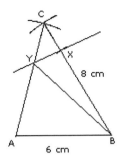 $\angle BYX$ = **69°**

13.(a) Amt. petrol = $\dfrac{2 \times 318}{12}$ + 10 ℓ (b) Cost = 53 ℓ x \$1.20 /ℓ

        = **63 ℓ**   = **\$63.60**

14.(a) Let c be the capital.   (b) Current profit is 120% of previous profit.
        30% of c = \$72,000   Let p be previous profit.
        $c = \$\dfrac{72,000}{30} \times 100$ 120% of p = \$72,000
        = **\$240,000** $p = \$\dfrac{72,000}{120} \times 100$
                                                           = **\$60,000**

   (c) Percent profit = $\dfrac{60,000}{240,000} \times 100\%$ = **25%**

Paper II (pp. 414-416)

1. (a) $\dfrac{1}{2}(2x + 1) + \dfrac{1}{4}(x + 5) = 2\dfrac{3}{8}$ (b) $\dfrac{1}{x + y} + \dfrac{1}{y - zw} = \dfrac{1}{\dfrac{1}{4} + 6} + \dfrac{1}{6 - \left(-\dfrac{1}{2}\right)(0)}$

        $x + \dfrac{1}{2} + \dfrac{x}{4} + \dfrac{5}{4} = \dfrac{19}{8}$ $= \dfrac{1}{\dfrac{25}{4}} + \dfrac{1}{6}$

        $\dfrac{8x}{8} + \dfrac{4}{8} + \dfrac{2x}{8} + \dfrac{10}{8} = \dfrac{19}{8}$ $= \dfrac{4}{25} + \dfrac{1}{6}$

        $8x + 4 + 2x + 10 = 19$ $= \dfrac{24 + 25}{150}$
        $10x + 14 = 19$
        $10x = 5$ $= \dfrac{49}{150}$
        $x = \dfrac{1}{2}$

2. (a) $\angle BCX$ = **57°**   corr. $\angle$s, BY // CX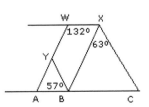

   (b) $\angle CBX$ = 180 - 63° - 57° $\angle$sum of a Δ
        = 60°
        $\angle BXW$ = **60°**   alt. $\angle$s, AC // WX

   (c) $\angle BAW$ = 180° - 132°   int. $\angle$s, AC // WX
        = 48°
        $\angle BYW$ = 48° + 57°   ext. $\angle$ of a Δ
        = **105°**

3.   pattern 1   2   3   4   (a)   5th term is 12 + 3 = **15**
     dots   3   6   9   12   (b)   10th term is 15 + (3 x 5) = **30**
     Each term is 3 more than previous term.   (c) nth term is **3n**

4. (a)
     Price with discount of $7\frac{1}{2}$% is $92\frac{1}{2}$% of cost.

     $92\frac{1}{2}$% of \$640 = $\dfrac{185}{200}$ x \$640 = **\$592**

   (b)   Let m be his monthly installments.   (c)   Let m be his monthly installments.
         $688 = \dfrac{640}{4} + 12m$ His hire purchase price is 120% of \$640.
         $688 = 160 + 12m$ $\dfrac{120}{100}(640) = 24m$
         $528 = 12m$ $768 = 24m$
         $m = 44$ $32 = m$
         His monthly installment is **\$44**.   He paid **\$32** per month.

5. (a)   (i) First, third, and last dials are counterclockwise. Reading is **76,564.5**.
         (ii) Electricity used = 907.3 - 45.2 = **862.1**
         (iii) Average consumption = $\dfrac{862.1}{5}$ = **172.4**

   (b) $AB : BC : CD$ is 1 : 2 : 4. If p is a part then $1p + 2p + 4p = 14$; $7p = 14$; $p = 2$. So AB
         = 2 cm, BC = 4 cm, and CD = 8 cm. If AB = 2 XB and AB = 2 cm, then XB = 1 cm. X
         can be on either side of B.

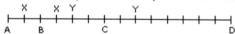

         If $CD = 4YC$, and $CD = 8$, then $YC = 2$. Y can be on either side of C.

         So XY can be **1 cm, 3 cm, 5 cm, or 7 cm**.

6. (a)   Hourly rate = $\dfrac{\$210}{40}$ (b)   Overtime = 160% of regular pay
                      = **\$5.25**   = $\dfrac{160}{100}$ x \$5.25
                                                              = **\$8.40**

   (c)   50 hours is 40 hours at regular pay and   (d)   He saves $\dfrac{2}{5}$ of his base salary + his
         10 hours at overtime.
         Pay = \$210 + (10 x \$8.40)   overtime pay.
             = \$210 + \$84   Savings = $(\dfrac{2}{5}$ x \$210$) + (5$ x \$8.40$)$
             = **\$294**
                                                                    = \$84 + \$42
                                                                    = **\$126**

7. (a)(i) Length of strip is $\frac{3}{4}$ of the circumference, $2\pi r$.

Length $= \frac{3}{4}$ x 2 x 3.142 x 48 cm

$= \textbf{226.22 cm}$

(ii) Area is area of $\frac{3}{4}$ of a circle + area of the triangle with base and height of OA and OB.

Area $= \frac{3}{4}(3.142)(48^2) + \frac{1}{2}(48)(48)$

$= 5,429.38 + 1,152$

$= \textbf{6,581.38 cm}^\textbf{2}$

(b) Area of rectangle $= 96$ x 104 cm$^2 = 9,984$ cm^2

% wasted $= \dfrac{9,984 - 6,581.38}{9,984}$ x 100% = **34.1%**

8. (a)(i) $\triangle BAC$ is isosceles, with C the apex.

$\angle BAC = \frac{1}{2}(180^\circ - 35^\circ)$

$= \textbf{72}\frac{\textbf{1}}{\textbf{2}}^\textbf{o}$

(ii) $\triangle BMC$ is isosceles, with M the apex.

$\angle BMC = 180^\circ - 2(35^\circ)$

$= \textbf{110}^\textbf{o}$

(b) (i) $\angle ABC = \dfrac{180^\circ(n-2)}{n}$ where n is the number of angles

$= \dfrac{180^\circ \times 3}{5} = \textbf{108}^\textbf{o}$

(ii) $\triangle CDE$ is isosceles, $\angle CDE = 108^\circ$

$\angle CDE = \frac{1}{2}(180^\circ - 108^\circ) = 36^\circ$

$\angle BCE = 108^\circ - 36^\circ = \textbf{72}^\textbf{o}$

(iii) $\angle ABC + \angle BCE = 108^\circ + 72^\circ = 180^\circ$.

∴ they are corresponding angles, and BA // EC

ABCE is a trapezoid (trapezium).